9 ∞

PROBLEMS IN PHYSICS

В. Г. ЗУБОВ и В. П. ШАЛЬНОВ

ЗАДАЧИ ПО ФИЗИКЕ

Пособие для самообразования

Издательство «Наука»

V. ZUBOV AND V. SHALNOV

PROBLEMS IN PHYSICS

MIR PUBLISHERS • MOSCOW

Translated from the Russian by A.N. Troitsky
Translation edited by J.B. Williams

First published 1974
Second printing 1985
Third printing 1989

На английском языке

Printed in the Union of Soviet Socialist Republics

ISBN 5-03-000513-7

The authors will ...

PREFACE

For the most part, this is a collection of modified problems discussed in extracurricular circles and at tutorials and olympiads at the Moscow University.

In selecting and preparing the problems for this collection the authors attempted to focus the attention of the reader on those postulates and laws of physics where students make the most mistakes. Some problems were specially selected to explain comprehensively the application of the most important laws —something which students often fail to grasp properly. A number of problems concern the subjects usually omitted in secondary school text-book problems. Some problems are intended for discussion in extracurricular circles or for independent study by those wishing to acquaint themselves with material beyond the scope of the school syllabus.

The most difficult problems and the problems outside the scope of the secondary school syllabus are provided with detailed explanations in order to give the student a better understanding of the general principles of solution. With this end in view, some sections are also supplemented with brief information about the most frequent mistakes and the simplest means of solution.

In selecting and preparing the problems for olympiads and extracurricular circles which are included in this book the authors cooperated with Prof. S. G. Kalashnikov, Prof. V. I. Iveronova, Prof. S. P. Strelkov, Assistant Professors I. A. Yakovlev, B. I. Spassky, E. G. Shvidkovsky and A. S. Anikeev. In addition, a number of the most instructive and readily solvable problems from such popular collections of higher school problems as those by I. V. Meshchersky, D. I. Sakharov and I. S. Kosminkov, A. V. Tsinger and others are included in this book.

The manuscript of this book was meticulously reviewed by Assistant Professor I. A. Yakovlev and editor E. B. Kuznetsova, whose critical comments helped considerably to improve it.

The authors will be extremely grateful for readers' comments and suggestions for improvements.

V. Zubov,
V. Shalnov

CONTENTS

		Answers and Solutions
Preface	5	
	Problems	

Chapter I. MECHANICS 9 141

1. Rectilinear Uniform Motion — 9 — 141
2. Rectilinear Uniformly Variable Motion — 15 — 148
3. Curvilinear Motion — 18 — 152
4. Rotational Motion of a Solid Body — 19 — 154
5. Dynamics of the Rectilinear Motion of a Point — 20 — 155
6. Power Impulse. Momentum — 28 — 164
7. Work. Energy. Power — 33 — 169
8. Dynamics of a Point Moving in a Circle — 37 — 176
9. Statics — 45 — 188
10. Universal Gravitational Forces — 53 — 194
11. Oscillations — 54 — 197
12. Hydro- and Aerostatics — 56 — 201

Chapter II. HEAT AND MOLECULAR PHYSICS 63 207

13. Thermal Expansion of Bodies — 63 — 207
14. Quantity of Heat. Heat Exchange — 65 — 210
15. The Gas Laws — 66 — 211
16. Surface Tension — 73 — 219
17. Humidity of Air — 77 — 224

Chapter III. ELECTRICITY 78 224

18. Coulomb's Law — 78 — 224
19. Electric Field. Field Intensity — 81 — 229
20. Work Done by Forces in an Electrostatic Field. Potential — 85 — 235
21. Electric Field in a Dielectric — 88 — 239
22. Capacitance and Capacitors — 89 — 241
23. The Laws of Direct Current — 93 — 244
24. Thermal Effect of Current. Power — 102 — 255

	Problems	Answers and Solutions
25. Permanent Magnets	105	257
26. Magnetic Field of a Current	112	263
27. Forces Acting in a Magnetic Field on Current-Carrying Conductors	116	267
28. Electromagnetic Induction	120	270
Chapter IV. OPTICS	124	271
29. The Nature of Light	124	271
30. Fundamentals of Photometry	126	273
31. The Law of Rectilinear Propagation and Reflection of Light	128	275
32. Spherical Mirrors	133	279
33. Refraction of Light at Plane Boundary	136	283
34. Lenses and Composite Optical Systems	137	285

PROBLEMS

Chapter I

MECHANICS

1. Rectilinear Uniform Motion

In solving the problems both in this section and in Secs 2 and 3, special attention should be paid to the general rules for compounding and resolving motion as well as to the vectorial nature of the principal kinematic quantities (velocity and acceleration). Such problems are sometimes difficult to solve, especially in the case of curvilinear motion or the relative motion of two bodies (for example, the motion of a ball falling to the ground relative to that of a ball thrown vertically upwards).

These difficulties can only be obviated by considering the separate components of motion independently and using the rules for compounding and resolving vectors correctly. Many difficulties can be overcome if a correct general approach is used to solve problems on curvilinear motion.

Most of the solutions in Sec. 3 are intended to show how the correct resolution of motion into components can reduce a complicated problem on curvilinear motion to a simple, familiar problem involving two independent rectilinear motions.

When considering a uniformly variable motion, it is necessary to use the true physical sense of the equations for the path and velocity of this motion correctly. For instance, when solving problems on the motion of a body projected into the air, students frequently break the solution down into two independent stages, considering first the uniformly retarded motion upwards until the body comes to rest and then the uniformly accelerated motion downwards from rest.

This method affords a comparatively simple solution when only one body is in motion, but can hardly be applied when the problem describes the simultaneous motion of several bodies (for example, Problems 31 and 35 where two bodies thrown upwards one after the other meet in the air). This approach ignores the fact that the equation $S = v_0 t - \frac{at^2}{2}$ is the general distance-time expression for uniformly variable motion in which the body moves with uniform retardation up to time $t = \frac{v_0}{a}$ (the moment when the directional component of velocity changes), and with uniform acceleration after this time.

In Secs 2 and 3, one should pay attention to the meaning of the equation $S = v_0 t - \frac{at^2}{2}$ used in solving the problems and to the associated simplifications employed in the solution.

A number of serious difficulties arise because the correct sequence of operations is not adhered to. Students sometimes do not take enough care when specifying the starting point of the motion and the displacements of the bodies. Then they try to avoid deriving basic equations in the general case and attempt to write out mathematical formulae for the unknown quantities. When solving problems involving the motion of several bodies projected at different moments or from different heights, they fix different starting points for the displacement and time for each body. The relations between the separate motions, which are needed in the course of solution, are determined only at the end by means of additional and often confusing recalculations. This method leads to unwarranted complications even when very simple problems are to be solved.

Most of the problems in Secs 1-3 are intended to show once again the basic rules in selecting the origin of time and displacement common to all the bodies considered in the problem.

It is worth noting in these problems the general sequence of operations, the order in which the basic equations are derived and the methods of utilizing the available data for some points on the path to obtain the mathematical equations.

Many problems in Secs 1-3 can be solved graphically. Since the ability to apply and understand graphs is very important, the student should try to solve the problems graphically even when this is not specifically stated.

The resistance of the air is disregarded in all the problems related to kinematics except for otherwise specified cases.

1. Two men, one in an opera house and the other sitting at home near his radio, are listening to the same music.

(1) At what distance from the orchestra should the man in the opera house be in order to hear the first sounds of the overture at the same time as the radio listener if the latter is at a distance of 7,500 km from the opera house?

(2) At what distance from the radio should the listener be in order to hear the sounds simultaneously with the man in the opera house sitting a distance of 30 metres from the orchestra? The microphone is in the orchestra. The velocity of sound is 340 m/s. The velocity of propagation of radio waves is 3×10^{10} cm/s.

2. The distance between the towns M and K is 250 km. Two cars set off simultaneously from the towns towards each other. The car from M travels at a speed of $v_1 = 60$ km/hr and the one from K at a speed of $v_2 = 40$ km/hr.

Draw graphs of path versus time for each car and use them to determine the point where they will meet and the time that will elapse before they meet.

3. A car leaves point A for point B every 10 minutes. The distance between A and B is 60 km. The cars travel at a speed of 60 km/hr.

Draw graphs of the path versus time for the cars. Use these graphs to find the number of cars that a man driving from B to A will meet en route if he starts from B simultaneously with one of the cars leaving A. The car from B travels at a speed of 60 km/hr.

4. An anti-tank gun fires point-blank at a tank. The burst of the shell is observed by the crew after $t_1 = 0.6$ s and the sound is heard $t_2 = 2.1$ s after the shot is fired.

What is the distance between the gun and the tank? What is the horizontal velocity of the shell? The velocity of sound is 340 m/s. Neglect the resistance of the air.

5. How long will a passenger sitting at the window of a train travelling at a speed of $v_1 = 54$ km/hr see a train

passing by in the opposite direction with speed $v_2 =$
$= 36$ km/hr, if the length of the latter is $l = 150$ m?

6. A passenger in an electric train notices that a train
coming in the opposite direction and consisting of a locomotive and ten carriages takes 10 s to go past.

What is the speed of the electric train if the length of
each carriage in the other train is 16.5 m, the length of the
locomotive with the tender is 20 m and the distance between
the carriages is 1.5 m? Both trains are travelling at the
same speed when they meet.

7. Will it require the same time for a launch to cover
a distance of 1 km up and down a river (the speed of the
current is $v_1 = 2$ km/hr) and on a lake (in stagnant water)
if the speed of the launch relative to the water is $v_2 =$
$= 8$ km/hr in both cases?

Solve this problem analytically and graphically.

8. Determine the distance traversed by the launch relative to the water in the river assuming the conditions of
the previous problem.

9. It takes one minute for a passenger standing on an
escalator in the underground to reach the top. If the escalator does not move it takes him three minutes to walk up.

How long will it take for the passenger to arrive at the
top if he walks up the escalator when it is moving?

10. A launch takes 3 hours to go downstream from point
A to point B and 6 hours to come back.

How long does it take for this launch to cover the distance
AB downstream with its engine cut off?

11. An aircraft flies from point M to point B and back
with a speed of $v_1 = 300$ km/hr (relative to the air).

How much time is needed for the entire flight if the wind
blows continuously with a velocity of $v_2 = 60$ km/hr along
the flight path? The distance between M and B is 900 km.

12. Two launches were going downstream with different
velocities. When one overtook the other a ring-buoy was
dropped from one of the launches. Some time later both
launches turned back simultaneously and went at the same
speeds as before (relative to the water) to the spot where
the ring-buoy had been dropped.

Which of the launches will reach the ring-buoy first?
Solve this problem also for the cases in which the launches:

(1) went upstream; and (2) were approaching each other before they met.

13. A pipe which can be swivelled in a vertical plane is mounted on a cart (Fig. 1). The cart moves uniformly along a horizontal path with a speed $v_1 = 2$ m/s.

At what angle α to the horizon should the pipe be placed so that drops of rain falling plumb with a velocity $v_2 = 6$ m/s move parallel to the walls of the pipe without touching them? Consider the velocity of the drops as constant due to the resistance of the air.

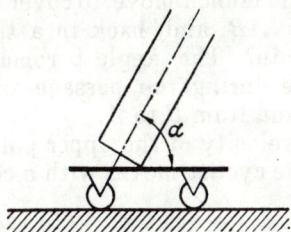

Fig. 1

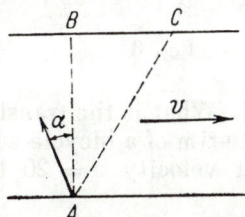

Fig. 2

14. An ice-boat glides in a straight line over a smooth surface of ice with a speed v. The wind blows with a velocity $u = 2v$ perpendicular to the course of the ice-boat.

At what angle β relative to the surface of the sail will the weather vane mounted on the mast of the ice-boat arrange itself?

The sail is set at an angle of 45° to the direction of the wind.

15. A man in a boat crosses a river from point A (Fig. 2). If he rows perpendicular to the banks then, 10 minutes after he starts, he will reach point C lying at a distance $S = 120$ m downstream from point B. If the man heads at a certain angle α to the straight line AB (AB is perpendicular to the banks) against the current he will reach point B after 12.5 minutes.

Find the width of the river l, the velocity of the boat u relative to the water, the speed of the current v and the angle α. Assume the velocity of the boat relative to the water to be constant and of the same magnitude in both cases.

16. A launch plies between two points A and B on the opposite banks of a river (Fig. 3), always following the line AB. The distance S between points A and B is 1,200 m. The velocity of the river current $v = 1.9$ m/s is constant over the entire width of the river.

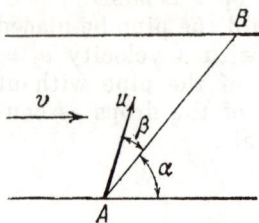

The line AB makes an angle $\alpha = 60°$ with the direction of the current.

With what velocity u and at what angle β to the line AB should the launch move to cover the distance AB and back in a time $t = 5$ min? The angle β remains the same during the passage from A to B and from B to A.

Fig. 3

17. What is the translational velocity of the upper points of the rim of a bicycle wheel if the cyclist moves with a constant velocity $v = 20$ km/hr?

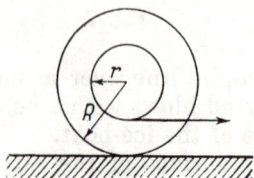
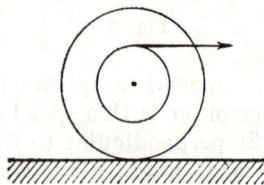

Fig. 4   Fig. 5

18. A bobbin with thread wound around it lies on a horizontal table and can roll along it without sliding.

With what velocity and in what direction will the axis of the bobbin move if the end of the thread is pulled in a horizontal direction with a velocity v (Fig. 4)? The inner radius of bobbin is r and the external one R.

19. Solve the previous problem if the thread is unwound from the bobbin as shown in Fig. 5.

20. When two bodies move uniformly towards each other the distance between them diminishes by $S_1 = 16$ m every $t_1 = 10$ s. If the bodies move with velocities of the same magnitude and in the same direction as before the distance between them will increase by $S_2 = 3$ m every $t_2 = 5$ s.

What is the velocity of each body?

2. Rectilinear Uniformly Variable Motion

21. A point moving with a uniform acceleration travels distances $S_1 = 24$ m and $S_2 = 64$ m during the first two equal consecutive intervals of time, each of duration $t = 4$ s.

Determine the initial velocity and the acceleration of the moving point.

22. In his laboratory register M. V. Lomonosov noted the following results of measurements on the distances traversed by falling bodies: "...as they fall, bodies traverse a distance of $15^1/_2$ rhenish feet during the first second, 62 in two seconds, $139^1/_2$ in three seconds, 248 in four seconds and $387^1/_2$ in five seconds (one rhenish foot = 31.39 cm).

Use these results to calculate the acceleration of gravity.

23. Drops of water fall at regular intervals from the roof of a building of height $H = 16$ m, the first drop striking the ground at the same moment as the fifth drop detaches itself from the roof.

Find the distance between the separate drops in the air as the first drop reaches the ground.

24. A body leaving a certain point O moves with an acceleration which is constant in magnitude and direction. At the end of the fifth second its velocity is 1.5 m/s. At the end of the sixth second the body stops and then begins to move backwards.

Find the distance traversed by the body before it stops.

Determine the velocity with which the body returns to point O.

25. Fig. 6 is the velocity-time graph for the motion of a certain body. Determine the nature of this motion. Find the initial velocity and acceleration and write the equation for the variation of displacement with time.

What happens to the moving body at point B? How will the body move after this moment?

26. Two bodies fall freely from different heights and reach the ground simultaneously. The time of descent for the first body is $t_1 = 2$ s and for the second, $t_2 = 1$ s.

At what height was the first body situated when the other began to fall?

27. Two bodies begin to fall freely from the same height, the second τ s after the first.

How long after the first body begins to fall will the distance between the bodies be equal to l?

28. In the last second of free fall a body traversed half its path.

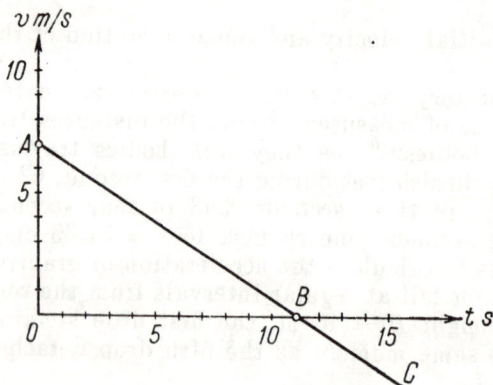

Fig. 6

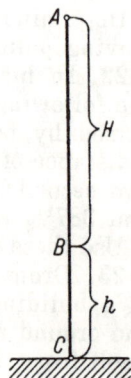

Fig. 7

From what height h was the body dropped and what time t did it require to reach the ground? Indicate two ways of solving the problem.

29. One body falls freely from a point A at a height $H + h$ (Fig. 7) whilst another body is projected upwards with an initial velocity v_0 from point C at the same time as the first body begins to fall.

What should the initial velocity v_0 of the second body be so that the bodies meet at a point B at a height h? What is the maximum height attained by the second body for the given initial velocity? Consider the case $H = h$ separately.

30. How long before or after the first body starts to fall and with what initial velocity should a body be projected upwards from point C (see Problem 29) to satisfy simultaneously the following conditions: (1) the bodies meet at point B at a height h; and (2) the height h is the maximum height which the projected body reaches?

31. Two bodies are projected vertically upwards from one point with the same initial velocities v_0, the second τ s after the first.

How long after will the bodies meet?

32. A balloon rises with a constant velocity v_0. A load is tied by a rope to the basket.

How will the load move relative to the earth if the rope holding it is cut when the balloon is at an altitude H_0? How long does it take for the dropping load to reach the earth? With what velocity will it land?

33. Prove that for a body thrown vertically upwards: (1) the initial projection velocity v_0 is equal to the final velocity upon contact with the earth; (2) the time for ascent is equal to the time for descent.

34. A heavy elastic ball falls freely from point A at a height H_0 onto the smooth horizontal surface of an elastic plate. As the ball strikes the plate another such ball is dropped from the same point A.

At what time t, after the second ball is dropped, and at what height will the balls meet?

35. Two bodies are thrown vertically upwards with the same initial velocities v_0, the second τ s after the first.

(1) With what velocity will the second body move relative to the first? Indicate the magnitude and direction of this relative velocity. According to what law will the distance between the bodies change?

(2) Solve this problem when the initial velocity of the second body v_0 is half the initial velocity of the first.

36. Two motor-cyclists set off from points A and B towards each other. The one leaving point A drives uphill with a uniform acceleration $a = 2$ m/s² and an initial velocity $v_1 = 72$ km/hr, whilst the other goes downhill from point B with an initial velocity $v_2 = 36$ km/hr and with an acceleration of the same magnitude as the other car.

Determine the time of motion and the distance covered by the first motor-cyclist before they meet, if the distance between A and B is $S = 300$ m. Show how the distance between the motor-cyclists will change with time. Plot the change of distance between the motor-cyclists against time. Use this graph to find the moment when the motor-cyclists meet.

3. Curvilinear Motion

37. A body is dropped freely from the window of a railway car. Will the time of the free fall be equal, if: the car is stationary, the car moves with a constant velocity v, the car moves with an acceleration a?

38. A machine-gun stationed high up on the sheer bank of a lake fires in a horizontal direction. The initial velocity of the bullets is v_0. What will the velocity of the bullets be as they strike the water if the height of the bank is h?

39. Two solid bodies are simultaneously thrown in a horizontal direction from two points on a sheer bank which are at certain heights above the water surface. The initial velocities of the bodies are $v_1 = 5$ m/s and $v_2 = 7.5$ m/s, respectively. Both bodies fall into the water at the same time. The first body enters the water at a point $S = 10$ m from the bank.

Determine: (1) the duration of flight for the bodies; (2) the heights from which they were thrown; (3) the point where the second body dropped into the water.

40. A shell is fired from a long-range gun with an initial velocity $v_0 = 1,000$ m/s at an angle $\alpha = 30°$ to the horizon.

How long will the shell be in the air? At what distance S from the gun will it fall to the ground? The gun and the point where the shell lands are on a horizontal line.

41. At what angle α to the horizon should a body be thrown to get the maximum range with a given initial velocity?

42. Two bodies are thrown with the same initial velocity at angles α and $(90° - \alpha)$ to the horizon.

Determine the ratio of the maximum heights reached by the bodies.

43. The initial velocity of a body thrown at an angle to the horizon is v_0. The maximum range is S.

At what angle α to the horizon should the body be thrown to have a range equal to l? $(l < S)$.

44. Field guns open fire on a shooting range.

What is the minimum safe altitude for bombers flying over the shooting range if the initial velocity of the shells is $v_0 = 800$ m/s? The shells are fired at an elevation angle of $\alpha = 15°$ to the horizon.

45. At what angle to the horizon should a jet of water be directed so that its elevation is equal to its range?

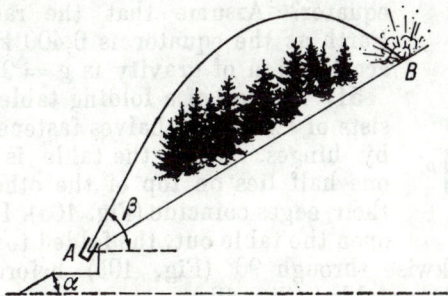

Fig. 8

46. A trench mortar fires at a target situated on the side of a hill (Fig. 8).

At what distance l ($l = AB$) will the shells fall if their initial velocity is v_0, the slope of the hill is $\alpha = 30°$ and the angle of fire is $\beta = 60°$ to the horizon?

4. Rotational Motion of a Solid Body

47. The minute-hand of the Moscow University tower clock is 4.5 m long.

With what linear velocity does the end of the hand move? What is the angular velocity of the hand?

48. Determine the velocity v and the acceleration a of the terrestrial points in latitude 60° due to the daily rotation of the Earth. The radius of the Earth is 6,400 km.

49. A pulley of radius $R = 20$ cm is rotated by a weight suspended from a thread which is gradually being wound off the pulley (Fig. 9). Initially the weight is at rest and then it begins to go down with an acceleration $a = 2$ cm/s².

Find the angular velocity of the pulley when the weight has travelled a distance $S_1 = 100$ cm. Determine the magnitude and direction of the acceleration of point A at this moment.

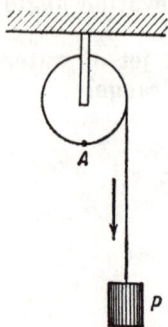

Fig. 9

50. What horizontal velocity should be imparted to a body so that it moves parallel to the terrestrial surface along the equator? Assume that the radius of the Earth at the equator is 6,400 km and the acceleration of gravity is $g = 9.7$ m/s^2.

51. The top of a folding table 1 m^2 consists of two equal halves fastened together by hinges. When the table is folded up, one half lies on top of the other so that their edges coincide (Fig. 10a). In order to open the table out, the folded top should be turned clockwise through 90° (Fig. 10b) before the two halves can be unfolded (Fig. 10c).

Find the position of the centre of rotation of the table top.

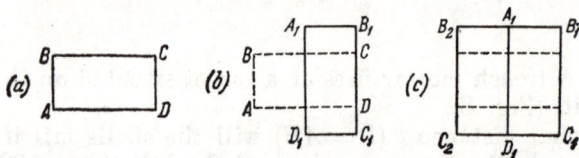

Fig. 10

5. Dynamics of the Rectilinear Motion of a Point

Since we have to calculate the forces and the accelerations which result from them, in almost every branch of physics it is extremely important to know how to solve problems involving the application of Newton's laws. Methods for solving them are therefore illustrated in this section.

Students often try to reduce such problems to a direct calculation from the equation $F = ma$ without discovering beforehand the physical meaning of the force F in the equation. For example, if when faced with the task fo finding the tension F_2 in a thread by which a body is set in motion from the acceleration of the body and the known force of friction F_1, a student will first determine the "motive" force $F = ma$ (considering it as one of the component forces and not as a resultant), and then, by adding to it the "retarding" force F_1, will find the force of tension in the thread which actually causes the motion of the body.

This method does not reveal the true picture of the physical interactions of bodies, leads to nonexistent properties being ascribed to individual forces and sometimes makes it altogether impossible to get the correct result without additional artificial and unwarrantedly complex reasoning. In particular, the method causes difficulties in problems involving interacting forces (for example, when determining the pressure exerted by a load on a moving support or the readings of a dynamometer which is being pulled in opposite directions with different forces).

In this section a method is followed for solving problems which involve the use of Newton's second law. This requires the student to have a clear picture of the interactions of bodies which give rise to the forces. He must then introduce these forces in an intelligible form (as an algebraic sum) into Newton's second law equation. Only when he has written all the equations correctly can he begin to calculate the unknown quantities directly.

As a good deal of practice is required to master this method, the student is advised to work through all the problems in this section systematically.

Particular attention should be paid to problems dealing with the motion of several interconnected bodies. In this case the first thing to do is to derive equations from Newton's second law for all the bodies in the moving system. When solving the problems in this section, one should take note of the way in which the interacting forces in a moving system depend on the distribution of masses along the link (for example, the way the tension in a thread depends on the ratio of the masses which it joins during the motion). One is also well advised to follow the relationship between the linking force and the motion in the system (for example, the relationship between the tension in a thread wrapped over a fixed pulley and linking two weights and the acceleration with which these weights move).

Since it is sometimes difficult to calculate the forces of

friction, especially when the force of friction $F < kN$ (k is the coefficient of friction and N is the perpendicular force between the surfaces in contact), this section includes several problems illustrating such calculations.

52. A body moving under the action of a constant force F travels a distance $S = 25$ cm in the first second.

Determine the force F if the mass of the body is 25 g.

53. A stone sliding over a horizontal ice surface stops after moving a distance $S = 48$ m.

Determine the initial velocity of the stone v_0 if the force of sliding friction of the stone against the ice is 0.06 of the weight of the stone.

54. A tramcar travelling at a speed of $v_0 = 36$ km/hr brakes sharply, its wheels not rotating but simply sliding along the rails.

What distance will be covered by the tramcar from the moment the brakes are applied until it stops, if the coefficient of friction of sliding of the wheels against the rails is $k = 0.2$?

55. A car weighing $P = 845$ kgf is standing on a railway truck.

What are the tensions in the ropes which hold the car on the truck if the train, on braking, has a deceleration of $a = 0.5$ m/s²? Disregard the friction.

56. A tractor pulls a sledge loaded with logs over an icy road at a constant speed of 15 km/hr.

With what speed will the tractor pull the same sledge and its load in summer over a ledger road if the power developed by the engine is the same in both cases? The coefficient of friction for motion over the icy road is $k_1 = 0.01$ and over the ledger road $k_2 = 0.15$.

57. A body weighing $P = 2.5$ kgf moves vertically downwards with an acceleration $a = 19.6$ m/s².

Find the force which acts on the body simultaneously with the force of gravity P during the fall. Neglect the resistance of the air.

58. With what force does a weight P bear on a support if the latter moves downwards with the weight and has an acceleration in the upwards direction?

59. A ball of mass m hangs on a thread fastened at point O. With what acceleration and in what vertical direction should the point of suspension O be displaced for the tension in the thread to be equal to half the weight of the ball?

60. High-speed passenger lifts move at a speed of 3.6 m/s. The weight of the lift and passengers may reach 1,500 kgf. The variation in the speed of the lift as it ascends is plotted in Fig. 11.

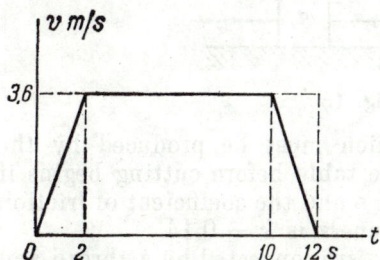

Fig. 11

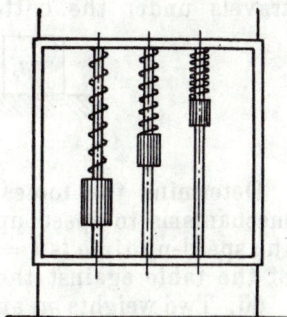

Fig. 12

Determine the tension in the cable holding the lift at the beginning, in the middle and at the end of the ascent. Assume $g = 10$ m/s².

61. In a device designed by N. A. Lyubimov* which was intended to demonstrate the interaction of bodies in a free fall, three weights 1 kgf, 2 kgf and 3 kgf are suspended from a light frame on identical springs (Fig. 12).

How will the position of the weights change and what will be the tension in each spring when the frame is in free fall?

62. Determine the force of air resistance acting on a parachutist if he descends with a constant velocity. The weight of the parachutist $P = 80$ kgf.

63. A body is thrown vertically upwards with an initial velocity $v_0 = 30$ m/s and reaches its highest point of rise after $t_1 = 2.5$ s.

---

* N. A. Lyubimov (1830-1897) was a professor of physics at the Moscow University and one of the teachers of the prominent Russian physicist A. G. Stoletov (1839-1896).

What is the mean value of the force of air resistance acting on the body during the ascent? The mass of the body is 40 g.

64. A man standing on the platform of a decimal balance performs rapid squatting motions. How will the readings of the balance change at the beginning and end of squatting?

65. The table of a small shaping machine weighs 100 kgf with the workpiece and the speed with which the table travels under the cutter is $v = 1$ m/s.

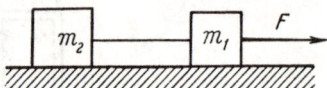

Fig. 13

Determine the forces which must be produced by the mechanisms to speed up the table before cutting begins if the speed-up time is $t = 0.5$ s and the coefficient of friction of the table against the runners is $k = 0.14$.

66. Two weights m_1 and m_2 are connected by a thread and lie on a smooth horizontal surface of a table (Fig. 13).

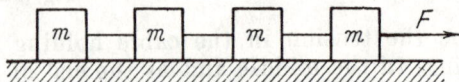

Fig. 14

With what acceleration will the weights move if a force $F = 10^5$ dynes parallel to the surface of the table is applied to the weight m_1? What is the tension in the thread linking the bodies in this case? The masses of the weights are $m_1 = 200$ g, $m_2 = 300$ g.

Determine the maximum force F at which the thread will be broken if this force is applied to: (a) the weight m_1; (b) the weight m_2. The thread can endure a maximum load of $T = 1$ kgf. Disregard the friction between the bodies and the table. In calculations assume $g = 10$ m/s^2.

67. Four identical blocks, each of mass m, are linked by threads and placed on a smooth table (Fig. 14). Force F is applied to the first block.

Find the tensions in all the threads. Disregard the forces of friction between the blocks and the table.

68. In order to start a heavy railway train the engine-driver first backs his train up and then engages the forward gear.

Why is it easier to start the train with this method? (The train is composed of freight-cars with loose couplings.)

69. If a locomotive starts a railway train with a sudden jolt the couplings between the freight-cars are sometimes broken.

Why, in what part of the train and in what other conditions does this occur most frequently?

70. A dynamometer D (Fig. 15) is attached to two weights of mass $M = 10$ kg and $m = 10$ g. Forces $F = 2$ kgf and $f = 1$ kgf are applied to the weights.

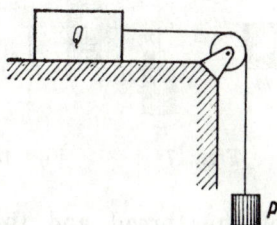

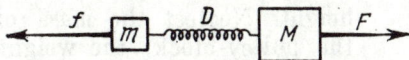

Fig. 15   Fig. 16

What will happen to the weights and what will the dynamometer show if: (1) the force F is applied to the larger weight and the force f to the smaller one; (2) the force F is applied to the smaller weight and f to the larger one; (3) what will the dynamometer show if the masses of the weights M and m are both equal to 5 kg?

71. Two bodies of weight Q and P are linked by a thread as shown in Fig. 16.

With what acceleration does the body Q move if its coefficient of friction against the table top is k? What is the tension in the thread connecting the bodies? Disregard the mass of the pulley-block and the weight of the thread. The surface of the table is horizontal.

72. Two identical weights of mass M are linked by a thread wrapped around a pulley-block with a fixed axis. A small weight of mass m is placed on one of the weights (Fig. 17).

(1) With what acceleration will the weights move? (2) What is the tension in the thread when the weights are moving? (3) What pressure will be exerted on the axis of the pulley-block as the weights move? (4) With what force

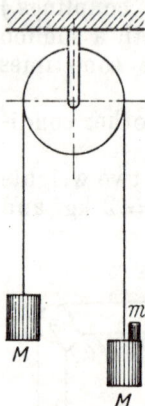
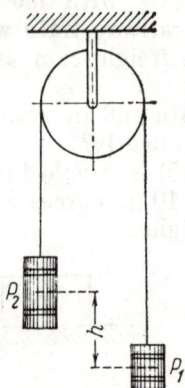

will the smaller weight m press against the weight M? Neglect the mass of the pulley-block, the weight of the thread and the air resistance.

73. Two weights $P_1 = 1$ kgf and $P_2 = 2$ kgf are linked by a thread strung over a fixed pulley-block. Initially the distance between the centres of gravity of these weights is $h = 1$ m (Fig. 18).

How long after the weights start to move will their centres of gravity be at the same height? Neglect the mass of the pulley-block, the weight of the thread and the air resistance.

Fig. 17   Fig. 18

74. Weights P_1 and P_2 are connected by a thread strung over a fixed pulley-block. Initially the centres of gravity of the weights are at the same height.

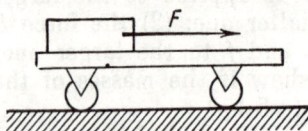
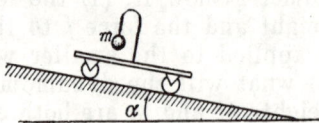

Fig. 19   Fig. 20

Determine with what acceleration and in what vertical direction the centre of gravity of the combination of weights will move if $P_1 > P_2$.

75. A cart weighing 20 kgf can roll without friction along a horizontal path. The cart carries a block weighing 2 kgf (Fig. 19). The coefficient of friction between the block and the cart is $k = 0.25$. First a force $F_1 = 200$ gf is applied to the block and then a force $F_2 = 2$ kgf.

Find the force of friction between the block and the cart and their accelerations in both cases.

76. A light cart rolls without friction down an inclined surface. A plumb line is fastened on the cart (a ball of mass m on a thread) (Fig. 20).

What will the direction of the plumb line be when the cart rolls freely down the slope? Before the cart started rolling, the thread was held perpendicular to the inclined surface.

77. A log of weight P is pulled at a constant velocity and with a force F by means of a rope of length l. The distance between the end of the rope and the ground is h (Fig. 21).

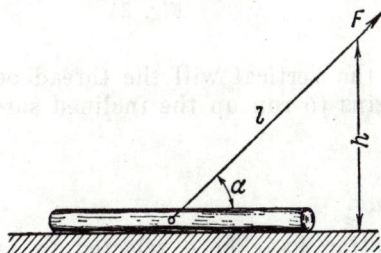
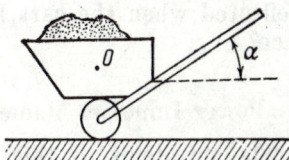

Fig. 21   Fig. 22

Find the coefficient of friction between the log and the ground. The rope is attached to the centre of gravity of the log. Will the force of friction change if the rope is fastened to the end of the log?

78. A man wheels a barrow at a constant speed (Fig. 22). First he pulls it after him and later he pushes it forward. In both cases the handles of the barrow make the same angle α with the horizontal.

In which case must the man apply the greater effort in order to wheel the barrow? The weight of the wheelbarrow is P, its centre of gravity O is above the axis of the wheel and the coefficient of friction of the wheels aganst the ground is equal to k.

79. A cart weighing 500 kgf moves down a funicular railway inclined at $\alpha = 30°$ to the horizontal (Fig. 23).

Determine the tension in the cable as the cart is braked at the end of descent if its speed before braking was $v_0 =$

= 2 m/s and the braking time $t = 5$ s. Assume the coefficient of friction to be $k = 0.01$.

80. A small cart with a ball suspended from a thread (Fig. 24) moves with a velocity v_0 towards an inclined surface.

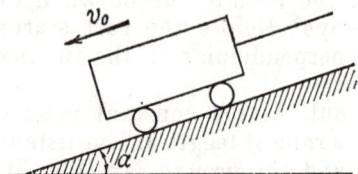

Fig. 23

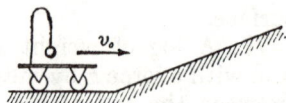

Fig. 24

In which direction from the vertical will the thread be deflected when the cart begins to run up the inclined surface?

6. Power Impulse. Momentum

The problems in this section have been selected so as to give the reader a comprehensive understanding of the extremely important concepts of dynamics —power impulse and momentum, and with the law of conservation of momentum albeit in its simplest form. This broadens considerably the range of problems which can be solved by a student and also provides a new and deeper insight into problems which he previously solved by Newton's laws. In solving the problems in this section, attention should be paid first of all to those in which the vectorial nature of the impulse and momentum is revealed and to the rules for calculating these quantities.

Most of the problems in this section can easily be solved either by determining accelerations from Newton's laws and then calculating the velocities by the equations of kinematics, or by calculating the velocities directly from the impulses and from the law of conservation of momentum. It is recommended that these problems be solved using both methods. As you solve the problems, remember that if the solution does not require every part of the motion to be determined and only the final velocities have to be found from the given initial velocities, then the application of the concepts of impulse and momentum, and the law of conservation of momentum will always result in the simplest and neatest methods of solution.

It is advisable to try and solve some problems from Sec. 5, utilizing the concepts of impulse and momentum, in order to develop good habits when selecting the best method for a particular problem.

When attempting the problems in this section the reader should select the simplest method of applying the law of conservation of momentum to the calculation of velocities. Experience shows that this will allow him to avoid many unpleasant technical errors in calculations.

81. A ball of mass m flies perpendicularly upwards a wall with a velocity v (Fig. 25), strikes it elastically and rebounds with the same speed in the opposite direction.

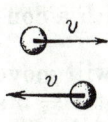

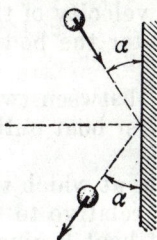

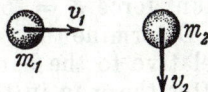

Fig. 25   Fig. 26   Fig. 27

Indicate the magnitude and the direction of the impulse imparted to the ball by the wall. What is the average force with which the ball acted on the wall if the impact continued for t seconds?

82. Determine the magnitude of the impulse received by the ball from the wall (see the previous problem) if the impact was completely inelastic.

83. A ball strikes a wall elastically at an angle α (Fig. 26). The mass of the ball is m, the velocity before and after impact has the same value v and the angle of incidence is equal to the angle of reflection. Determine the magnitude and direction of the vector representing the change in momentum of the ball.

84. Two balls of mass $m_1 = 2$ g and $m_2 = 3$ g move in a horizontal plane with velocities $v_1 = 6$ m/s and $v_2 = 4$ m/s, respectively. The balls move at an angle of $\alpha = 90°$ (Fig. 27) to each other.

What is the sum of the momenta of these balls?

85. A body is acted upon by a constant force $F = 5$ kgf for a time $t = 10$ s.

Find the mass of the body if the resulting change in velocity is $\Delta v = 5$ m/s.

86. A train weighs 3,000 tons. The coefficient of friction $k = 0.02$.

What should the tractive force of the locomotive be for the train to acquire a speed of 60 km/hr two minutes after the motion has commenced?

87. A body of weight P slides down a rough inclined surface. The angle of inclination is $\alpha = 30°$, the length of the inclined surface $l = 167$ cm and the coefficient of friction $k = 0.2$. The initial velocity of the body is zero.

How long does it take for the body to reach the bottom of the inclined surface?

88. A rope is stretched between two boats on the surface of a lake. A man in the first boat pulls the rope with a constant force $F = 5$ kgf.

Determine the velocities at which the first boat will move relative to the bank and relative to the other boat $t = 5$ s after the man in the first boat begins to pull the rope. The combined weight of the first boat and the man in it is $P_1 = 250$ kgf and the weight of the second boat and its load is $P_2 = 500$ kgf. Neglect the resistance of the water.

Indicate several ways of solving the problem.

89. A man of mass m stands on a rope-ladder which is tied to a free balloon of mass M. The balloon is at rest.

In what direction and at what speed will the balloon move if the man starts to climb the rope-ladder at a constant velocity v relative to the ladder?

90. A compressed spring is situated between two carts of mass m_1 and m_2 (Fig. 28). When the spring expands and assumes its initial state it acts on each cart with an average force F for a time τ.

Prove that after the spring is fully expanded and its action ceases the carts will move along horizontal rails in such a way that their centre of mass (centre of gravity) remains at rest. Disregard friction.

91. A grenade flying in a horizontal direction with a velocity $v_0 = 10$ m/s bursts into two fragments weighing $P_1 = 1$ kgf and $P_2 = 1.5$ kgf. After the burst the velocity of the larger fragment remains horizontal and increases to $v_2 = 25$ m/s.

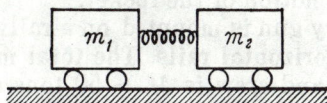

Fig. 28

Find the speed and direction of the smaller fragment.

92. The world's first reactive projectile invented by the Russian general A. D. Zasyadko (1779-1838) weighed about 2 kgf (without the propellant charge). The explosion of the propellant charge ejected 200 g of powder gases from the projectile at a velocity $u = 600$ m/s.

At what distance from the point of projection will such a body fall, if it is launched at an angle $\alpha = 45°$ to the horizontal? Disregard the air resistance.

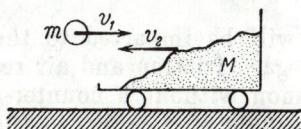

Fig 29.

93. A cart filled with sand rolls at a speed $v_2 = 1$ m/s along a horizontal path without friction (Fig. 29). A ball of mass $m = 2$ kg is thrown with a horizontal velocity $v_1 = 7$ m/s towards the cart. The ball meets the cart and gets stuck in the sand.

In what direction and with what velocity u will the cart move after the ball strikes it? The mass of the cart is $M = 10$ kg.

94. Assume that the jet engine of a rocket ejects the

products of combustion in portions whose masses are $m =$ $= 200$ g and whose velocity on exit from the nozzle of the engine is $v = 1,000$ m/s.

Assuming it flies horizontally with what velocity will the rocket move after the ejection of the third portion of the gas? What will the velocity of the rocket be at the end of the first second of motion if the engine produces twenty bursts per second? The initial mass of the rocket is $M =$ $= 300$ kg and its initial velocity is zero. Disregard the air resistance to the motion of the rocket.

95. An artillery gun is mounted on a railway truck standing on straight horizontal rails. The total mass of the truck with gun, shells and crew is $M = 50$ tons and the mass of

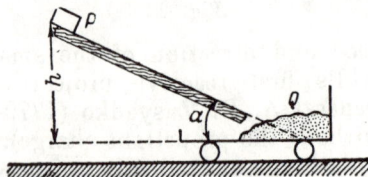

Fig. 30

each shell is $m = 25$ kg. The gun fires in a horizontal direction along the railway. The initial velocity of the shells is $v_0 = 1,000$ m/s.

What velocity will be imparted to the truck after the second shot? Disregard friction and air resistance.

96. An old cannon without a counter-recoil mechanism fires a ball at an angle of $\alpha = 40°$ to the horizontal. The mass of the ball is $m = 10$ kg and the initial velocity $v_0 =$ $= 200$ m/s.

What will the velocity of recoil of the cannon be if its mass $M = 500$ kg? Disregard friction.

97. A body of weight P slides without friction down an inclined board onto a cart standing at rest.

What velocity v will be imparted to the cart when the body drops on it? The weight of the cart is Q, the initial height of the body above the level of the cart is h and the angle at which the board is inclined to the horizontal is α (Fig. 30). The cart moves without friction.

7. Work. Energy. Power

Usually, in solving the kind of problems in this section the most serious difficulties are encountered when the original store of energy of any system is distributed, during motion, between several bodies simultaneously (for example, when a body slides down a moving triangular prism, Problems 106, 107). For this reason, in addition to problems which explain the concepts of work, energy and power, this section includes a series of problems which require simultaneous calculation of the energy of several interacting bodies.

When solving such problems, one should pay attention to the fact that if, for an elastic impact, the bodies are in motion before and after interaction, the law of conservation of momentum and the law of conservation of energy need to be applied simultaneously in order to calculate the velocities. The methods pertaining to the use of these laws should be considered carefully.

The problems in this section utilize the concepts of perfectly elastic and inelastic impacts. When solving the problems, one should observe the specific behaviour of the interacting bodies in these two cases.

Most of the problems dealing with the calculation of energy of rotating bodies are to be found in Sec. 8. In solving such problems it is worth noting those cases in which a body's original store of energy is converted instantaneously into two other kinds of energy (for example, the case considered in Problem 136). Just as in Sec. 6, it is advisable to follow the entire sequence of operations when applying the law of conservation of energy.

98. A gun whose barrel weighs 450 kgf fires in a horizontal direction. The weight of the shell is 5 kgf and its initial velocity $v_0 = 450$ m/s. When the shell is fired the barrel recoils a distance of 45 cm.

Determine the mean braking force developed in the gun's counter-recoil mechanism.

99. A body falls with an initial velocity $v_0 = 14$ m/s from a height $h = 240$ m and penetrates into sand a depth $S = 0.2$ m.

Determine the mean resistive force of the sand. The body weighs 1 kgf. Disregard the air resistance. Solve the problem by two different ways: with the aid of Newton's laws and on the basis of the law of conservation of energy.

100. A sledge slides down an icy hill of height h (Fig. 31) and stops after covering a distance CB. The distance AB is equal to S.

Determine the coefficient of friction k between the sledge and the icy surface. Calculate the acceleration of the sledge over the path DC and over the path CB.

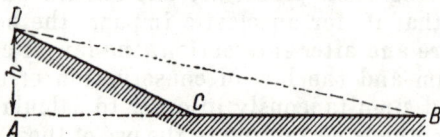

Fig. 31

101. Will the distance S change (see the previous problem) if the hill is sloping but has the same height h? Will the sledge move on a hill whose base is $AB = S$ (Fig. 31) and whose height is h as before?

102. A uniform rectangular parallelepiped of mass m and with sides l, $2l$ and $4l$ is placed in turn on each of its three sides on a horizontal surface.

What is the potential energy of the parallelepiped in each of these positions? What position will be the most stable?

103. A bullet fired from a rifle with an initial velocity $v_0 = 1,000$ m/s strikes the ground with a velocity $v = 500$ m/s. What work has been expended during the flight to overcome the air resistance if the bullet weighs 10 g?

104. A boy leaning against a fence throws a stone horizontally with a velocity $v_1 = 5$ m/s.

(1) What velocity v_2 can the boy impart to the stone if he throws it with the same force while standing on skates on smooth ice? The mass of the stone $m = 1$ kg, the mass of the boy $M = 49$ kg.

(2) Will the boy produce the same power in each case?

(3) What will the velocity of the stone be relative to the boy in the second case?

105. A man in a boat A, of mass $m_1 = 300$ kg, pulls a rope with a force $F = 10$ kgf. The other end of the rope is tied first to a tree on the bank and then to a boat B of mass $m = 200$ kg.

Determine the velocity of the boat A in both cases at the end of the third second. What work will be done in this time and what power will the man develop in these two cases by the end of the third second? Disregard the weight of the rope and the resistance of the water.

106. A heavy body slides smoothly down a triangular prism (Fig. 32). The prism lies on a horizontal surface and can move along it without friction. The prism is fixed in the first case and free in the second.

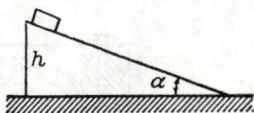

Fig. 32

Will the velocity of the body when it reaches the end of the prism be the same in both cases if the body slides each time from the same height?

107. Determine the direction in which a load slides down a movable prism (see the previous problem). The mass of the load is m and the mass of the prism is M. The prism moves in a horizontal direction due solely to the pressure exerted by the load. There is no friction.

108. Two identical perfectly elastic balls roll towards each other along a smooth horizontal surface. The velocities of the balls are v_1 and v_2.

With what velocities will the balls move after head-on collision? The impact is perfectly elastic. There is no friction.

109. Two boats set on parallel courses move under their own momentum through the stagnant water of a lake towards each other and with the same velocity $v = 6$ m/s. As soon as they come abreast a load is shifted from the first boat onto the second. After that, the second boat continues to move in the original direction but with a velocity $v_2 = 4$ m/s.

Find the mass of the second boat if the first boat weighs $P_1 = 500$ kgf empty and the weight of the load is $p =$

= 60 kgf. Calculate the energy store of the boats and the load before and after the load has been transferred. Explain why this energy store has changed. Neglect the resistance of the water.

110. What power must be developed by an aircraft engine to raise it to an altitude of 1 km if the aircraft weighs 3,000 kgf and the time of ascent is 1 min?

111. The motors of an electric train moving with a velocity $v = 54$ km/hr consume a power of $N_1 = 900$ kW. The efficiency of the motors and the drive mechanisms is $k = 0.8$.

Determine the tractive force of the motors.

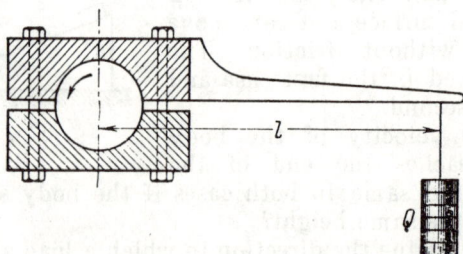

Fig. 33

112. The power of an engine is frequently determined experimentally with the aid of the so-called absorption dynamometer which consists of two shoes tightly gripping the shaft of the engine. A lever with a weight on the end is attached to one of the shoes (Fig. 33). The weight is selected so as to equalize the force of friction and hold the lever in a horizontal position.

Determine the power of the engine if the number of shaft revolutions is $n = 60$ rpm, the length of the lever from the centre of the shaft is $l = 1$ m and the weight is $Q = 50$ kgf. Disregard the weight of the lever.

113. A cyclist rides up a hill at a constant velocity.

Determine the power developed by the cyclist if the length of the connecting rod of the pedal is $r = 25$ cm, the time for one complete revolution of the rod is $t = 2$ s and the mean force exerted by his foot on the pedal is $F = 15$ kgf.

114. In order to take off, an aircraft must have a velocity $v = 80$ km/hr. The take-off run is $S = 100$ m, the weight of the aircraft is $P = 1,000$ kgf and the coefficient of friction during the run is $k = 0.2$.

What must the minimum power of the engine be so that the aircraft can take off? Consider the motion during the run as uniformly accelerated.

115. The stone of a grinding machine has a diameter $d = 60$ cm and revolves at $n = 120$ rpm. The workpiece is pressed against the stone with a force $F = 100$ kgf.

What power is expended on grinding if the coefficient of friction between the stone and the workpiece is $k = 0.2$?

116. A pulley is rotated by a drive belt (Fig. 34). The radius of the pulley is $r = 25$ cm and the number of revolutions it makes $n = 120$ rpm. The tension in the driving part of the belt is twice that in the driven part. Both parts of the belt are parallel.

Fig. 34

Find the tensions in the driving and driven parts of the belt when it transmits power of $W = 15$ kW to the pulley.

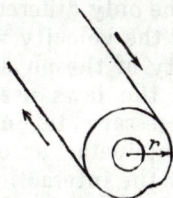

8. Dynamics of a Point Moving in a Circle

Calculating the forces which act on a body moving in a circle is, perhaps, one of the most difficult tasks in physics.

The difficulties arise as a rule when the centripetal acceleration in rotational motion and the acceleration in rectilinear motion are regarded as two physical quantities which differ in principle, each obeying its own laws: one can be calculated from the "usual" Newton's law and the other from the "special" centripetal and centrifugal forces. When such an incorrect contraposition of the laws and characteristics of rectilinear motion and motion along circular path is made, it is very difficult to solve correctly problems in which the concept of a centrifugal force as a force acting on the physical link between the point and the centre cannot be employed (for example, problems on the determination of the force which a moving car exerts on a convex bridge).

In this section the problems and the solutions that go with them are chosen so as to help the reader get rid of this misconception, if it is present.

In solving problems involving the calculation of motion in a circle, it should be remembered that acceleration in rectilinear motion and centripetal acceleration are the same in their physical nature (both change the velocity). The only difference is that the former changes the magnitude of the velocity vector and the latter its direction. The identity of the physical nature also predetermines the identity of the laws used to calculate these quantities. It is not necessary to introduce any "special" forces to calculate centripetal accelerations apart from the forces generated by the interaction of bodies.

Just as in calculating rectilinear motion, it is necessary in the case of rotational motion to specify first the nature of the change in the velocity vector, the direction and magnitudes of the acceleration vectors, and then to get a clear insight into the interaction of the bodies which produce the forces, obtain the sum of these forces and apply Newton's second law to calculate the sought-for quantities.

This sequence of operations is adopted for solving all the problems in this section. This is something which should be given a special attention.

One should carefully consider those problems in which the necessary centripetal accelerations are provided by the simultaneous action of two or several forces (for example, Problems 124-140).

When solving the problems, consider the origination of the forces in rotational motion needed to produce sufficient accelerations for various kinds of interaction between bodies (centripetal accelerations due to friction forces, tensions in an elastic cord, forces exerted by rails, etc.). Also observe the change in the magnitude of these forces, their direction and the points of application when the velocity of a body along the circle is increased. Notice the behaviour of a body when the forces of interaction are not enough to set up the accelerations necessary for it to move in a circle (for example, Problem 133).

It is advisable in solving the problems requiring the use of the law of conservation of energy to compare their solutions with the problems in Sec. 7.

117. Two balls of mass $M = 9$ g and $m = 3$ g are attached by threads AO and OB whose combined length is $l = 1$ m to a vertical axis at O (Fig. 35) and are set in rotational motion in a horizontal plane about this axis with a constant angular velocity ω.

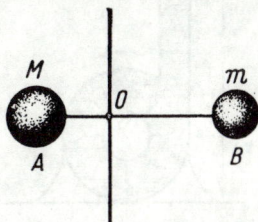

Determine the ratio of the lengths AO and OB for which the tensions in the threads will be the same. Disregard the weight of the threads.

118. Two identical balls A and B are attached to the ends of a

Fig. 35

thread passed through a tube as shown in Fig. 36. The ball B rotates in a horizontal plane. The distance from the axis of the tube to the ball B is $r = 20$ cm.

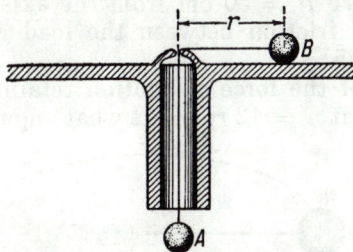

Fig. 36

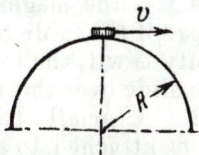

Fig. 37

With what angular velocity should the ball B rotate so that the ball A neither rises nor sinks? Will the equilibrium be stable? Disregard the friction.

119. A small washer is placed on the top of a hemisphere of radius R (Fig. 37).

What minimum horizontal velocity should be imparted to the washer to detach it from the hemisphere at the initial point of motion?

120. Determine the centripetal acceleration of bodies on the terrestrial equator. Find the reduction in the weight of bodies on the equator due to the participation of these bodies in the rotational motion of the Earth. The radius of the Earth is about 6,400 km.

121. A centrifugal pump has vanes of radius R. The pump can raise water to a maximum height h (Fig. 38).

Find: (1) the number of revolutions of the pump; (2) the difference in pressure between points lying on the axis and points on the external circumference of the vanes of the pump; (3) prove that the sum of all the forces acting on water particles which are at a distance R from the axis of rotation is $m\omega^2 R$

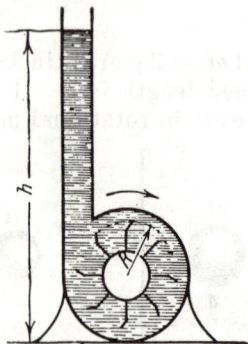

Fig. 38

(m is the mass of these particles).

122. A load weighing $P = 1$ kgf is placed on a horizontal revolving table at a distance $R = 50$ cm from the axis of rotation. The coefficient of friction between the load and the table surface is $k = 0.25$.

What is the magnitude of the force of friction retaining the load if the table rotates at $n = 12$ rpm? At what angular velocity ω will the load begin to slide over the table?

123. A small ball of mass m attached to a rubber cord moves in a circle through a horizontal plane with an angular velocity ω (Fig. 39).

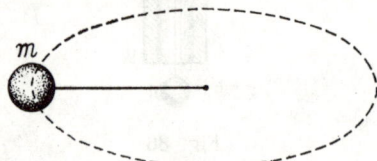

Fig. 39

Determine the radius of the circle along which the ball will move and the tension in the cord. The original length of the unstretched rubber cord is l_0. The force of tension in the cord increases in proportion to the amount it is stretched. When the length is increased by 1 cm the cord produces a force f_0.

124. A car weighing P kgf moves with a constant velocity

v: (1) over a horizontal flat bridge; (2) over a convex bridge; (3) over a concave bridge. The radius of curvature of the bridge in the last two cases is R.

What pressure is exerted by the car on the bridge in each of these cases as it passes the middle point of the bridge?

125. Determine the force that presses the pilot against his seat at the upper and lower points of a loop if the weight of the pilot is $P = 75$ kgf, the radius of the loop is $R = 200$ m and the velocity of the plane looping the loop is constant and equal to $v = 360$ km/hr.

126. A pendulum string of length l is moved up to a horizontal position (Fig. 40) and released.

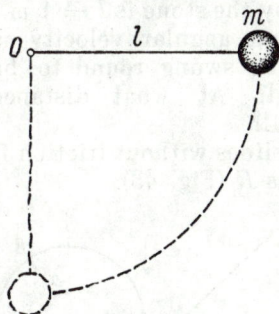

Fig. 40

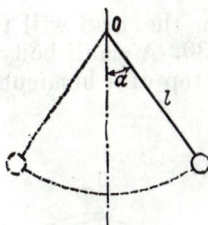

Fig. 41

What should the minimum strength of the string be to withstand the tension as the pendulum passes through the position of equilibrium? The mass of the pendulum is m. Disregard the mass of the string and air resistance.

127. A pendulum consisting of a small heavy bob suspended from a rigid rod oscillates in a vertical plane (Fig. 41). When the bob passes through the position of equilibrium the rod is subjected to a tension equal to twice the weight of the bob.

Through what maximum angle α from the vertical will the pendulum be deflected? Disregard the weight of the rod and the resistance of the air.

128. A ball of mass m is suspended from a thread of length l. The ball is moved up from the position of equilibrium to the suspension point and is then released.

At what value of α (the angle between the thread and the vertical, Fig. 41) will the thread be broken if it can withstand twice the weight of the ball? What will the trajectory of the ball be like after the thread is broken?

129. A man swings a stone of mass 1 kg uniformly round in a vertical plane (Fig. 42). The stone is attached to a thread that can withstand a tension of 4 kgf. The axis of rotation is at a distance of $h = 4$ m from the ground. The radius of the circle described by the stone is $l = 1$ m.

With what angular velocity must the stone be swung round to break the thread? At what distance S from the man will the stone fall?

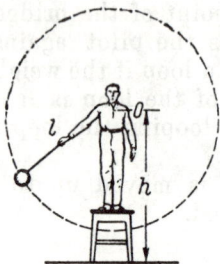

Fig. 42

130. A small body of mass m slides without friction from the top of a hemisphere of radius R (Fig. 43).

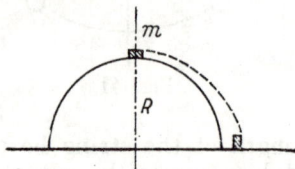

Fig. 43

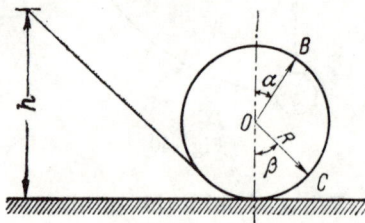

Fig. 44

At what height will the body be detached from the surface of the hemisphere?

131. A ball slides without friction down an inclined chute from a height h and then moves in a loop of radius R (Fig. 44).

What is the pressure exerted by the ball on the chute at a certain point B if the radius drawn from the centre of the loop to the point B makes an angle α with the vertical? The mass of the ball is m and the height $h = 5/2R$. Consider the size of the ball as negligible.

132. Determine the pressure exerted by the ball at the point C (Fig. 44) for the conditions of motion specified in the previous problem.

133. A heavy ball of mass m slides without friction down an inclined chute which forms a loop of radius R (Fig. 45).

At what height will the ball leave the chute and to what maximum height will it rise afterwards if it begins to run down the chute without initial velocity from a height $h = 2R$? Consider the size of the ball as negligible.

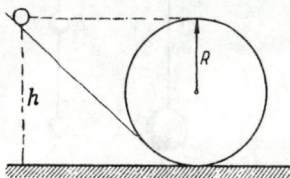
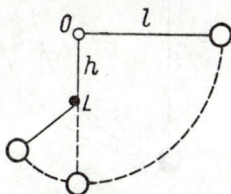

Fig. 45   Fig. 46

134. A heavy ball of mass m is suspended from a thread of length $l = 2h$ which is fixed at point O. A nail L is hammered in at a distance h from the point O (Fig. 46). The thread is moved an angle $\alpha = 90°$ from the position of equilibrium and released.

How will the ball move when the thread meets the nail L? What maximum height will the ball attain after passing the position of equilibrium?

135. At what minimum distance h from the point of suspension should the nail L be driven in (see the conditions of the previous problem) so that the ball deflected through an angle $\alpha = 90°$ will move in a circle whose centre is at L?

136. Two balls A and B with the same mass m are suspended one on a rigid thread and the other on a rubber cord. Both balls are deflected from the position of equilibrium through an angle $\alpha = 90°$ and released. When the balls pass through the position of equilibrium the length of the rubber cord becomes equal to that of the thread l (Fig. 47).

Which of the balls will have the larger linear velocity when passing through the point of equilibrium?

137. A weightless rod of length l carries first a mass $2m$ at its end and then two equal masses m, one secured at the end and the other in the middle of the rod (Fig. 48). The rod can revolve in a vertical plane around the point A.

What horizontal velocity must be imparted to the end of the rod C in the first and second cases to deflect it to the horizontal position?

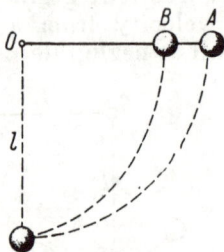

Fig. 47

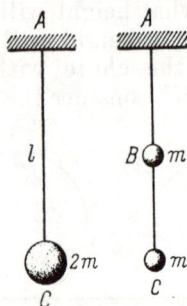

Fig. 48

138. A cyclist rides at a constant velocity of 36 km/hr along a circle of radius 34 m.

At what angle to the vertical should he incline his bicycle?

139. What is the minimum radius of a circle along which a cyclist can ride with a velocity $v = 28.8$ km/hr if the coefficient of friction between the tyres and the road is $k = 0.3$? What is the maximum angle at which the bicycle must be inclined to prevent the rider from falling over?

140. What is the maximum speed at which a railway carriage can move without toppling over along a curve of iadius $R = 200$ m if the distance from the centre of gravity of the carriage to the level of the rails is $h = 1.5$ m, the distance between the rails is $l = 1.5$ m and the rails are laid horizontally?

141. When can a spirit level (a bubble of air in a tube filled with a liquid) be used in a moving train to determine the gradient of the railway bed?

142. A load is weighed on a spring balance in the carriage of a train which is moving along a curve of radius $R = 404$ m at a speed $v = 72$ km/hr. The weight of the load rs $P = 5$ kgf.

What will the reading of the spring balance be?

143. An aircraft weighing $P = 300$ kgf flies at a speed $v = 360$ km/hr and makes a turn of radius $R = 2,500$ m. Determine the aircraft's bank angle and the magnitude of the lift needed to perform the turn in a horizontal plane. The lift is always directed perpendicularly to the plane of the aircraft wings.

144. A ball of mass m (Fig. 49) is attached to the end of a thread fastened to the top of a vertical rod which is secured to a horizontally revolving round table.

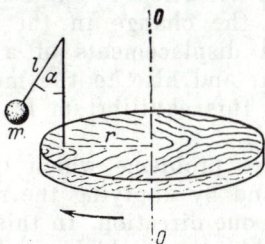   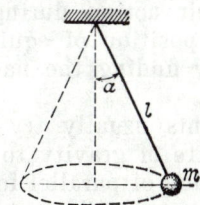

Fig. 49   Fig. 50

With what angular velocity ω will the table rotate if the thread forms an angle of $\alpha = 45°$ with the vertical? The length of the thread is $l = 6$ cm and the distance of the rod from the axis of rotation is $r = 10$ cm.

145. A heavy ball of mass m is suspended from a thread of length l. The ball rotates uniformly in a circle in a horizontal plane (conical pendulum) (Fig. 50). The thread makes an angle α with the vertical.

Find the time for one complete revolution of the ball.

9. Statics

Most of the problems in statics covered by the school curriculum can be solved using various independent methods —either from the general conditions of equilibrium (the sum of forces and the sum of moments of forces are equal to zero) or with the help of the "golden rule" of mechanics. It is extremely important to master thoroughly these methods for solving problems involving simple machines.

The problems in this section are selected so as to enable the reader to trace the application of each rule to the calculation of various systems. It is advisable to follow carefully the sequence of operations for each method in those problems which are to be solved by several different ways.

Serious difficulties are encountered when the "golden rule" of mechanics is applied to determine the nature of equilibrium for separate bodies or systems. Several problems in this section on stability or instability of bodies are intended to draw the student's attention to the sequence of operations for determining the change in the forces and their action during small displacements of a body from a position of equilibrium, and also to the methods used for finding the nature of this equilibrium from the changes.

Students usually try to solve problems which require the centre of gravity to be found by applying the rule of summation of parallel forces in one direction. In this case, even the most elementary problems in which the centre of gravity can only be determined by using the rule of resolution of parallel forces or the rule of summation of parallel forces oppositely directed usually become extremely difficult. Pay special attention to the solution of Problem 170 in which the sequence of applying the above rules to determine the centre of gravity of an intricate figure is considered.

146. Find the resultant R of five forces equal in magnitude applied to one point and arranged in one plane if the angles between all the forces are the same (Fig. 51).

147. In which case will a rope have the greater tension:

(1) Two men pull the ends of the rope with forces F equal in magnitude but opposite in direction.

(2) One end of the rope is fastened to a fixed support and the other is pulled by a man with a force $2F$.

148. Two uniform rods each of weight $P = 16$ kgf and length $L = 1.2$ m are suspended horizontally from ropes (Fig. 52). The lengths of the ropes AC, BC, AD and BE are the same and equal to $l = 1$ m.

Determine the tension in the ropes and the forces acting

on the rods in both cases. The rope DA is parallel to CB and BE is parallel to AC.

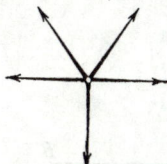

Fig. 51

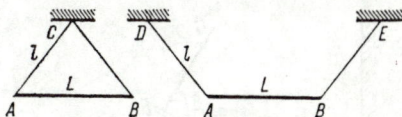

Fig. 52

149. A noose is placed around a log and used to pull it with a force F (Fig. 53).

How will the tension of the ropes forming the loop depend on the magnitude of the angle α? In what conditions will

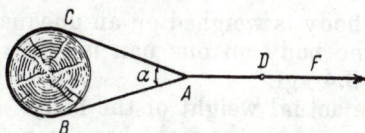

Fig. 53

the tension of the rope in the sections AB and AC be larger than in the section AD?

150. To rescue a car stuck on a bad road the driver ties one end of a rope to the car and the other to a tree a distance $l = 12$ m in front. Putting the weight of his body on the middle of the rope in a perpendicular direction to it with a force $F = 40$ kgf, the driver moves $S = 0.6$ m.

What force is acting on the car at the last moment? Consider the rope as inelastic.

151. One end of a heavy uniform board of weight P and length l presses against a corner between a wall and a floor. A rope is attached to the other end of the board (Fig. 54).

Determine the tension in the rope BC if the angle between the board and the rope is $\beta = 90°$. How will the tension in the rope change as the angle α between the board and the floor increases if the angle β remains constant?

152. A uniform beam rests on a truck with one end overhanging (Fig. 55). The length of the overhanging end is 0.25 the length of the beam. A force P acts on the end of

the beam at point B. When P is equal to 300 kgf the opposite
end of the beam A begins to rise.

What is the weight of the beam Q?

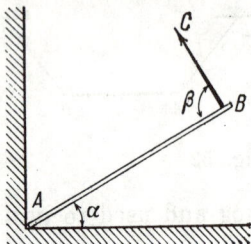

Fig. 54

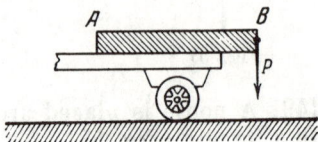

Fig. 55

153. When a body is weighed on an unequal-arm balance
the weight of the body on one pan is $P_1 = 3$ kgf and on
the other $P_2 = 3.4$ kgf.

Determine the actual weight of the body.

154. A man stands on the right-hand pan of a large beam
balance and is counterbalanced by a weight placed on the

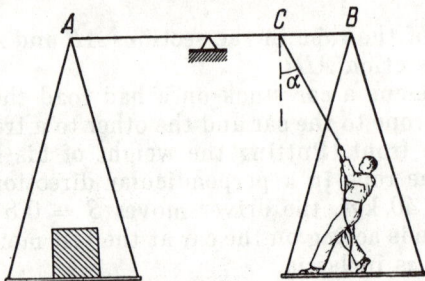

Fig. 56

other pan. A rope is tied to the middle of the right-hand
arm of the balance at point C (Fig. 56).

Will the equilibrium be disturbed if the man standing
on the pan begins to pull the rope with a force $F < P$ at
an angle of α to the vertical? The weight of the man is P
and the length of the beam $AB = l$. This is an equal-arm
balance. Disregard the weight of the rope.

155. One end of a beam is fixed to a wall. The beam is in a horizontal position (Fig. 57). (Neglect the deflection of the beam under the action of the force of gravity.) A force $P = 100$ kgf is applied to the free end of the beam at an angle $\alpha = 30°$ to the horizontal.

Find the magnitude of the force causing the tension and deflection of the beam.

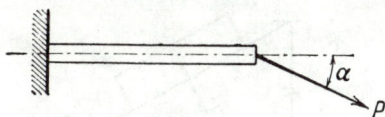

Fig. 57

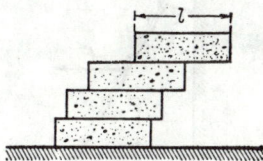

Fig. 58

156. A bricklayer lays four bricks to make the cornice of a building so that a portion of each brick protrudes over the one below (Fig. 58).

Determine the maximum lengths of the overhanging parts when the bricks in the cornice are still in equilibrium without mortar. The length of each brick is l.

157. A uniform beam of length l and weight P is balanced on a trihedral prism.

Will the equilibrium change if a quarter of the beam is cut off and placed on the shortened end of the beam on top and level with it (Fig. 59)?

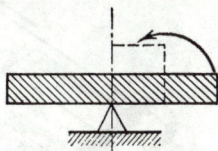

Fig. 59

If the equilibrium does change, what force is needed to restore the equilibrium and at which end of the beam should it be applied?

158. A ladder of weight P and length l is placed against a smooth vertical wall at an angle $\alpha = 30°$. The centre of gravity of the ladder is at a height h from the floor (Fig. 60). A man pulls the ladder at its middle point in a horizontal direction with a force F.

What is the minimum value of the force F which will permit the man to detach the upper end of the ladder from the wall? The friction against the floor is such that the bottom of the ladder does not slide.

159. Which is the easier way to set a railway carriage in motion: by applying a force to the body of the carriage, or by applying it to the top of the rim of the wheel?

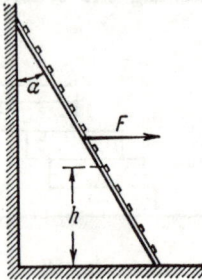

Fig. 60

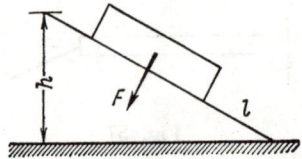

Fig. 61

160. A wooden block lies on an inclined surface (Fig. 61). With what force should this block be pressed against the surface to retain it in equilibrium? The weight of the block

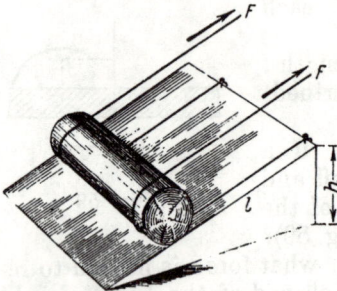

Fig. 62

is $P = 2$ kgf, the length of the inclined surface $l = 1$ m and the height $h = 60$ cm. The coefficient of friction of the block against the inclined surface is $k = 0.4$.

161. A heavy log is pulled up an inclined surface with the aid of two parallel ropes secured as shown in Fig. 62. The weight of the log is $P = 400$ kgf, the height of the inclined surface $h = 1$ m, and its length $l = 2$ m.

What force F should be applied to each rope to pull the log up? Indicate two methods for solving the problem.

162. What force should be applied to the end of the lever of a differential winch to retain a load $P = 50$ kgf?

The length of the lever is $l = 1$ m, the radius of the larger cylinder of the winch $r_1 = 20$ cm, the radius of the smaller cylinder $r_2 = 10$ cm (Fig. 63). Indicate two methods for solving the problem.

163. To what height h can a load P be raised (see the previous problem) if the winch performs 10 revolutions?

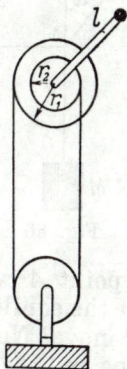

Fig. 63

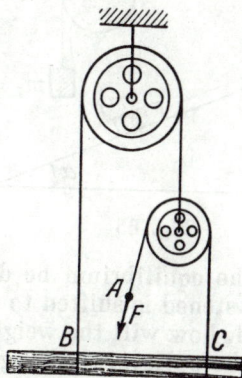

Fig. 64

164. The system of pulleys shown in Fig. 64 is used to raise a log of weight P. With what force F should the end of the rope A be pulled for the purpose? How should the ends of the rope B and C be fastened to keep the rising log in a horizontal position?

Indicate two methods for determining the force.

165. A system of weights m_1, m_2 and m_3 is in equilibrium (Fig. 65).

Find the mass m_3 and the pressure force exerted by the mass m_1 on an inclined surface if the masses m_1, m_2 and the angle α between the inclined surface and the horizontal are known. Disregard the masses of the pulleys, the weight of the threads and friction.

166. M of weight 10 kgf is balanced by two weights P and Q (Fig. 66). The thread holding the weight Q is horizontal from point A.

Find the weight Q and the angle α if $P = 18$ kgf.

167. A system composed of fixed and movable pulleys (Fig. 67) is in equilibrium. Determine the weight Q if $P = = 10$ kgf.

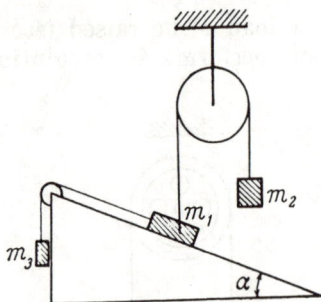

Fig. 65

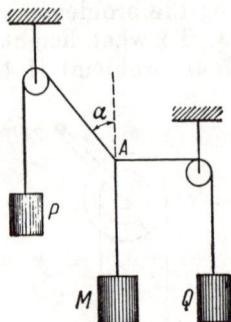

Fig. 66

Will the equilibrium be disturbed if point A where the rope is fastened is shifted to the right? If the equilibrium is disturbed, how will the weights P and Q move? Neglect the mass of the pulleys, the weight of the rope and the friction.

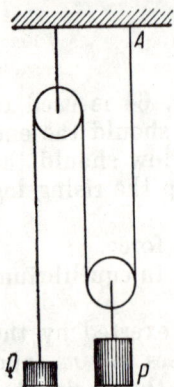

Fig. 67

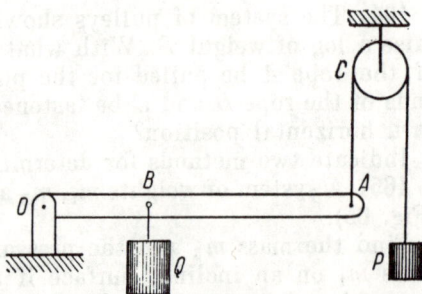

Fig. 68

168. A light rod is secured at point O and can revolve in a vertical plane (Fig. 68). The end of the rod at point A is attached to a thread wrapped around a fixed pulley. The weight P is suspended from the other end of the thread. A weight Q is attached to the rod at point B. The length of the rod is l and the distance $OB = l/3$. The system is in equilibrium when the rod is horizontal and the section of the thread AC is vertical.

Determine the weight Q if $P = 3$ kgf. How will the rod move if it is displaced from the position of equilibrium by

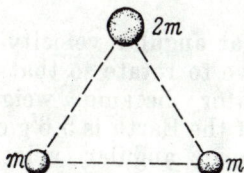

Fig. 69

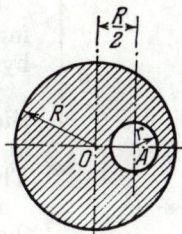

Fig. 70

moving the end A slightly up or down? Disregard the mass of the rod, the pulley and the thread and also the friction.

169. Two balls each of mass m are placed on two vertices of an equilateral triangle. A ball of mass $2m$ is situated at the third vertex (Fig. 69).

Determine the centre of gravity of this system.

170. Find the position of the centre of gravity of a uniform disk of radius R from which a hole of radius r is cut out (Fig. 70). The centre of the hole is at a distance $R/2$ from the centre of the disk.

10. Universal Gravitational Forces

171. The gravity constant in the law of universal gravitation is equal to $\gamma = 7 \times 10^{-8}$ cm³/g·s².

Determine the numerical value and the units of this constant in the MKS system.

172. The great Russian scientist M. V. Lomonosov noted that "if there was a big variation in the force of gravity for small variations in distance a 'wrong' balance could be built" (Fig. 71).

Determine the ratio between the lengths of the threads carrying loads at which such a balance would produce an error of 0.01 gf on the earth surface when a load of 10 kgf is being weighed. Consider the threads to be weightless. The mean density of the Earth is 5.6 g/cm³.

173. The radius of the Earth is $r = 6,400$ km, the distance from the Earth to the Sun is $R = 1.5 \times 10^8$ km, the density of the Earth $\rho = 5.6$ g/cm^3, the period of revolution of the Earth around the Sun is $T = 365$ days.

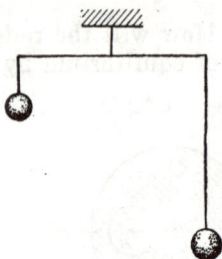

Use these data to calculate the mean force of attraction exerted on the Earth by the Sun.

174. At what angular velocity would the Earth have to rotate so that bodies at the equator became weightless? The density of the Earth is 5.6 g/cm^3.

Fig. 71

175. The mean angular velocity of the Earth around the Sun is 1° in twenty-four hours. The distance from the Earth to the Sun is 1.5×10^8 km.

Determine the mass of the Sun.

176. The maximum altitude reached by the Soviet-made balloon "Osoaviakhim" was $h = 22$ km.

Determine the change in the acceleration of the force of gravity during such an ascent.

177. In what seasons of the year is the linear velocity of the Earth around the Sun larger and when is it smaller?

178. Assume that a certain body moves inside the Earth from the surface to its centre.

How will the force of gravity acting on the body depend on the distance from the body to the centre of the Earth? Consider the Earth as a sphere of uniform density.

11. Oscillations

This section is focussed on a brief review of the basic laws of oscillations of a simple pendulum and the elucidation of the problems which deal with the relationship between the period of oscillations and the mass of the oscillating body as well as the nature of the forces acting on it. These problems also demonstrate the relationship between the magnitude of the forces necessary to generate oscillations and the amplitude, the frequency of oscillations and the mass of the body. A qualitative analysis of these relationships can easily be grasped by the reader and it is essential for understanding the laws of oscillatory motion.

Pay special attention to the behaviour of a pendulum on a cart moving with an acceleration (Problem 182) and discuss in detail the solutions of Problems 183 and 184 at extracurricular circles.

179. An accurate astronomical clock with a seconds pendulum is mounted in the basement of the main building of the Moscow University.

How much will this clock lose in twenty-four hours if it is transferred to the upper storey of the University which is 200 m higher than the basement?

180. Two pendula begin to swing simultaneously. During the first fifteen oscillations of the first pendulum the other pendulum makes only ten swings.

Determine the ratio between the lengths of these pendula.

181. A pendulum is attached to a board which can fall freely without friction down guide ropes (device designed by Prof. Lyubimov). Before the board is released the pendulum is deflected from the position of equilibrium (Fig. 72).

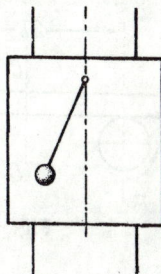

Fig. 72

Will the pendulum swing as the board is falling?

182. A pendulum is secured on a cart rolling without friction down an inclined surface. The period of the pendulum on an immobile cart is T_0.

How will the period of the pendulum change when the cart rolls down the slope?

183. The Soviet scientist N. N. Andreyev suggested the following approximate method to estimate the small amplitudes of oscillation of the surface of vibrating bodies: a thin layer of dry sand is scattered over the surface being investigated. When the surface is made to oscillate the sand grains also begin to oscillate with it. If the amplitude is increased sufficiently the grains are detached from the surface and begin to bob up and down. If different parts of the surface oscillate with different amplitudes (as, for example, a telephone membrane), the grains are gradually accumulated at the points of minimum amplitude.

Explain the cause of such behaviour of the grains. Will the behaviour of the grains be affected by their mass? Will the frequency of oscillations be of any importance?

184. A hydrometer consisting of a ball filled with shot and a cylindrical tube of cross section S is placed in a liquid of density ρ. The hydrometer is immersed in the liquid somewhat deeper than actually needed for equilibrium and then released. It then begins to perform free oscillations near the position of equilibrium.

Show how the period of oscillation of the hydrometer will change when: (a) its mass is increased; (b) the diameter of the tube is decreased; (c) the density of the liquid is increased.

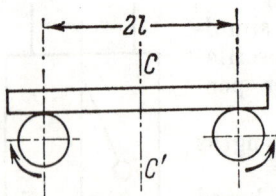

Fig. 73

185. A board is placed horizontally on two rollers revolving in opposite directions as shown in Fig. 73. The weight of the board is P and the distance between the axes of the rollers is $2l$. The coefficient of friction between the board and each of the rollers is k. Initially, the board was placed so that its centre of gravity was a certain distance x from the middle line CC'.

Determine the type of motion that will be performed by the board under the action of the forces of friction produced by the rollers.

12. Hydro- and Aerostatics

186. A piston fitted tightly against the inner walls of a long cylindrical tube is moved with the aid of a long rod. The tube with the piston at its lowest point is sunk into a well. As soon as the bottom of the tube is immersed in the water the piston is raised by means of the rod (Fig. 74).

To what height h from the level of the water in the well can the water in the tube be raised by this method? The atmospheric pressure is 760 mm Hg.

187. Under what pressure P_0 must water be supplied by a pumping station arranged in a basement so that the pressure of the water in the pipes is not less than $P =$

= 1.5 kgf/cm^2? The height of the upper storey above the basement is $h = 200$ m.

188. A hole of area 5 cm^2 is formed in the side of a ship three metres below the water level.

What minimum force is required to hold on a patch covering the hole from the inside of the ship?

189. A vessel contains air compressed to four technical atmospheres. A force of $F = 9.3$ kgf has to be applied to hold in place a plug in the round aperture in the vessel. The radius of the aperture is $r = 1$ cm.

Determine the atmospheric pressure.

190. The limbs of a glass U-tube are lowered into vessels A and B (Fig. 75). Some air is pumped out through the top of the tube C. The liquid in the left-hand limb then rises to a height h_1 and in the right-hand one to a height h_2.

Determine the density of the liquid in limb B if water is present in limb A, $h_1 = 10$ cm and $h_2 = 12$ cm.

Fig. 74

191. To what height h should a cylindrical vessel be filled with a homogeneous liquid to make the force with which the liquid will press on the side of the vessel equal to the pressure on the bottom of the vessel?

192. Some air is pumped out of a tube one end of which is immersed in water. The water in the tube rises above tap A (Fig. 76).

Will the water flow out from tap A if it is opened?

193. A barometer shows an air pressure of 75 cm Hg.

Find the pressure at a depth of 10 m under the surface of water.

194. A cylindrical opening in the cover of a large vessel filled with water is tightly closed by a piston (Fig. 77). A vertical tube of radius $r = 5$ cm is attached to the piston. The radius of the piston is $R = 10$ cm and the weight of the piston and the tube is $Q = 20$ kgf.

How high will the water in the tube rise when the piston is in equilibrium?

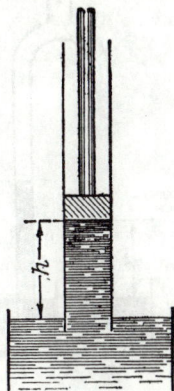

195. Equal amounts by weight of mercury and water are poured into a cylindrical vessel. The total height of the two layers of the liquids is $h_0 = 29.2$ cm.

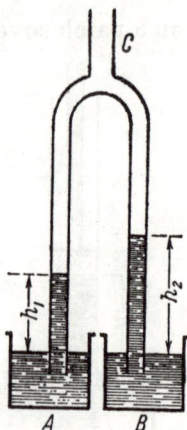

Fig. 75

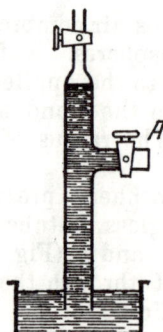

Fig. 76

Fig. 77

What pressure does the liquid exert on the bottom of the vessel. The specific gravity of the mercury is 13.6 gf/cm³.

196. Two cylindrical communicating vessels with equal cross section $S = 11.5$ cm² contain mercury. One litre of water is poured into one vessel on top of the mercury and a body weighing $p = 150$ gf is lowered into the water.

What distance will the mercury level move in the second vessel after pouring in the water and lowering the body?

197. Water and oil are poured into the two limbs of a U-tube containing mercury (Fig. 78). The interfaces of the mercury and the liquids are at the same height in both limbs.

Determine the height of the water column h_1 if that of the oil $h_2 = 20$ cm. The density of the oil is 0.9.

198. Two communicating vessels contain mercury. The diameter of one vessel is four times larger than the diameter of the other (Fig. 79). A column of water of height $h_0 = 70$ cm is poured into the left-hand vessel.

How much will the mercury level rise in the right-hand vessel and how much will it sink in the left one? How much will the mercury level rise in the narrow vessel if a column of water of the same height is poured into the broad vessel?

199. Mercury is poured into a U-tube in which the cross-sectional area of the left-hand limb is three times smaller

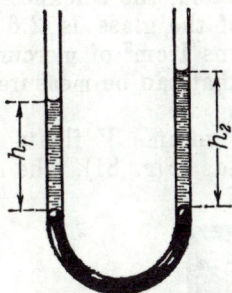

Fig. 78

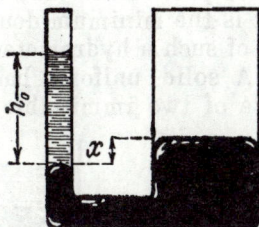

Fig. 79

than that of the right one. The level of the mercury in the narrow limb is a distance $l = 30$ cm from the upper end of the tube.

How much will the mercury level rise in the right-hand limb if the left one is filled to the top with water?

200. Cylindrical communicating vessels with the same diameters and the same height contain mercury (Fig. 80). A column of water of height $h_0 = 32$ cm is poured into one of the limbs on top of the mercury.

How will the levels of the mercury be arranged with respect to each other in both vessels if they are filled to the top with kerosene? The specific gravity of mercury $\gamma_1 = 13.6$ gf/cm³ and of kerosene $\gamma_2 = 0.8$ gf/cm³.

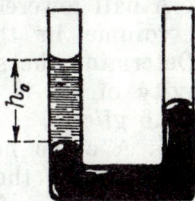

Fig. 80

201. A vessel containing water is equalized on a balance and then the end of a wooden rod is immersed in the water, its other end being held by hand.

What additional weight should be placed on the other pan to restore the equilibrium if the volume of the submerged part of the wood is 50 cm³?

202. A swimmer floats face up motionless, the whole of his body being submerged in the water except for a small part of the face. The swimmer weighs 75 kgf. Find the volume of his body.

203. A hydrometer takes the form of a glass cylindrical tube soldered at both ends, having a length $l = 20$ cm and an external diameter $D = 1.2$ cm; the thickness of the walls is $h = 1$ mm, the density of the glass is 2.6 g/cm³. The lower part of the tube contains 1 cm³ of mercury.

What is the minimum density that can be measured with the aid of such a hydrometer?

204. A solid uniform ball of volume V floats on the interface of two immiscible liquids (Fig. 81). The specific

Fig. 81

gravity of the upper liquid is γ_1 and of the lower one γ_2, whilst the specific gravity of the ball is γ ($\gamma_1 < \gamma < \gamma_2$).

What fraction of the volume of the ball will be in the upper liquid and what fraction in the lower one?

205. A vessel is filled first with mercury and then with oil. A ball lowered into the vessel floats with exactly half its volume in the mercury (Fig. 81).

Determine the specific gravity of the ball. The specific gravity of oil is $\gamma_1 = 0.9$ gf/cm³ and of mercury $\gamma_2 = 13.6$ gf/cm³.

206. A cubic body floats on mercury with 0.25 of its volume below the surface.

What fraction of the volume of the body will be immersed in the mercury if a layer of water poured on top of the mercury covers the body completely?

207. Determine the density of a uniform body weighing $P_1 = 280$ gf in air and $P_2 = 169$ gf in water. Neglect weight losses in air.

208. The weight of a body in water is one third of its weight in air. What is the density of the body?

209. On one pan of a balance is placed a piece of silver weighing 105 gf and on the other a piece of glass weighing 130 gf.

Which pan will move down when the balance is immersed in water? The density of silver $d_1 = 10.5$ g/cm^3 and of glass $d_2 = 2.6$ g/cm^3.

210. A copper ball with a hollow centre weighs $P_1 = 264$ gf in air and $P_2 = 221$ gf in water.

Determine the volume of the hollow centre of the ball. The density of copper is $d = 8.8$ g/cm^3.

211. A piece of iron weighs 400 gf in water. Determine its volume. The density of iron is 7.8 g/cm^3.

212. The capillary of a mercury thermometer weighs $P_1 = 66$ gf in air and $P_2 = 44$ gf in water.

Find the weight of the mercury filling the tube. The specific gravity of mercury is $\gamma_1 = 13.6$ gf/cm^3 and of glass $\gamma_2 = 2.6$ gf/cm^3.

213. Two bodies with volumes V and $2V$ are equalized on a balance. The larger body is then immersed in oil of density $d_1 = 0.9$ g/cm^3.

What must be the density of the liquid in which the smaller body is simultaneously immersed so as not to disturb the equilibrium of the balance?

214. Calculate the change in the potential energy of a body raised in water to a height h.

Will the potential energy of the water in the vessel change when the body rises? What will happen when the density of the body is larger and smaller than the density of the water? The density of the body is d, the density of the water is d_0 and the volume of the body is V.

215. A body of volume $V = 500$ cm^3 being weighed in air is equalized on a balance by copper weights totalling $P_1 = 440$ gf.

Determine the true weight of the body. The specific gravity of copper is $\gamma_1 = 8.8$ gf/cm^3 and of air $\gamma_0 = 1.29$ gf/l.

216. In accurate weighing a correction is usually introduced to account for weight losses in air for the body being weighed and for the set of small weights.

In what case may this correction be dispensed without impairing the accuracy of weighing?

217. If a vessel is filled with air its weight is $P_1 = 126.29$ gf. When this vessel is filled with carbon dioxide its weight becomes $P_2 = 126.94$ gf, and when it is filled with water, $P_3 = 1,125$ gf.

Determine the specific gravity of carbon dioxide γ_1, the volume V_0 and the weight P_0 of the vessel. The specific gravity of air is $\gamma_0 = 1.29$ gf/l.

218. The envelope of a balloon has a volume of 100 m³ and is filled with hydrogen. The weight of the envelope with the hydrogen is 50 kgf.

Find the lift of the balloon and the density of the layer of the air in which the balloon will be in equilibrium. The density of the air near the terrestrial surface is 1.29 g/l.

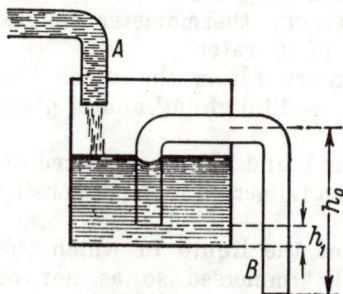

Fig. 82

219. What must the ratio of volumes of water and alcohol be for their mixture to have a density $d_0 = 0.9$ g/cm³? When the alcohol is mixed with the water the volume of the mixture diminishes. The volume of the mixture is 0.97 of the initial volume of the water and the alcohol.

220. What ratio by volume of carbon dioxide and water is needed to prepare a mixture in which a rubber ball filled with air could float without sinking or rising? The volume of the ball is $V = 5$ l and the weight of its shell $P = 1.5$ gf. Under normal conditions the specific gravity of the air is $\gamma_1 = 1.29$ gf/l and that of the carbon dioxide is $\gamma_2 = 1.98$ gf/l.

221. Plot the variation with time of the water level in the open vessel shown in Fig. 82 if the velocity of the water flowing from the infeed pipe A is less than the velocity of water flowing from the siphon pipe B.

Chapter II

HEAT AND MOLECULAR PHYSICS

13. Thermal Expansion of Bodies

222. At a temperature t_0 the pendulum of a clock has a length of l_0 and the clock then goes accurately. The coefficient of linear expansion of the pendulum material is $\alpha = 1.85 \times 10^{-5}$.

How much will the clock gain or lose in twenty-four hours if the ambient temperature is 10°C higher than t_0? In deriving the formula allow for a small value of the coefficient of linear expansion of the pendulum.

223. A steel rod with a cross-sectional area S = 10 cm² is set lengthwise between two rigidly secured massive steel plates.

With what force will the rod press against each plate if the temperature of the rod is increased by $t = 15°C$? The modulus of elasticity of steel is $E = 2.1 \times 10^6$ kgf/cm², and the coefficient of linear expansion of steel is $\alpha = 1.1 \times 10^{-5}$.

224. A bar measured with a vernier caliper is foudn to be 180 mm long. The temperature during the measurement is 10°C.

What will the measurement error be if the scale of the vernier caliper has been graduated at a temperature of 20°C?

225. A steel cylindrical component machined on an engine lathe is heated to a temperature of 80°C. The diameter of the component should be 5 cm at a temperature of 10°C and the permissible error should not exceed 10 microns from the specified dimension.

Should corrections for the thermal expansion of the component be introduced during the process of machining?

226. When making a certain physical instrument it was found necessary to ensure that the difference between the lengths of an iron and a copper cylinder remained the same whatever the temperature change.

How long should these cylinders be at 0°C so that the difference between them is 10 cm whatever the temperature change? The coefficient of linear expansion of iron is $\alpha_1 = 1.1 \times 10^{-5}$ and of copper $\alpha_2 = 1.7 \times 10^{-5}$.

227. The brass scale of a mercury barometer has been checked at 0°C. At 18°C the barometer shows a pressure of 760 mm.

Reduce the reading of the barometer to 0°C. The coefficient of linear expansion of brass is $\alpha = 1.9 \times 10^{-5}$ and the coefficient of volume expansion of mercury $\beta = 1.8 \times 10^{-4}$.

228. The volume occupied by a thin-wall brass vessel and the volume of a solid brass sphere are the same and equal to 1,000 cm³ at 0°C.

How much will the volume of the vessel and that of the sphere change upon heating to 20°C? The coefficient of linear expansion of brass is $\alpha = 1.9 \times 10^{-5}$.

229. In observing thermal expansion of liquids a certain part of a glass vessel is filled with a mixture whose coefficient of volume expansion is $\beta_2 = 8 \times 10^{-5}$ in order to exclude the effect of the change in volume of the vessel during heating.

Determine what fraction of volume of the vessel should be filled with the mixture so as to compensate completely for the thermal expansion of the vessel. The coefficient of volume expansion of glass is $\beta_1 = 3 \times 10^{-5}$.

230. In the past, temperature was measured in laboratories using the so-called "weight" thermometer which consisted of a hollow platinum sphere filled with mercury and provided with a capillary hole. An increase in temperature was estimated from the amount of mercury flowing out of the hole.

How much mercury should flow out of the hole of such a thermometer when the temperature is increased by 1°C if the completely filled sphere of the thermometer contained 700 gf of mercury at 0°C? The coefficient of volume expansion of platinum is $\beta_1 = 2.7 \times 10^{-5}$ and of mercury $\beta_2 = 1.8 \times 10^{-4}$.

231. In his work "On the Free Movement of Air in Mines"

the Russian scientist M. V. Lomonosov discovered the plysical causes for the appearance of permanent streams of air in mines. In particular, Lomonosov studied the flow of air in mines of the type shown in Fig. 83.

Determine the direction in which the air will flow in such a mine in winter and in summer. Prove that these

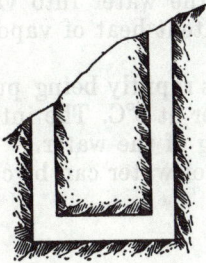

Fig. 83

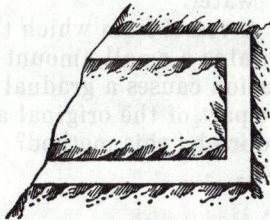

Fig. 84

streams arise of necessity by themselves. Consider the temperature of air as constant and the same at all points in the mine and in all the seasons of the year.

232. M. V. Lomonosov also described the flow of air in mines of the kind shown in Fig. 84.

Prove that the flow takes place and find the direction of motion of air in such a mine in winter and summer. Use the same assumptions as in Problem 231.

14. Quantity of Heat. Heat Exchange

233. 300 g of ice at a temperature of —20°C are immersed in a calorimeter containing 200 g of water at a temperature of 8°C.

What will be the temperature of the calorimeter and its contents after thermal equilibrium is reached?

234. A piece of iron of mass $m = 325$ g is placed in a calorimeter filled with thawing ice.

Determine the amount of ice that will melt by the time thermal equilibrium is reached if the volume of the piece of iron being lowered into the calorimeter is $V = 48$ cm³.

The density of iron at 0°C is $d_0 = 6.8$ g/cm^3, its thermal capacity $C = 0.12$ cal/g·deg and the coefficient of volume expansion of iron is $\beta = 0.33 \times 10^{-4}$.

235. It takes 15 minutes to raise a certain amount of water from 0°C to boiling point using an electric heater. After this one hour and twenty minutes are required in the same conditions to convert all the water into vapour.

Use these data to determine the latent heat of vapourization of water.

236. A vessel from which the air is rapidly being pumped out contains a small amount of water at 0°C. The intensive evaporation causes a gradual freezing of the water.

What part of the original amount of water can be converted into ice by this method?

15. The Gas Laws

The ideal gas laws acquire their simplest form when the absolute temperature scale is used. This form allows a visual and much deeper insight into the essence of the laws and makes it possible at the same time to simplify appreciably the solution of all problems and reduce errors.

Experience shows, however, that some students underestimate the importance of this method of writing the laws of an ideal gas. For this reason some of the problems in this section require the formulas showing the dependence of volume and pressure of a gas on absolute temperature to be derived and only absolute temperatures are used in this section. One should watch the order when applying the laws in this way, solve the problems using the usual equations with the binomial of volume expansion and pay attention to the simplifications when solving them for the first time.

A number of problems involving a simultaneuos change in the temperature, pressure and volume of a gas are included in this section to help the reader master the laws which govern the simplest proccesses that may occur in an ideal gas. With the same aim in view, some problems deal with simultaneous constant pressure, constant volume or constant temperature processes that occur in a given mass of gas.

Graphical methods of solving the problems are extremely

helpful in the study of the laws of an ideal gas. A proper understanding of the plots showing the change in the state of an ideal gas and the ability to interpret the nature of changes of all the parameters that determine the state of a gas (for example, the change in gas pressure from the plot of gas volume versus temperature) are essential to attain a thorough knowledge of this branch of physics.

Many graphical problems in this section are intended to develop these skills and throw some light on the essence of the equations representing the simplest processes that can take place in an ideal gas.

When solving problems involving the application of Gay-Lussac's law most of the errors are caused by the incorrect use of the coefficient of volume expansion of a gas.

We know that the change in the volume of a gas on heating is always related to the volume occupied by a given mass of gas at nought degrees Centigrade. Some pupils forget this, and relate the change in the volume of a gas not to the state at zero degrees but to some other "initial" volume corresponding to the "initial" temperature specified in the conditions of the problem. This widespread error is discussed in Problem 253. A thorough examination of this problem is recommended.

At the end of the section there are some elementary problems on the calculation of the work done by a gas and the expenditure of heat required to raise the temperature of a gas in various conditions. Study the theory of the subject again before you tackle the problems.

237. Using Gay-Lussac's law $V = V_0 (1 + \alpha t)$ and the definition of absolute temperature, derive the formula for the relationship between volume and absolute temperature at constant pressure. Plot this dependence.

238. Derive the formula showing the dependence of pressure on absolute temperature in this process if at constant volume $P = P_0 (1 + \alpha t)$. Plot this dependence.

239. A certain mass of gas is heated first in a small vessel and then in a large one. During heating the volumes of the vessels remain constant.

How will the pressure-temperature graphs differ in the first and the second case?

240. The gas in a cylinder is enclosed by a freely moving piston. Plot the dependence of volume on temperature: (a) when the gas is heated with a small load on the piston; and (b) with a large load.

How will the position of the volume versus temperature curve change at constant (internal) pressure when the external pressure is altered?

241. What will the relative arrangement of the isothermal lines of a gas be on the volume-pressure graph for the expansion of the same mass of gas at a low and a high temperature?

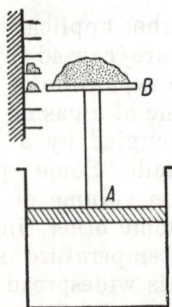

Fig. 85

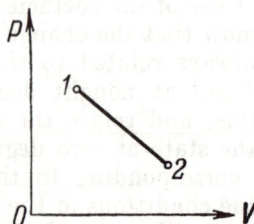

Fig. 86

242. Draw curves showing the dependence of volume on temperature for gases at constant pressure, constant volume and constant temperature.

243. How will constant volume, constant pressure and constant temperature processes be depicted on a diagram showing the relationship between pressure and temperature?

244. Plot the dependence of pressure on volume for gases at constant temperature, constant pressure and constant volume.

245. The gas in a cylinder is enclosed by a piston A (Fig. 85). The piston end has an area B supporting a certain amount of sand that exerts the necessary pressure on the piston. If some sand is pushed in small portions onto the shelves near the support the pressure exerted on the piston will gradually change. It is also possible to change the temperature of the gas by placing the cylinder on heaters or coolers.

A plot of pressure versus volume for a gas expanding in such a cylinder made from direct measurements is illustrated in Fig. 86.

How can this plot be used to determine the nature of change in the temperature of the gas?

246. A curve showing the dependence of pressure on absolute temperature was obtained for a certain gas (Fig. 87). Does compression or expansion take place when the gas is being heated?

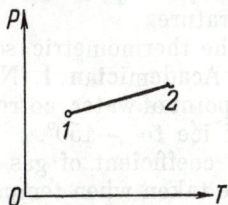

Fig. 87

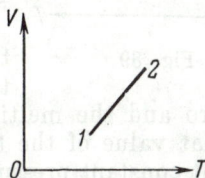

Fig. 88

247. Use the volume-temperature curve (Fig. 88) to find graphically the nature of change in the pressure of a gas during heating.

248. A constant volume vessel is used to heat first m grams of a certain gas and then $2m$ grams of the same gas.

Draw the curves showing the dependence of pressure on temperature in each case. Indicate the difference in the positions of the curves.

249. A movable piston is inserted in a cylinder closed on both ends. One end of the cylinder contains m grams of a certain gas and the other $2m$ grams of the same gas.

What fraction of the cylinder by volume will be occupied by $2m$ grams of the gas when the piston is in equilibrium?

250. A gas of molecular weight μ is heated in a cylinder enclosed by a freely moving piston. A gas of molecular weight 2μ is then heated in the same cylinder. The masses of the gasses and the pressure exerted by the load on the piston are the same in each case.

Will the plots of volume versus temperature be the same in each case?

251. The piston in a gas-filled cylinder is loosely fitted against the wall of the cylinder and can slowly let the gas go past. The volume-temperature curve for the gas at constant pressure has the form shown in Fig. 89.

Use this curve to determine whether the amount of gas in the cylinder has increased or decreased.

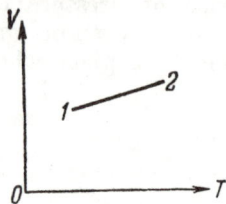

Fig. 89

252. Plot the variation in the density of a gas with temperature at constant pressure and the dependence of the gas density on pressure at constant temperature.

253. On the thermometric scale of the Russian Academician I. N. Delil the boiling point of water corresponds to zero and the melting point of ice to −150°.

What value of the temperature coefficient of gas expansion at constant pressure should be taken when temperature is measured on Delil's scale?

254. A hollow ball with a capacity of 100 cm³ is fitted with a long graduated tube. The internal volume of the tube between graduations is 0.2 cm³. The ball and a part of the tube contain air which is separated from the atmosphere by a drop of water. At a temperature of 5°C the drop of water arranges itself near the 20th graduation. The drop sets itself at the 50th graduation in the room where the temperature is being measured.

What is the temperature in the room? Neglect the change in the volume of the vessel.

255. Air separated from the atmosphere by a column of mercury of length $h = 15$ cm is present in a narrow cylindrical tube soldered at one end. When the tube is placed horizontally the air occupies a volume $V_1 = 240$ mm³. When it is set vertically with its open end upwards the volume of the air is $V_2 = 200$ mm³.

What is the atmospheric pressure during the experiment?

256. A narrow cylindrical tube 80 cm long and open at both ends is half immersed in mercury. Then the top of the tube is closed and it is taken out of the mercury. A column of mercury 22 cm long then remains in the tube.

What is the atmospheric pressure?

257. The limbs of a U-tube are equal in length. One of the limbs is soldered and contains a column of air 28 cm high. The air is separated from the atmosphere by mercury and its pressure is equal to the external pressure.

What will the height of the air column be in the soldered limb if the second limb is filled with mercury to the top? The external pressure is 76 cm Hg.

258. An open glass tube is immersed in mercury so that an end of length $l_1 = 8$ cm projects above the mercury. The tube is then closed and raised 44 cm.

What fraction of the tube will be occupied by the air after it has been raised? The atmospheric pressure is $P = 76$ cm Hg.

259. A cylindrical glass is lowered upside down into water and floats so that the inside of its base is at the same level with the surface of the water in the vessel. The glass weighs $Q = 408$ gf, the area of the base is $S = 10$ cm^2. The pressure of the air in the glass before it is submerged is $P = 76$ cm Hg.

What part of the glass will be occupied by the air after it is submerged?

260. A cylindrical vessel is half-filled with mercury and then hermetically sealed by a cover through which a siphon tube is passed. The height of the vessel is 60 cm.

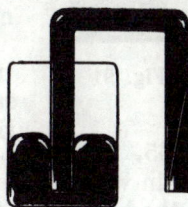

Fig. 90

The siphon has been filled with mercury in advance, has equal limbs and the end of one tube is located at the bottom of the vessel (Fig. 90).

At what pressure in the vessel will the mercury cease to flow through the siphon? By how much will the mercury level then have dropped? The external pressure is 750 mm Hg.

261. A column of mercury of length $h = 10$ cm is contained in the middle of a narrow horizontal tube soldered at both ends. The air in both halves of the tube is under a pressure of $P_0 = 76$ cm Hg.

What distance will the mercury column move if the tube is placed vertically? The length of the tube is 1 m.

262. A cylinder closed at both ends is divided into two equal parts by a heat-proof piston. Both parts of the cylinder contain the same masses of gas at a temperature $t_0 = 27°C$ and a pressure $P_0 = 1$ atm.

What distance from the middle of the cylinder will the piston be displaced if the gas in one of the parts is heated to $t = 57°C$? What will be the pressure in this case in each part of the cylinder? The length of half the cylinder is $l = 42$ cm.

263. A glass tube 15 cm long soldered at one end and containing a certain amount of air is immersed in mercury so that 10 cm of the tube projects above the surface (Fig. 91). The level of the mercury inside the tube at 0°C is 5 cm higher than the mercury level in the vessel.

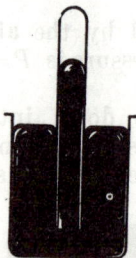

By how much should the temperature of the air in the tube be increased for it to occupy the entire volume of the tube? The atmospheric pressure is 75 cm Hg. The mercury level in the vessel is invariable.

264. Calculate the value of the constant in the combined law of Boyle and Gay-Lussac for one gram-molecule of gas in calories and in CGS units.

Fig. 91

265. Two vessels of equal volume and weight are immersed in water to a depth h. One of the vessels has an opening at the bottom which admits water.

Is the same work required to immerse each of the cylinders in the water?

266. One gram-molecule of oxygen is heated at a constant pressure from 0°C.

What amount of heat should be imparted to the gas to double its volume? The heat capacity of oxygen in these conditions is $C_p = 0.218$ cal/g·deg.

267. A gas is heated by 1°C in a cylinder fitted with a piston. The weight of the piston is G and its area S. During heating the gas does work to lift the piston. Express this work: (a) in terms of the pressure and the change in volume of the gas; (b) in terms of the constant R in the combined equation of Boyle and Gay-Lussac. Disregard the pressure of the outside atmosphere.

268. A vertical cylinder with a base of area $S = 10$ cm^2 is filled with gas. The cylinder is fitted with a piston weighing $G = 20$ kgf which can move without friction. The original volume of the gas is $V_0 = 11.2$ l and the temperature $t_0 = 0°C$.

What quantity of heat is needed to raise the temperature of the gas in these conditions by 10°C if the thermal capacity of this mass of gas with the piston secured in the initial position is $C_V = 5$ cal/deg? Disregard the pressure of the outside atmosphere.

269. Explain why a gas can only expand at constant temperature if a certain quantity of heat is supplied to it.

270. A certain amount of gas initially occupying a volume V_0 at a pressure P_0 and a temperature T_0 expands first at constant pressure and then at constant temperature to a volume V_1.

In which of these two cases will the gas do more work?

271. A cylinder filled with gas is placed in a heat-proof jacket.

How will the temperature of the gas change if the volume of the cylinder is gradually increased?

16. Surface Tension

272. The Russian scientist M. V. Lomonosov recorded the following results from his experiments on raising a liquid in capillaries: "rise of liquids in a capillary tube to the lines: water 26, alcohol 18, volatile alcohol of ammonium salt 33". One line = $= 2.56$ mm.

Use these data to determine the relationship between the surface tensions of these substances. Find the radius of the capillary used by M. V. Lomonosov. The surface tension of water is $\alpha = 70$ dyn/cm. The densities of both alcohols are the same and equal to 0.8 g/cm³.

273. A capillary tube of radius r and height h_1 is connected to a broad tube as shown in Fig. 92. The broad tube is gradually filled with drops of water falling at equal intervals.

Fig. 92

Plot the changes in the levels of the water in both tubes with time and changes in the difference between these levels.

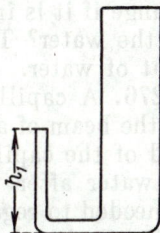

Calculate the maximum water level in the broad tube and the maximum difference in the levels. The surface tension of water is α.

274. The following design of a perpetuum mobile has been suggested. A capillary of radius r is chosen which

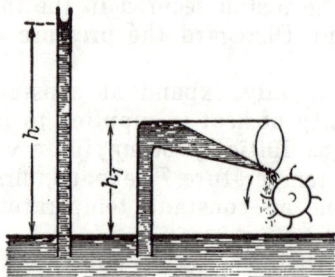

Fig. 93

allows water to rise to a height h (Fig. 93). At a height h_1, smaller than h, the capillary is bent and its upper end is made into a broad funnel as shown in the diagram. The surface tension is enough to raise the liquid to the height h_1 and introduce it into the funnel. The liquid in the broad part of the funnel detaches itself from its upper surface and flows down unimpeded. A water wheel can be installed in the path of the drops falling back into the vessel, thus providing a perpetuum mobile.

Will this perpetuum mobile actually operate? Find the error in the reasoning above.

275. Will the results of measurements on the density of liquids using a hydrometer be affected by the action of surface tension? How will the position of the hydrometer change if it is in water and several drops of ether are added to the water? The surface tension of ether is smaller than that of water.

276. A capillary tube with very thin walls is attached to the beam of a balance which is then equalized. The lower end of the capillary is brought in contact with the surface of water after which an additional load of $P = 0.135$ gf is needed to regain equilibrium.

Determine the radius of the capillary. The surface tension of water is $\alpha = 70$ dyn/cm.

277. Explain the following experiment performed by M. V. Lomonosov: "Mercury can be removed from a vessel in twenty-four hours by using a sheet of lead folded into a siphon and immersed with one end in the mercury."

278. A rectangular wire frame with one movable side is covered by a soap film (Fig. 94).

What force should be applied to the movable side to counterbalance it? What work will be done if this side of the frame is moved a distance $S = 2$ cm? What will be the source of this work when the surface of the film is reduced and into what kind of energy will the work be transformed? The length of the movable side is $l = 6$ cm. The surface tension of the soap film is $\alpha = 40$ dyn/cm.

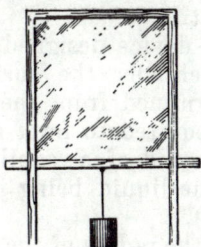

Fig. 94

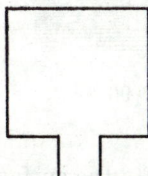

Fig. 95

279. A light open rigid paper frame as shown in Fig. 95 floats on the surface of water.

What will happen to the frame if some soap solution is dropped inside it? What force will act on the frame and in what direction will it act?

280. When some useless work is done it is commonly said that it is the same as carrying water in a sieve.

When can water really be carried in a sieve without it seeping through? What is the maximum height of the water layer that can be carried in a sieve if the diameter of the mesh is $d = 1$ mm? Can the water poured into a sieve be drained over its edge? The surface tension of water is $\alpha = 70$ dyn/cm.

281. Part of a capillary is lowered into a wetting agent.

Can the loss of weight of the capillary be calculated by Archimedes' law? What will the answer be in the case of a non-wetting agent?

282. A capillary of radius r is lowered into a wetting agent with surface tension α and density d.

Determine the height h_0 to which the liquid will rise in the capillary. Calculate the work done by surface tension and the potential energy acquired by the liquid in the capillary and compare the two. Explain the difference in the results obtained.

283. In order to remove paraffine and other fatty spots from fabric they are usually ironed hot through paper. Why does paraffine or fat soak into the paper in this case and not spread over the fabric? Should the paper used for ironing be sized or not?

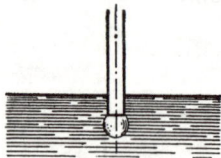

Fig. 96

284. In a device designed by Academician Rebinder the surface tension is determined from the pressure difference required to form a bubble of air at the end of a capillary immersed in the liquid being investigated (Fig. 96).

Calculate the surface tension if the radius of the capillary is $r = 1$ mm and the difference in the pressures during bubble formation is $\Delta P = 14$ mm of water column. The end of the capillary is near the surface of the liquid.

285. The internal radius of one limb of a capillary U-tube is $r_1 = 1$ mm and the internal radius of the second limb is $r_2 = 2$ mm. The tube is filled with some mercury, and one of the limbs is connected to a vacuum pump.

What will be the difference in air pressure when the mercury levels in both limbs are at the same height? Which limb of the tube should be connected to the pump? The surface tension of mercury is 480 dyn/cm.

286. A long capillary tube of radius $r = 1$ mm open at both ends is filled with water and placed vertically.

What will be the height of the column of water left in the capillary? The thickness of the capillary walls is negligible.

287. A capillary tube sealed at the top has an internal radius of $r = 0.05$ cm. The tube is placed vertically in water, open end first.

What should the length of such a tube be for the water in it to rise in these conditions to a height $h = 1$ cm? The pressure of the air is $P_0 = 1$ atm. The surface tension of water is $\alpha = 70$ dyn/cm.

17. Humidity of Air

288. A test-tube of height h is filled to the top with water and its open end is lowered into a glass of water.

At what temperature will the level of water move away from the bottom of the test-tube? What will occur in the test-tube if the water is further heated to 100°C? Disregard the action of surface tension.

289. The temperature of the air is $t_1 = 20°C$ and the dew point $t_2 = 8°C$. Find the absolute and relative humidity of the air if the elasticity of the saturated vapour pressure at t_1 is $p_1 = 17.54$ mm Hg and at t_2, $p_2 = 8.05$ mm Hg.

290. In what conditions can the relative humidity diminish when the absolute humidity of the atmospheric air increases?

291. Two vessels contain air saturated with vapour — one at a temperature of 20°C and the other at a temperature of 10°C.

What amount of dew will be deposited when these two masses of air are mixed if the volumes of the vessels are the same and equal to 1 m³? Assume that within the chosen range the saturated vapour pressure is proportional to the temperature and equal to 9 mm Hg at 10°C and 17 mm Hg at 20°C.

Disregard heat losses due to the heat exchange with the walls of the vessel during mixing.

292. A vessel contains air at a temperature of 10°C and humidity of 60 per cent.

What will be the relative humidity of this air if it is heated to 100°C and its volume is simultaneously decreased to one third? The absolute humidity corresponding to the saturated vapours at 10°C is 9.43 g/m³.

293. What amount of dew is deposited when a certain volume of air is reduced to one quarter if the initial volume of the air is 1 m³, the temperature 20°C and the humidity 50 per cent? The temperature is constant throughout.

Chapter III

18. Coulomb's Law

When studying the fundamentals of electrostatics it is especially important to master first Coulomb's law for calculating the forces produced by a system of electric charges and, particularly, to understand clearly how the principle of independent action of electric charges can be used to solve problems.

The problems in this section and their solutions are presented so as to indicate the sequence in which this principle can best be applied, especially when solving the problems in Secs 19, 20 and 21. At the same time these problems allow the reader to revise the methods commonly used for finding the equilibrium of separate bodies and systems.

In solving the problems on calculation of electric charges, pay attention to the stability of the equilibrium of charges (for example, if the equilibrium of the charge q in Problem 299 is stable with respect to the movement along a straight line connecting all the three charges it will be unstable with respect to motion in all the other directions). This is a particular case of the general theorem which states that it is impossible to attain a stable equilibrium in a system of free electric charges.

294. How should Coulomb's law be written in order to obtain the force in kilograms if the charges are in coulombs and the distances in metres?

295. Determine the force of electrostatic interaction between the electron and the nucleus in a hydrogen atom. The mean distance of the electron from the nucleus of the atom is 1×10^{-8} cm and the charge of the electron is $e = 4.8 \times 10^{-10}$ cgs electrostatic units.

296. An electron with a charge e and mass m rotates in a circular orbit of radius r around a nucleus of charge Ze.

Determine the velocity of the electron in this orbit. Perform a numerical calculation for a hydrogen atom.

297. The distance between two fixed positive charges $4e$ and e is l.

How should a third charge q be arranged for it to be in equilibrium? Under what conditions will the equilibrium of the charge q be stable and when will it be unstable?

298. Two free positive charges $4e$ and e are a distance a apart.

What charge is needed to achieve equilibrium for the entire system and where should it be placed?

299. A negative point charge $2e$ and a positive charge e are fixed at a distance l from each other.

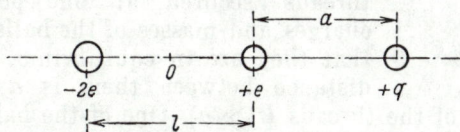

Fig. 97

Where should a positive test charge q (Fig. 97) be placed on the line connecting the charges for it to be in equilibrium? What is the nature of equilibrium of the test charge with respect to longitudinal motions. Plot the dependence of the force acting on this charge on the distance between it and the charge $+e$.

300. Two identical balls each have a mass of 10 g. What charges should these balls be given so that their interaction equalizes the forces of universal gravitation acting between them? The distance between the balls is large in comparison to their radii.

301. Two small identical metal balls having positive charges of 5 and 20 cgs electrostatic units are placed 10 cm apart.

Will the force of interaction between the balls change after they have been connected for a short time by a wire? What will the charges on the balls be after this experiment?

302. The distance between two equal balls having unlike charges is $l = 2$ cm. The radii of the balls are much less than l. The attractive force between the balls is $F_1 = 4$ dynes. After the balls have been connected by a wire and the latter has been removed, the balls repel each other with a force $F_2 = 2.25$ dynes.

Determine the original charges on the balls.

303. A small cork ball with a mass $m = 0.58$ g is suspended from a thread 10 cm long. Another ball is fixed at a distance $l = 10$ cm from the point of suspension and at a distance $l/2$ from the thread as shown in Fig. 98.

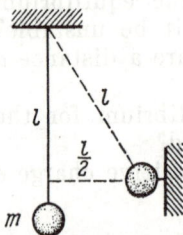

Fig. 98

What should the magnitude of the like and equal charges on the balls be to deflect the thread through 30°?

304. Two small equally charged conducting balls are suspended from long threads secured at one point. The charges and masses of the balls are such that they are in equilibrium when the distance between them is $a = 10$ cm (the length of the threads $L \gg a$). One of the balls is then discharged.

How will the balls behave after this? What will be the distance b between the balls when equilibrium is restored?

305. The Russian professor Rikhman was the designer of one of the world's first electrometers. His device consisted of a vertical metal bar at the top of which was attached a linen thread that was deflected from the bar under the action of an electric charge (Fig. 99). The readings were taken on a quadrant graduated in degrees. The length of the thread is l and its mass is m.

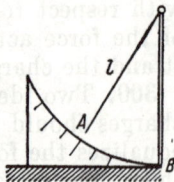

Fig. 99

What will be the charge when the thread of such an electrometer is deflected through an angle α. Make the following assumptions: (a) the charge on the electrometer is equally distributed between the bar and the thread; (b) the charges are concentrated at point A on the thread and at point B on the bar.

306. Two point charges with the same sign and magnitude $q = 3.4$ cgs electrostatic units are 17 cm apart.

With what force and in what direction will these charges be acting on a unit positive charge located 17 cm from each of them? What is the magnitude and direction of this force if the former two charges are unlike?

307. Four identical free positive charges e are located at the four corners of a square of side a.

What charge should be placed at the centre of the square to obtain equilibrium? Will this equilibrium be stable?

19. Electric Field. Field Intensity

The basic concept of an electric field and the quantities that describe it is one of the most difficult parts of the curriculum but is something that must be thoroughly mastered.

For this reason this section mainly concentrates the simplest problems involving the application of the equation $F = eE$, on the distribution of charges on the surface of conductors placed in an electric field and on the motion of charged bodies under the action of the electric field forces.

Most of the problems in this section are of a qualitative nature and they are designed not simply to calculate the forces but to illustrate the behaviour of charges in conductors under the influence of an external electric field and also the nature of the changes that take place in a field when conductors are introduced into it.

Special attention should be paid to the solutions of Problems 319-325 which show the simplest ways of calculating the motion of bodies produced by an electric current.

308. Find the intensity of an electric field set up by a point charge of one cgs electrostatic unit at a distance of 1 m from the charge. Express the intensity in the absolute and practical electrical units.

309. Two equal like point charges of 2 cgs electrostatic units each are situated a distance $2a = 100$ cm apart.

Calculate the intensity and the potential at a point A situated halfway between the two charges.

310. A charge q is placed on a metal wire ring of radius R.

Determine the intensity of the field set up by this charge:

(a) in the centre of the ring O (Fig. 100); (b) at the point A lying on the axis of the ring at a distance R from the centre O.

311. A small metal ball is brought into contact alternately with points A, B and C of the charged body shown in Fig. 101. After each contact the charge of the ball is determined approximately by touching it against an electroscope.

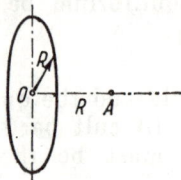

Fig. 100

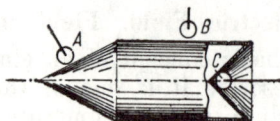

Fig. 101

Will the leaves of the electroscope be deflected similarly in these three cases?

312. An uncharged conducting ball is placed in the uniform electric field of a plane capacitor. How will the form and the arrangement of the lines of force in the field change after the ball has been introduced and what causes this change in the field? Draw the system of equipotential surfaces. Show what induced charges will appear on the ball and where they will appear.

313. How can a positively charged ball be used to electrify two other balls—one positively and the other negatively—without reducing its own charge?

314. A positively charged ball is placed into a hollow conductive uncharged sphere. Indicate: (a) the location and the kind of the electric fields produced; (b) the charges, if any, on the sphere; (c) the changes in the electric field when the ball moves inside the sphere and where these changes occur; (d) the change in the field inside and outside the sphere if the ball is fixed and a charged body is brought close to the sphere from the outside.

315. A ball of charge e is placed in a hollow conductive uncharged sphere. After this the sphere is connected with earth for a short time and the ball is then removed from the sphere. The ball has not been brought into contact with the sphere.

What charge will the sphere have after these operations? Where and how will this charge be distributed? What will be the nature of the field and how will it be located?

316. Two large metal plates tightly fitted against each other are placed between two equal and unlike point charges perpendicular to the line connecting them (Fig. 102).

What will happen to the plates if they are released?

What changes will occur in the electric field in this case? Draw the lines of force of the changed field.

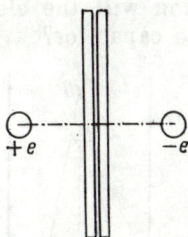

Fig. 102

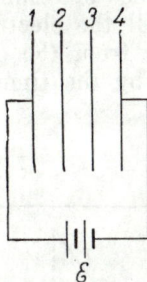

Fig. 103

317. The plates considered in the previous problem are introduced into a field so that they do not touch each other and are then drawn a certain distance apart. Draw the distribution of the lines of force of the electric field after the plates are drawn apart and show how the induced charges are distributed in them.

318. Two parallel metal plates are inserted at equal distances into a plane capacitor as shown in Fig. 103. Plates *1* and *4* are connected to a battery with an electromotive force $\mathcal{E}$.

(a) What are the potentials of each of the four plates?

(b) How will the potentials of plates *2* and *3* and the intensities of the fields in each of the three spaces change after plates *2* and *3* have been closed for an instant by a wire? What will happen in this case to the charges on plates *1* and *4*?

(c) Will there be charges on plates *2* and *3* before and after shorting?

6*

319. A ball has a mass of 10 g and a charge of 5 cgs electrostatic units of electricity.

With what acceleration will the ball move in a uniform electric field of intensity 300 V/cm?

320. The control plates in a cathode-ray tube form a plane capacitor. The distance between the plates is $d = 10$ mm and the length of the plates is $l = 5$ cm. The plates receive a direct voltage of 50 V. An electron moves into the capacitor with a velocity $v = 20,000$ km/s parallel to the plates at a distance of 5 mm from the lower plate.

How will the electron move inside the capacitor? What distance h from the original position will the electron be displaced by the time it leaves the capacitor?

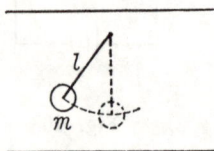

Fig. 104

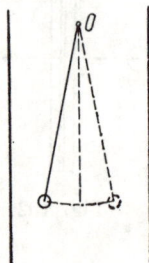

Fig. 105

321. A speck of dust of mass 10^{-9} g and charge $9.60 \times \times 10^{-8}$ cgs electrostatic units is located between the horizontal plates of a charged plane capacitor.

What is the intensity of the field in the capacitor if the weight of the speck of dust is equalized by the action of the electric field force on it?

322. A small metal ball of mass m (Fig. 104) is suspended from a thread of length l between the plates of a large plane capacitor.

How will the period of oscillations of such a pendulum change if a charge $+e$ is placed on the ball and the upper plate of the capacitor is charged: (a) positively; (b) negatively?

323. A ball of mass $m = 1$ g is suspended from a thread in a capacitor (see the previous problem). In the absence of any charges the period of oscillation of the ball is $T_1 =$

= 0.628 s. After the capacitor and the ball are charged the period of oscillation becomes $T_2 = 0.314$ s.

What force has the electric field of the capacitor exerted on the ball? What is the length of the thread from which the ball is suspended? Determine the period of oscillation if the sign of the charge on the ball is reversed.

324. A metal ball on a long thread is placed between the plates of a capacitor as shown in Fig. 105.

How will the oscillations of this pendulum change if the ball and the plates of the capacitor are charged? The pendulum swings in a plane perpendicular to the plates.

325. What is the charge on the Earth if the intensity of the electric field near the terrestrial surface is 1.30 V/cm? Consider the Earth as a sphere of radius 6,400 km.

20. Work Done by Forces in an Electrostatic Field. Potential

In the study of the potential of an electrostatic field the student comes across one of the most important properties of an electric field—the fact that the work done by the field forces is independent of the path. Since it is usually difficult to get into the habit of using this property correctly some of the problems in this section are intended to illustrate the meaning of this fundamental property of an electrostatic field and indicate how best to apply it when solving problems.

A series of problems at the beginning of the section require the use of the independent action of electric fields to calculate the potentials of separate points in a field and the work done when charges move in a field.

In analyzing the results of the solution of Problem 336 and the problems that follow it attention should be paid to the best method of using the relative arrangement of the lines of force and the equipotential surfaces of an electrostatic field when carrying out the simplest calculations. The problems in this section are recommended for discussion amongst senior grades in secondary schools.

326. The distance between the plates of a capacitor is $d = 5$ cm, and the intensity of the electric field in the capacitor is constant and equal to $E = 2$ cgs electrostatic units. An electron moves along one of the lines of force from one plate of the capacitor to the other. The initial velocity of the electron is zero.

What velocity is imparted to the electron en route due to the work done by the electric field forces?

327. The intensity of the electric field in a plane capacitor is 2 cgs electrostatic units and the potential difference between the plates is 3,000 V.

What is the distance between the plates of the capacitor?

328. The radius of a charged metal sphere R is 10 cm and its potential is 300 V. Find the charge density on the surface of the sphere.

329. Two like point charges of 5 cgs electrostatic units each are at some distance from each other.

Determine the potential at a point 10 cm from each of the charges.

How will this potential change if the space around the charges is filled with a dielectric of permittivity $\varepsilon = 2$?

330. The potential at a point A in an electric field is $V_A = 300$ V and at point B, $V_B = 1,200$ V.

What work must be done to move a positive charge of 3×10^{-8} coulomb from point A to point B?

331. Two identical metal balls of radius $r = 2.5$ cm are at a distance $a = 1$ m from each other and are charged, one with a potential $V_1 = + 1,200$ V and the other with a potential $V_2 = - 1,200$ V.

What are the charges q_1 and q_2 on these balls?

332. Two metal concentric spheres have radii a and b. There is a charge q on the inner sphere and a charge Q on the outer sphere.

Find the expressions for the intensity and the potential of the field outside the spheres and inside the first and second sphere.

333. A charge is uniformly distributed over the surface of two concentric conductive spheres (with the same density σ).

What is the magnitude of this charge if a quantity of work of 10 ergs is required to transfer one positive unit of electricity from infinity to the common centre of the spheres? The radii of the spheres are 5 and 10 cm.

334. The distance between the plates of a charged plane capacitor disconnected from the battery is $d = 5$ cm and the intensity of the field in it is $E = 300$ V/cm. An uncharged metal bar 1 cm thick (Fig. 106) is introduced into the capacitor parallel to its plates.

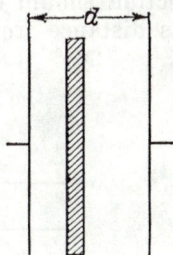

Determine the potential difference between the plates of the capacitor before and after the bar is introduced.

335. The test ball in Problem 311 is connected by a wire to an electroscope and passed around the entire contour of the body (Fig. 101).

Will the readings of the electroscope change in this case when it moves from point A to points B and C?

Fig. 106

336. The equipotential surfaces of a certain field are shown in Fig. 107. It is known that $V_1 > V_2$. Use this pattern to reproduce approximately the lines of force of this field and indicate their direction.

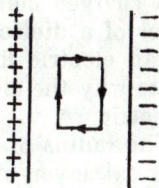

Fig. 107   Fig. 108

Determine the region in which the intensity of the field is highest.

337. The intensity of an electric field inside a capacitor is E.

Calculate the work needed to move a charge q in a closed rectangular circuit (Fig. 108).

338. Use the solution of the previous problem to prove that it is impossible to produce an electric field in which all the lines of force would be parallel straight lines and the density of their distribution would constantly increase in a direction perpendicular to the lines of force (Fig. 109).

339. Prove that if the lines of force are shaped like arcs of concentric circles with their centre at point O in a certain section of a field (Fig. 110) the intensity of the field in this section should at each point be inversely proportional to its distance from point O.

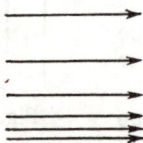

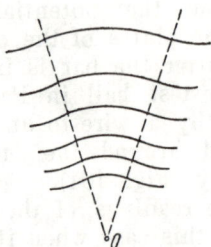

Fig. 109   Fig. 110

21. Electric Field in a Dielectric

340. A charged metal ball is surrounded by a thick spherical layer of a dielectric. Draw the pattern of the lines of force of an electric field inside and outside the dielectric.

Indicate why the electric field changes at the boundary of the dielectric.

341. The radius of a metal ball is 5 cm, the thickness of the spherical layer of a dielectric surrounding the ball is 5 cm, the permittivity of the layer is $\varepsilon = 3$ and the charge of the ball, $q = 10.8$ cgs electrostatic units.

Calculate the intensity of the field at the points lying a distance $r_1 = 6$ cm and $r_2 = 12$ cm from the centre of the ball.

342. The reduction in the intensity of an electric field when a charged body is immersed in a dielectric can be explained by the appearance of polarizing charges in the dielectric near the surface of the charged body which screen the action of the charges of the body with their field.

Determine the magnitude and the sign of such a polarizing charge and the density of its distribution if a metal ball of radius R and charge q is inside the dielectric of permittivity ε.

343. Charged balls suspended by long threads as in Problem 304 are placed into transformer oil. The density of the balls d is greater than that of the oil d_0.

Find the distance b between the balls after they have been immersed in the oil. The permittivity of the oil is ε.

22. Capacitance and Capacitors

One of the most difficult problems concerns the relationship between the magnitude of charges on capacitor plates and the field intensity in a capacitor. It is also difficult to determine how the charges on the plates and the forces of interaction between bodies change when these bodies (or a capacitor) are placed in media with various dielectric properties.

As regards the change of interaction of two charged bodies immersed in a dielectric when the charges of these bodies are invariable or when their potentials are kept the same, students sometimes think that this interaction decreases in all conditions in proportion to the permittivity of the medium.

In order to avoid such misconceptions the student should carefully consider the physical meaning of capacitance as a quantity which simultaneously takes into account the effect of the shape, dimensions and position of a body and the properties of the medium on the relationship between the potential and the charge of the body. Proper attention should also be paid to getting a mental picture of the changes in an electric field when a body is placed in various media and to the dependence of these changes on the conditions in which the media are changed.

The first few problems in this section consider those cases in which an increase in the permittivity of a medium causes the force of interaction between the charged bodies to increase at the same time.

When analysing the solutions of Problems 344-346, follow carefully the change in the magnitude of charges and the field intensity after bodies have been immersed in a dielectric under various conditions.

The end of the section offers several problems on the calculation of the interaction of capacitor plates and the work needed to draw the plates apart. Although not within the scope of the school curriculum, these problems allow the student to get a much deeper insight into the processes occurring in a capacitor. These problems are recommended for discussion in extracurricular circles.

In Problem 354 pay attention to the changes in the distribution of charges for different methods of capacitor connection.

344. A plane capacitor is placed in a glass vessel and connected to a storage battery as shown in Fig. 111. Switch A is closed. The e.m.f. force of the battery is $\mathcal{E} = 12$ V, the area of the capacitor plates $S = 100$ cm^2 and the distance betwen the plates $d = 1$ mm. Determine the magnitude of the charges across the capacitor plates in the following two cases:

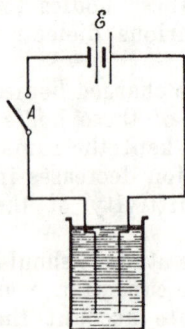

Fig. 111

(a) Switch A is opened and then the vessel is filled to the top with transformer oil of permittivity $\varepsilon = 2.2$.

(b) The vessel is first filled with oil and then switch A is opened.

Show how the intensity of the electric field will change in the capacitor in these two cases when the oil is poured in.

345. Two small charged bodies interact in air with a force F_1. What will the force of interaction between these bodies be after they are placed in a dielectric of permittivity ε if their potentials are kept the same as they were in air.

346. Two small charged balls permanently situated a large distance apart are placed consecutively in a number of media with increasing permittivities. The magnitude of the charges of the balls is then kept constant in one series of experiments while the potential difference remains the same in the other.

How will the force of interaction of the balls change as the permittivity increases in these cases?

347. A ball A of radius 5 cm has a charge $q_1 = + 20$ cgs electrostatic units of electricity and a ball B of radius 10 cm has the same charge $q_2 = + 20$ cgs electrostatic units. The balls are connected by a wire.

In what direction will the charges move along the wire? What quantity of electricity will be transferred from one ball to the other? What will the common potential and the charges of the balls be after connection? The balls are a long way apart.

348. A capacitor of 3 μF is charged to a potential difference of 300 V, and a capacitor of 2 μF to 200 V. Both charged capacitors are connected in parallel by the like poles.

What potential difference will be set up on the plates of the capacitors after connection?

349. After charging the capacitors in the previous problem their plates charged with unlike charges are connected.

What quantity of electricity will be transferred during connection and from what capacitor will this take place?

350. Identical charges $e = 2 \times 10^{-4}$ cgs electrostatic units are put on mercury drops of radius $r = 0.1$ cm. Ten such drops merge into one large drop.

What is the potential of the large drop?

351. Three capacitors of capacitance 0.002, 0.004 and 0,006 μF are connected in series.

Can a potential of 11,000 V be applied to this battery? What voltage will be received by each capacitor in the battery. The puncture voltage of each capacitor is 4,000 V.

352. Calculate the capacitance of a capacitor (see Problem 334) with a metal bar inserted into it if the area of each plate of this capacitor is $S = 100 \, \text{cm}^2$ and all the free space in the capacitor is filled with kerosene ($\varepsilon = 2.1$).

Will the capacitance of the capacitor be changed if the bar is moved parallel to itself from one plate to the other?

353. In a concentric-shape capacitor, the external and internal spheres are alternately connected to earth (Fig. 112).

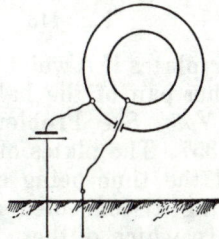

Fig. 112

Will the capacitance of this capacitor be the same in these two cases?

354. The charges on each plate of a plane capacitor are acted upon by the electric field set up by the charges on the other plate. Theoretical calculations show that the intensity of such a field set up by the charges of one plate in the capacitor is equal to

$$E = 2\pi \frac{Q}{S}$$

where Q is the charge on the plates and S is the area of each plate.

If Q and S are known, determine the force with which the plates of the plane capacitor will be mutually attracted. What work is needed to draw the capacitor plates apart by a distance d. Express this work in terms of the capacitance of the capacitor and the potential difference and in terms of the capacitance and the charge on the plates.

355. Find the charge density on the plates of a plane capacitor if its capacitance is 100 cm, the distance between the plates 2 mm and if the plates are mutually attracted by a force of 40 gf.

Note. See Problem 354.

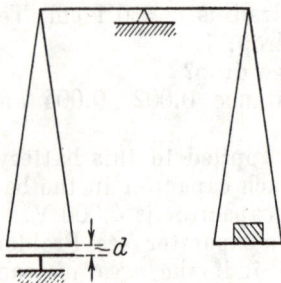

Fig. 113

356. One of the plates of a plane capacitor is suspended from the beam of a balance (Fig. 113). The distance between the capacitor plates is $d = 5$ mm and the area of the plates is 628 cm². What is the potential difference between the capacitor plates if a weight $P = 0.04$ gf has to be placed on the other pan of the balance to obtain equilibrium?

Note. See Problem 354.

357. The plates of a plane capacitor are first drawn apart all the time being connected to a voltage source and then being disconnected after receiving the initial charge.

In which of these two cases is more work required to draw the plates apart?

Note. See Problem 354.

358. A plane air capacitor is charged to a certain potential difference. A dielectric bar is put into the capacitor. The charge on the bar must then be increased three times to restore the former potential difference.

Determine the permittivity of the bar.

23. The Laws of Direct Current

This section requires special attention when solving problems involving the application of Ohm's law to an electric circuit containing several sources of e.m.f., and also the problems on current intensities in branched circuits and in the sections of a circuit containing the sources of e.m.f.

The errors in these problems usually occur because students confuse the signs of e.m.f. acting in a circuit and the directions of the currents and the electric field forces when writing the equations of Ohm's law.

Serious errors are also made when students forget that the intensity of current flowing in a section of a circuit with an acting source of e.m.f. is determined by the joint action of the electric potential difference at the ends of the section and the electromotive force of the source inside the section. For example, when calculating the current flowing through a storage battery of e.m.f. $\mathscr{E}$ and resistance R when it is charged from the mains having potential V, it is a common error to determine the current from the equation $IR = V$, frequently disregarding the proper equation $IR = V - \mathscr{E}$.

Errors are frequently caused by an inability to calculate the effect of the internal resistance of e.m.f. sources on the general functioning of the entire circuit. A number of problems in this section (for instance, 383, 385, 386, 392-395, etc.) are included to clarify this very point as well as the question of the best conditions for the operation of current sources.

When solving most of the problems in this section one should watch how the distribution of currents and potentials changes when separate resistances or sources are introduced or replaced in the circuit. It will be difficult to solve such problems as, for example, 379 and 380 if you do not know the relationship between the distribution of potentials and currents in branched circuits.

It is also important to show how and in what conditions one and the same measuring instrument can be utilized for various purposes (for example, the use of an ammeter as an ohmmeter, or a milliammeter as a voltmeter), and specify the most typical errors that can be made during measurement in various conditions (Problem 375). For this reason, some problems at the beginning of this section are based on the theory and operation of electrical measuring instruments.

359. The resistivity of copper is 1.7×10^{-6} ohm·cm. What is the resistivity of a copper wire 1 m long and 1 mm² in cross section?

360. One of the first attempts to get a standard unit of measurement for the resistance of conductors in all laboratories was made by the Russian Academician B. S. Yakobi. Yakobi's unit of resistance is equal to the resistance of a copper wire 6.358 feet long (1 ft = 30.5 cm) and 0.00336 in in diameter (1 in = 2.54 cm).

Express Yakobi's unit of resistance in ohms.

361. The resistance of a constantan wire is 10 ohms. Express this resistance in the units of the cgs electrostatic system.

362. How will the resistance of a telegraph line change from winter to summer if it is made of an iron wire 10 mm² in cross section? The temperature changes from —30°C to +30°C. In winter the length of the wire is 100 km, the resistivity of iron $\rho_0 = 8.7 \times 10^{-6}$ ohm·cm and the temperature coefficient of resistance $\beta = 6 \times 10^{-3}$ deg⁻¹.

How will the result change if the elongation of the wire on heating is taken into account? The coefficient of linear expansion of iron is $\alpha = 12 \times 10^{-6}$ deg⁻¹.

363. An electric lamp with a tungsten filament is rated at 220 V and consumes 40 W.

Determine the length of the filament in this lamp if its diameter is 0.01 mm. When the lamp burns the absolute temperature of the filament is 2,700°. The resistivity of tungsten which at 0°C is $\rho_0 = 5 \times 10^{-6}$ ohm·cm increases in proportion to the absolute temperature of the filament.

364. Determine the intensity of the current flowing in the electric lamp in the previous problem immediately after it is switched on. How much bigger will this current be than the current when the lamp burns normally?

365. A plane capacitor having plates of area S separated by a distance d is first filled with a dielectric of permittivity ε and then with an electrolyte of conductivity λ.

Find the ratio between the capacitance of the capacitor in the first case and its conductivity in the second.

366. In his experiments on the thermal effect of current the Russian Academician H.F.E. Lenz* assumed as a unit of current the intensity of that current which would evolve 41.16 cm³ of detonating gas in one hour at a pressure of 760 mm Hg and a temperature of 0°C when this current was passed through acidified water.

Express Lenz's unit of current in amperes. The density of oxygen at a pressure of 760 mm Hg is $d = 0.00143$ g/cm³.

367. What should the resistances of the sections of a rheostat R_1, R_2 and R_3 be (Fig. 114) in order to change the current passing through an instrument of resistance $R_0 = 30$ ohms by 1 A when the rheostat slide is shifted from one contact to another. The circuit is powered by a source of 120 V.

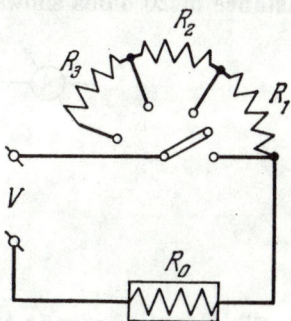

Fig. 114

368. It is required to measure the resistance of a circuit operating at 120 V. There is only one galvanometer with a response of 10^{-5} A per division.

How should the galvanometer be cut in to operate as an ohmmeter? What minimum resistance of the circuit can be measured with such a galvanometer if its full scale has 40 divisions? Construct the entire scale of such an ohmmeter in ohms per division. Disregard the internal resistance of the instrument.

369. A certain circuit with resistance $R = 100$ ohms is powered by a direct-current source. An ammeter with an internal resistance $R_0 = 1$ ohm is cut into the circuit to measure the current.

What was the current in the circuit before the ammeter was cut in if the ammeter shows 5 A?

370. What must the resistance of a shunt to a galvanometer be to reduce the response of the latter by 20 times? The internal resistance of the galvanometer is $R_0 = 950$ ohms.

* Heinrich Friedrich Emil Lenz (1804-1865) is famous for his law on the thermal effect of current and his rule applied to the phenomena of electromagnetic induction underlying today the theory of electric phenomena.

371. A milliammeter with a 20 mA scale is to be used as an ammeter to measure current up to 5 A. Calculate the resistance of the shunt if the internal resistance of the milliammeter is 8 ohms.

372. A sensitive milliammeter is utilized as a voltmeter. Determine the scale division of this instrument in volts if its internal resistance is 500 ohms and each division of the scale corresponds to 1 mA.

373. A voltmeter of internal resistance 400 ohms connected for measurement to a section of a circuit with a resistance of 20 ohms shows a reading of 100 V.

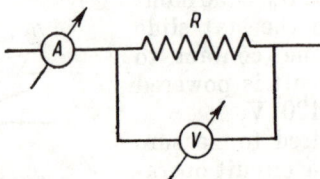

Fig. 115

What is the error in the readings of the voltmeter if the current in the circuit remains constant before branching?

374. The circuit shown in Fig. 115 is used to measure the resistance R. An ammeter shows a current of 2 A and a voltmeter a potential difference of 120 V.

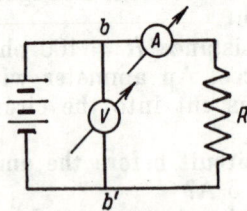
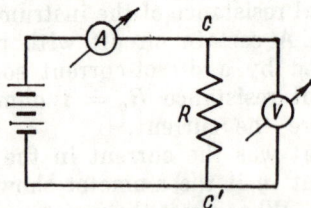

Fig. 116a   Fig. 116b

What is the magnitude of the resistance R if the internal resistance of the voltmeter is $R_0 = 3,000$ ohms? How large will the error in measuring R be, if the resistance of the voltmeter is assumed to be infinitely large in calculations?

375. A resistance R is calculated from the readings of a voltmeter and an ammeter connected as shown in Fig. 116a and 116b without any corrections being introduced for the internal resistances of the instruments.

Find the error which will be committed in measuring a resistance $R = 1$ ohm using these circuits if the internal resistance of the ammeter is $R_a = 0.1$ ohm and of the voltmeter $R_v = 1,000$ ohms. What will the error be in measuring a resistance $R = 500$ ohms? Which circuit should be used to measure low and high resistances?

376. A certain circuit with a resistance $R_1 = 10,000$ ohms is powered from a potentiometer of resistance $R_0 = 3,000$ ohms (Fig. 117). A voltage $V = 110$ V is supplied to the potentiometer. Determine the voltage V fed into the circuit when the slide is in the middle of the potentiometer.

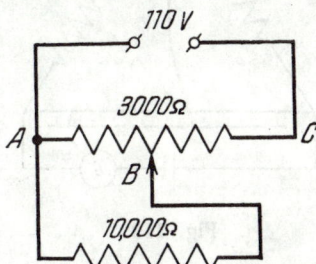

Fig. 117

377. A 60 W lamp burns in a room and an electric heating appliance of 240 W is switched on. The voltage in the mains is 120 V. The resistance of the wires connecting the electrical devices in the room with the mains is $R_0 = 6$ ohms.

By how much will the voltage supplied to the lamp be changed when the heating appliance is switched on?

378. A room is illuminated by n electric lamps each of which consumes a current I_0. The distance of the lead-in from the mains cable is l metres, the resistivity of the wires is ρ.

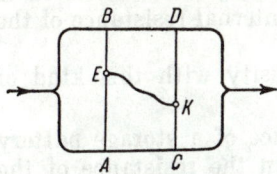

Fig. 118

Determine the minimum permissible cross section of the wires if the voltage loss in the line should not exceed V_1 volts.

379. Two conductors AB and CD are connected to the branches of an energized circuit (Fig. 118). The position of the points A, B, C and D is selected in a such a way that no current flows along these conductors. After that the two bridges are connected by a wire EK.

Will current flow in this case in the wire EK, and in the conductors AB and CD? What will happen to the potentials at the points A, B, C and D? What will be the potentials at the points E and K?

380. By mistake, a galvanometer and a switch were cut into the circuit of a bridge as shown in Fig. 119.

How can the balance of the bridge be established by observing the readings of the galvanometer when the switch is closed and opened?

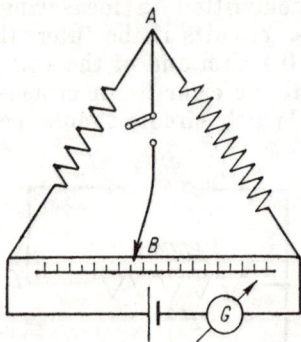

Fig. 119

381. In the system of electric units derived by Academician H.F.E. Lenz, the unit of e.m.f. is that e.m.f. which generates a current equal to Lenz's unit when the resistance of the circuit is equal to one of Yakobi's units (see Problems 360 and 366). Convert Lenz's unit for e.m.f. to volts.

382. The e.m.f. of a storage battery is 6 V. When the battery is connected to an external resistance of 1 ohm it produces a current of 3 A.

What will the current be when the battery is short-circuited?

383. An electric lamp of 110 V and 60 W is connected to a dry 120-volt storage battery. The internal resistance of the battery is 60 ohms.

Will the lamp burn at full intensity with this kind of connection?

384. What is the internal resistance of a storage battery if it produces a current of 1 A when the resistance of the external circuit is 1 ohm and a current of 0.5 A when the resistance is 2.5 ohms?

385. In order to determine the e.m.f. of a storage battery it was connected in series with a standard cell to a certain circuit and a 0.2-A current I_1 was obtained. When the storage battery is connected to the same circuit opposite to the standard cell a 0.08-A current I_2 flowing in the external circuit from the positive pole of the storage battery was obtained. What is the e.m.f. of the storage battery? The e.m.f. of the standard cell is $\mathscr{E}_2 = 2$ V.

386. What should the e.m.f. of the storage battery in Problem 385 be to obtain a 0.08-A current flowing in the external circuit from the negative to the positive pole of the storage battery when it is cut in the same direction as the standard cell?

387. The e.m.f. of a storage battery is 2 V, its internal resistance 0.4 ohm and the resistance of the external circuit 1 ohm. Determine the potential difference across its terminals.

388. A standard cell $\mathscr{E}_1$, a potentiometer with a resistance $R = 10$ ohms, a storage battery with an unknown e.m.f. $\mathscr{E}_2$ and a galvanometer G are connected as shown in Fig. 120.

Indicate the position of the slide A on the potentiometer at which no current will pass through the galvanometer. Determine the e.m.f. of the storage battery if the current ceases

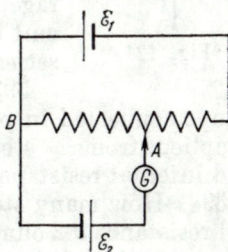

Fig. 120

to flow through the galvanometer when the resistance in the section of the potentiometer $AB = 9$ ohms. In this case the cell $\mathscr{E}_1$ produces a potential difference $V_0 = 2$ V at the ends of the potentiometer.

389. In the circuit in the previous problem (Fig. 120) the potentiometer has a scale 50 cm long with millimetre divisions, the response of the galvanometer is 10^{-4} A per division, and the internal resistance of the storage battery is $r = 0.5$ ohm.

What should the resistance of the galvanometer be to detect the disturbance of equilibrium when the slide is shifted from the position of equilibrium by one division of the potentiometer scale?

390. With the external circuit cut in, the potential difference across the poles of a storage battery is equal to 9 V and the current in the circuit 1.5 A.

What is the internal resistance r of the storage battery

and the resistance of the circuit R? The e.m.f. of the battery is 15 V.

391. Two identical storage batteries having e.m.f.s of 1.8 V and the same internal resistances are connected as shown in Fig. 121.

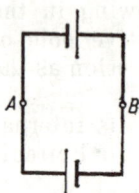

Determine the potential difference which will be established between points A and B. Disregard the resistance of the connecting wires.

392. A certain circuit with a resistance R is supplied with power simultaneously from N identical storage batteries.

At what internal resistance of the storage batteries will the current in the circuit be the same when they are connected in series and in parallel?

Fig. 121

393. How many 100 V, 50 W electric lamps connected in parallel can burn at full intensity when supplied from a storage battery with an e.m.f. $\mathscr{E} = 120$ V and internal resistance $r = 10$ ohms?

394. How many storage batteries of e.m.f. 2 V and internal resistance 0.2 ohm should be connected in series to obtain a current $I = 5$ A in the external circuit with a potential difference of $V = 110$ V across the poles of the battery?

395. When the resistance of the external circuit is 1.0 ohm the potential difference across the terminals of a storage battery is 1.5 V. When the resistance is 2 ohms the potential difference increases to 2 V.

Determine the e.m.f. and the internal resistance of the storage battery.

396. A storage battery of e.m.f. 6 V and internal resistance $r = 1.4$ ohms supplies power to an external circuit consisting of two parallel resistances of 2 and 8 ohms.

Determine the potential difference across the terminals of the storage battery and the currents in the resistances.

397. An external circuit with a resistance 0.3 ohm is powered by six storage batteries each of e.m.f. 2 V and internal resistance 0.2 ohm. The storage batteries are connected as separate groups in series and the groups are then connected in parallel.

What method of connecting the storage batteries in such

groups will provide the highest current in the circuit? What will this maximum current be?

398. A circuit with an external resistance R is powered by a storage battery consisting of N cells. The e.m.f. of each cell is $\mathscr{E}_0$ and the internal resistance is r_0. The storage battery is composed of identical groups connected in series. In turn, the groups consist of elements connected in parallel.

Find the number of the groups n and the number of the cells m in each group for which the maximum current will be observed in the circuit.

399. A current of 8 A is required in a circuit with a resistance of 5 ohms.

What is the minimum number of storage batteries needed to provide this current and how should they be connected into a compound battery if the e.m.f. of each battery is 2 V and the internal resistance 0.5 ohm?

400. A storage battery is connected to the mains for charging with voltage of 12.5 V (Fig. 122). The internal resistance of the storage battery is 1 ohm.

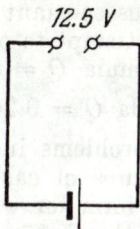

Fig. 122

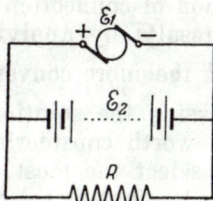

Fig. 123

What is the e.m.f. of this storage battery if a current of 0.5 A flows through it during charging?

401. A storage battery discharged to 12 V is connected for charging to 15-volt mains.

What auxiliary resistance should be connected to the circuit so that the charging current does not exceed 1 A? The internal resistance of the storage battery is 2 ohms.

402. A dynamo with an e.m.f. $\mathscr{E}_1 = 120$ V and an internal resistance $r = 0.5$ ohm, and a storage battery with an e.m.f. $\mathscr{E}_2 = 110$ V are connected to an external resistance R as shown in Fig. 123.

At what maximum value of R will no current pass through the storage battery? How will the battery operate when the resistance R is larger or smaller than the calculated value?

403. The e.m.f. of a storage battery is $\mathscr{E}_1 = 90$ V before charging and $\mathscr{E}_2 = 100$ V after charging. When charging began the current was 10 A.

What is the current at the end of charging if the internal resistance of the storage battery during the whole process of charging may be taken as constant and equal to 2 ohms and the voltage supplied by the charging plant as direct-current voltage?

24. Thermal Effect of Current. Power

Even if the reader is well versed in the Joule-Lenz law, he may sometimes fail to find the proper form of writing this law when solving some problems. For example, when solving Problem 411 on heating water in an electric kettle heater with two coils, students frequently forget that the voltage at the ends of the coils remains constant whatever their method of connection and they attempt to obtain the required results by applying the formula $Q = 0.24\ I^2Rt$ instead of the more convenient formula $Q = 0.24\ \dfrac{V^2}{R}\,t$.

In analysing the solutions to the problems in this section it is worth considering the features of each electric circuit to select the most convenient form for writing the Joule-Lenz law, noting the difference in the physical meaning of the forms of writing this law.

As we know the work done by the forces of an electric field in a given section of a circuit when a current is passed, is determined by the ratio $A = IVt$ while the amount of heat liberated in this section can be found from the equation $Q = I^2Rt$. If the section of the circuit being considered does not contain any sources of e.m.f. all the work done by the electric field forces is wholly expended on liberating Joule heat and both ratios produce the same results. If a source of e.m.f. is present inside this section some of the work done by the electric field forces is expended to overcome these electromotive forces and the relationships mentioned above yield different results.

Since the work done by the current in a section of a circuit having a source of e.m.f. is not included in the school curriculum the difference in the physical meaning of the formulas $A = IVt$ and $Q = I^2Rt$ usually escapes the attention of the student and he encounters serious difficulties in solving problems such as 409 and 410. Before solving problems of this kind refresh your knowledge of the work done by electric field forces and the thermal action of current.

A number of problems in this section (for instance, 406-408, 416, 417, etc.) are intended to draw the attention of the student to the nature of the dependence of the efficiency and useful power of current sources on the ratio between the resistance of an external circuit and the internal resistance of a source. This dependence is not always clear to some pupils who thus fail to give exhaustive answers to questions requiring calculation of the most favourable conditions for operation of current sources.

404. In one of his experiments on the thermal effect of current Academician H.F.E. Lenz heated 118 g of the alcohol with a current of 15.35 Lenz's units (see Problem 366).

Determine how long it took to raise the temperature of the alcohol by 1° if the resistance of the coil is 35.2 Yakobi's units (see Problem 360). The specific heat of the alcohol is 0.58 cal/g·deg. Disregard heat losses.

405. Use the data from the previous problem to calculate the time needed to heat the alcohol by 1°C with a current of 1 A and with a coil resistance of 1 ohm.

406. The coil of a heater has a resistance of 5 ohms and is supplied from a current source of internal resistance 20 ohms.

What should be the resistance of the shunt in the heater to reduce the amount of heat liberated in the heater to one ninth of the value without a shunt?

407. A storage battery of e.m.f. 12 volts and internal resistance $r = 0.8$ ohm supplies in turn external circuits rated at 0.4, 0.8 and 2 ohms.

Calculate for each of these three cases the useful power supplied by the battery and its efficiency. Explain the nature of the dependence of the efficiency and useful power on the resistance of the external circuit.

408. At the end of his article "Liberation of Heat in Conductors" Academician Lenz offers the following problem: "A circuit consisting of n cells is required to heat a wire of a definite diameter and length l. How many of these cells are needed to heat a wire of the same diameter but with a length pl?" In both cases the elements are connected in series. Solve this problem.

409. The voltage in the mains of a charging plant is 13 V. The internal resistance of a storage battery being charged is 0.4 ohm and its residual e.m.f. is 11 V.

What power will be expended by the plant in charging this storage battery? What part of this power will go on heating the storage battery?

410. An electric motor has an ohmic resistance of 2 ohms and is driven from mains of 110 V. When the motor is running the current passing through it is 10 A.

What power is consumed by this motor? What fraction of this power is converted into mechanical energy?

411. An electric kettle heater has two coils. When one coil is switched on, the water in the kettle begins to boil after 15 minutes and when the other is switched on—after 30 minutes.

How soon will the water in the kettle begin to boil if both coils are connected: (a) in series; (b) in parallel?

412. A current is passed along an iron wire with such an intensity as to heat it noticeably.

Explain why the cooling of one part of the wire (with water, for example) causes the other part to become more intensely heated than before the first part was cooled. The potential difference at the ends of the wire is kept constant throughout.

413. A fuse made of a lead wire with a cross section of 0.2 mm² is incorporated into a circuit of copper wire with a cross section of 2 mm². On short-circuiting the current reaches 30 A.

How long after the short-circuit occurs will the lead fuse begin to melt? How much will the copper wires heat up during this time? Neglect the loss of heat due to thermal conductivity. Take the specific heat of lead as constant and equal to $C_1 = 0.032$ cal/g·deg and of copper, $C_2 = =0.091$ cal/g·deg. The resistivity of lead is $\rho_1 = 22 \times \times 10^{-6}$ ohm·cm and of copper $\rho_2 = 1.7 \times 10^{-6}$ ohm·cm. The melting point of lead is $T_1 = 327°C$. The temperature of the wires before short-circuiting is $T_0 = 20°C$. The density of copper is $d_2 = 8.9$ g/cm³ and of lead $d_1 = 11.34$ g/cm³.

414. In one calorimeter there is a certain amount of water and in another the same mass of a liquid whose heat capacity is to be determined. Identical constantan wires connected in series to a current-carrying circuit are immersed in the calorimeters.

What is the specific heat of the liquid if the temperature of the water rises by 2.50°C and that of the liquid by 4.25°C some time after the wires are energized?

415. A steel wire has a resistance twice as great as a copper one.

Which wire will liberate more heat: (a) in parallel; (b) in series connection with both wires in a circuit powered by a direct-current voltage?

416. A wire with a resistance $R = 2$ ohms is first connected to a storage battery of internal resistance $r_0 = 2$ ohms and then another such wire is connected in parallel.

By how much will the quantity of heat liberated in the first wire change after the second is cut in?

417. A storage battery is shorted by an external circuit first with a resistance R_1 and then with a resistance R_2.

At what value R_0 of the internal resistance of the storage battery will the quantities of heat liberated in the external circuit be the same in both cases?

25. Permanent Magnets

418. Two magnetic poles repel each other with a force of 8 gf. The distance between the poles is 10 cm. The magnetic mass of one pole is twice as large as that of the other.

Determine the magnitude of the magnetic masses of these poles.

419. A bar magnet has a length $l = 10$ cm and the magnetic masses of its poles are $m = 10$ cgs electromagnetic units.

Determine the magnitude and direction of the field intensity vector produced by such a magnet at point A lying on the extension of the magnet's axis at a distance $a = 5$ cm from the south pole.

420. Two identical magnets with a length $l = 5$ cm and weight $p = 50$ gf each made of magnico alloy which was obtained by the Soviet scientists Zaimovsky and Lvov are arranged freely with their like poles facing in a vertical glass tube (Fig. 124). The upper magnet hangs in the air above the lower one so that the distance a between the nearest poles of the magnets is 3 mm.

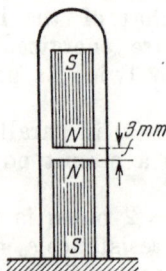

Fig. 124

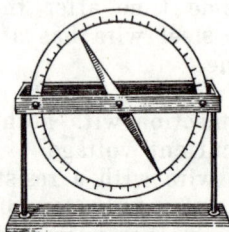

Fig. 125

Determine the magnetic masses of the poles of these magnets. Will remote poles change the distance between the magnets?

421. In order to keep the needle (Fig. 125) in a horizontal position a load of 0.01 gf is suspended from its top end.

Find the magnitudes of the horizontal and vertical components of the intensity of the terrestrial magnetic field. Calculate the total intensity of the terrestrial magnetic field. The dip angle $\alpha = 70°$. The magnetic masses of the poles of the needle are $m = 9.8$ cgs electromagnetic units.

422. If a magnetic needle is secured to a cork and the cork is floated on water the terrestrial magnetic field will cause the needle to turn and set itself along the magnetic meridian, but the needle will not move northwards or southwards. If the pole of a bar magnet is placed not far from the needle the field of the magnet will set the needle in the direction of the lines of force and will cause it to move towards the magnet.

What are the reasons for the different behaviour of the needle in the magnetic fields of the earth and the magnet?

423. One is given two outwardly identical long bars—one is made of soft iron and the other is a steel magnet.

By observing the interaction of the bars in various positions how can one determine which of them is a magnet.

424. The length of a thin bar magnet is $l = 10$ cm and the magnetic masses of the poles are $m = \pm 50$ cgs electromagnetic units.

Determine the force acting on a unit north magnetic pole at a point A lying on the perpendicular to the axis of the magnet in its middle point. The point A is at a distance 10 cm from the axis. Consider the poles as points.

425. A dip needle with a circular scale is secured on a horizontal axis (see Fig. 125).

How can the direction of the magnetic meridian be found with the aid of this needle?

Fig. 126   Fig. 127

426. Several steel needles are freely suspended on hooks from a small brass disk as shown in Fig. 126. If the pole of a strong magnet is brought up to the needles from below the needles will first be drawn apart and then will again assume a vertical position when the magnet is brought right up to them. As the magnet is removed, the needles will again be drawn apart forming a cone-shaped bunch.

Explain the causes of this behaviour.

427. Two long equally magnetized needles are freely suspended by their like poles from a hook as shown in Fig. 127. The length of each needle is 20 cm and the weight 10 gf. In equilibrium the needles make an angle $\alpha = 2°$ with each other.

Determine the magnetic masses of the poles of the needles. The magnetic masses are concentrated at the ends of the needles.

428. The following experiment can be carried out with the aid of strong magnets made of magnico alloy.

Identical magnets A and B are placed along one straight line with their like poles fitted tightly against each other. Then magnet B is raised so that it rests on its edge. The magnet will be held in equilibrum in this tilted position by the forces of interaction of the poles NN (Fig. 128).

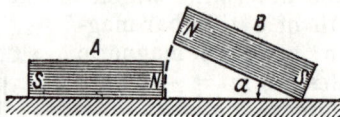

Fig. 128

Determine the force of interaction and the magnetic masses of the poles of the magnets when the magnet B of length $l = 10$ cm and weight $P = 100$ gf is in equilibrium at an angle $\alpha = 10°$. The magnetic masses of the poles can be taken as points and as being situated at the ends of the

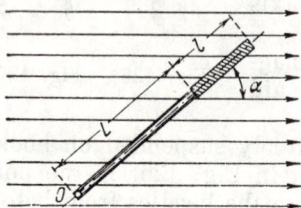

Fig. 129

magnets. Will the position of equilibrium of the magnet B be stable in this case?

429. The magnetic moment P of a magnetic needle is the product of the needle length l and the magnetic mass m of one of the poles: $P = ml$.

The needle is placed in a uniform magnetic field of intensity H. The direction of the needle forms an angle α with the direction of the lines of force of the field.

Determine the magnitude of the mechanical moment acting on the needle in this case. Express the mechanical moment in terms of the magnetic moment of the needle and the intensity of the field.

430. A magnetic needle uniform along its length has a magnetic moment $P = 50$ cgs electromagnetic units and a weight $Q = 5$ gf.

How should the point of support be arranged with respect to the centre of gravity of the needle to set it in a horizontal position in the terrestrial magnetic field in the northern hemisphere? The vertical component of the magnetic field is $H_v = 0.5$ cgs electromagnetic units.

431. A magnetic needle with length l and poles of magnetic masses $\pm m$ is attached to a wooden bar of length L (Fig. 129) and placed in a uniform magnetic field of intensity H. The bar and the needle can revolve around point O.

Find the magnitude of the mechanical moment that will cause the rotation of the bar around point O if the bar makes an angle α with the direction of the lines of force of the magnetic field.

432. A magnetic needle has a length l and the magnetic masses of its poles are $\pm m$. The needle is broken in two. What will the magnetic moments of the two halves be?

433. Draw the lines of force of the magnetic field inside a magnetized steel tube.

434. Indicate the positions and the nature of equilibrium of a number of magnetic needles arranged in a straight line at equal distances from one another.

435. A strong horseshoe magnet is closed by an iron plate A (Fig. 130). The weight of the plate corresponds to the lifting force of the magnet, and the magnet can easily hold the plate. If the poles of the magnet are now touched on the sides with a plate B made of soft iron, the plate A will drop at once. If the plate B is removed the magnet will again be capable of holding the plate A. Explain this phenomenon.

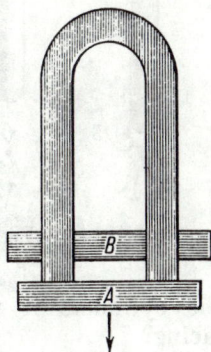

Fig. 130

436. A long rod made of soft iron is secured in a vertical position. If a strong magnet A is brought to the top of the rod as shown in Fig. 131 the rod will be magnetized so intensely as to retain at its other end several small pieces of iron. If the same magnet A is applied to the side of the rod near the bottom end (Fig. 132) the magnetization will be weak and the pieces of iron will fall. Explain why the magnet A acts differently in these two cases.

437. A strong magnet of magnico alloy can hold a chain consisting of several cylinders made of soft iron (Fig. 133).

What will happen to the cylinders if a similar magnet is brought up from below to this chain? The magnets are arranged with their like poles facing. What will happen to

Fig. 131

Fig. 132

Fig. 133

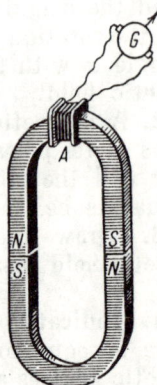
Fig. 134

the cylinders if the magnets have their opposite poles facing?

438. Two identical horseshoe magnets are linked by their opposite poles as shown in Fig. 134. One of the magnets has round it a coil A whose ends are connected to a galvanometer G. If the magnets are detached, the pointer of the galvanometer will be deflected at this instant through a certain angle. If the magnets are connected again the pointer of the galvanometer will also be deflected, but this time in the opposite direction.

Indicate the causes for the deflection of the pointer of the galvanometer.

439. Permalloy can be magnetized appreciably in the terrestrial magnetic field and does not possess residual magnetism, i.e., it is the softest material as far as magnetism is concerned.

How will a magnetic needle on a vertical axis near a long bar made of this alloy behave if:

(a) the bar is vertical (Fig. 135);

(b) the bar is horizontally placed along the magnetic meridian;

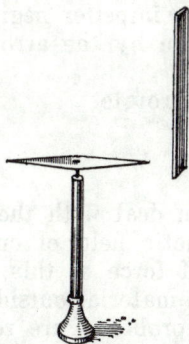

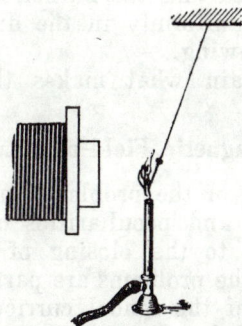

Fig. 135   Fig. 136

(c) the bar is in a horizontal plane perpendicular to the magnetic meridian.

Will the behaviour of the needle change in these three cases when the bar is turned?

440. A small thin iron nail is suspended from a light fire-proof thread. A strong electromagnet is placed near the nail (Fig. 136). The flame from a powerful gas burner is directed precisely between the nail and the magnet and licks the nail when it is deflected by the magnet. If the windings of the electromagnet are energized the nail will be at once deflected into the flame and will then be ejected from it to assume its original position. After a lapse

Fig. 137

of time the nail will again be drawn to the magnet.

Explain what causes these periodic oscillations of the nail.

441. F.N. Shvedov suggested the following design for a motor. Some 20-30 nickel rods similar to these used in an umbrella are attached to a small support bush fitted onto a sharp point. Nearby are arranged a strong electromagnet and a gas burner with a broad and intensive flame as shown in Fig. 137. When the windings of the electromagnet are energized and the burner is ignited the impeller begins to rotate uniformly in the direction shown by the arrow on the drawing.

Explain what makes the impeller rotate.

26. Magnetic Field of a Current

Most of the problems in this section deal with the properties and peculiarities of the magnetic field of current related to the closing of the lines of force of this field. Since the problems are partly based on material outside the scope of the school curriculum these problems are recommended for discussion in extracurricular circles. Pay special attention to the problems on the work done by the forces of the magnetic field of current in a closed loop.

442. Draw the lines of force of a magnetic field of a rectilinear current.

443. A current I flowing along a sufficiently long rectilinear conductor sets up, as we know, a magnetic field with an intensity

$$H = 0.2 \frac{I}{r} \text{ cgs electromagnetic units}$$

where r is the distance of the point in the field from the current-carrying conductor as measured in cm and I is the current in amperes.

Determine the intensity of the field at point A 5 cm away from the conductor if the current is 2 A. Draw the field intensity vector. Find the force acting at point A on a magnetic pole of $m = 5$ cgs electromagnetic units.

444. Given:

(a) The intensity of the magnetic field of a rectilinear current at a distance $R_0 = 1$ cm from the conductor is $H_0 = 0.2I$.

(b) The lines of force of the magnetic field of such a current are concentric circles.

(c) When a unit pole moves along a closed circuit the work done by the magnetic field forces is zero if this circuit is not penetrated by currents.

Use these data to derive the formula for the dependence of the intensity H of the magnetic field of the current on the distance R from the conductor.

445. A magnetic field at a certain point A is composed of the terrestrial magnetic field with a horizontal component of intensity $H_h = 0.2$ cgs electromagnetic units and the magnetic field of rectilinear current $I = 5$ A.

How should a current-carrying conductor be arranged with respect to the point A for the vector of the intensity of the resultant field be vertical at this point?

446. A conductor carrying a current is placed as in the previous problem.

At what points in space will the field intensity be equal to zero if the vertical component of the terrestrial magnetic field is $H_v = 0.5$ cgs electromagnetic units?

447. A current I flows along an infinite rectilinear thin-walled pipe.

What is the intensity of the magnetic field inside the pipe? The current is distributed uniformly along the entire section of the pipe.

448. A current I flows upwards along the inner conductor of a coaxial cable (Fig. 138) and returns down along the external shell of the cable.

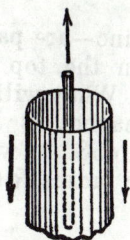

Fig. 138

What is the intensity of the magnetic field at points inside the cable?

449. A magnetic pole of $m = 5$ cgs electromagnetic units is passed around a circumference of radius R. A rectilinear conductor carrying a current of 2 A is laid perpendicularly to the plane of this circle through its centre.

Calculate the work done by the forces of the magnetic field of the current during this displacement of the magnetic pole.

450. When a magnetic pole moves along a closed path under the same conditions as the previous problem some work is obtained. Can this result be used to construct a perpetuum mobile?

451. A circular branching made from a uniform conductor is placed in a d-c circuit (Fig. 139).

What force will the magnetic field of the currents in the branching exert on the magnetic pole placed at its centre?

452. A cork floats in a broad vessel filled with a weak solution of sulphuric acid. Two small plates—copper and

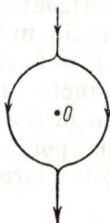

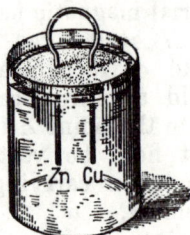

Fig. 139   Fig. 140

zinc—are passed through the cork. The plates are connected on the top by a copper wire (Fig. 140).

What will happen to the cork if the end of a strong bar magnet is brought up to it?

453. As we know, a current I flowing along a circumference of radius R creates in its centre a magnetic field of intensity

$$H = \frac{0.2\pi I}{R}$$

Determine the force acting on a unit magnetic pole placed at the centre of a circular current of 5 A if the radius of the circle is $R = 10$ cm. Indicate the direction of this force, assuming the direction of the current to be known.

454. Professor A. A. Eichenwald of the Moscow University carried out one of the basic experiments which directly revealed the generation of magnetic fields for any displacement of electric charges. In his experiment a certain charge was put on a massive disk which was then set in rapid rotation. The magnetic field set up by the charge on the disk was detected with the aid of a magnetic needle arranged above the instrument (Fig. 141).

Determine the direction in which the needle is deflected if a negative charge is put on the disk and the disk rotates in the direction shown.

455. Currents are sometimes measured with the aid of the so-called tangent galvanometer (Fig. 142) consisting of a small magnetic needle suspended from a light thread and placed in the centre of a circular current. The plane of the energized circle is arranged strictly in the plane of the magnetic meridian.

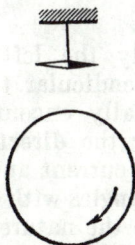

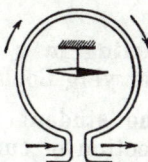

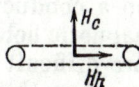

Fig. 141   Fig. 142

Determine the angle through which the needle of the tangent galvanometer will turn if a current $I = 1$ A is passed along the circle, if the radius of the circle is $R = 10$ cm and the horizontal component of the terrestrial magnetic field is $H_h = 0.2$ cgs electromagnetic units.

Note. See Problem 453.

456. A current I is passed along the ring of the tangent galvanometer in Problem 455 so that it establishes a field $H_c = 0.1$ cgs electromagnetic units in the centre of the ring. As the current is being passed the circle turns after the needle.

Determine the angle through which the circle should be turned so that the needle is in the plane of this circle in the case of equilibrium.

457. The magnetic field intensity inside a solenoid is proportional to the current I and the number of turns per unit length of the solenoid, i.e.,

$$H = 1.26 \frac{IN}{l}$$

where N is the total number of turns of the solenoid and l is its length.

Find the magnetic field intensity inside a long solenoid made of wire with a diameter 0.5 mm. The wire of the solenoid is wound so that the turns are close to one another. The current is 2 A.

27. Forces Acting in a Magnetic Field on Current-Carrying Conductors

Even if the student uses correctly the left-hand rule when the direction of current is perpendicular to the lines of force of a magnetic field he usually encounters some difficulties in applying it for finding the direction of the force acting on a conductor when the current and the lines of force of a magnetic field form acute angles with each other.

It is far more difficult to determine the nature of motion of a conductor when the lines of force form various angles with the direction of current in various sections of a conductor. It is just as difficult to take account of the effect exerted by the heterogeneity of a field on the behaviour of a conductor in the simplest cases. All the problems in this section deal precisely with these cases. In solving the problems, pay careful attention to the sequence of applying the left-hand rule when finding the forces acting on the separate elements of conductors in various conditions.

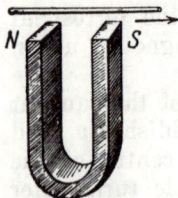

Fig. 143

458. A rectilinear current-carrying conductor is arranged above the poles of a horseshoe magnet as shown in Fig. 143. The conductor can move freely in all directions.

What will happen to the conductor under the action of the field of a magnet if the current passes in the direction indicated by the arrow?

459. A flexible free conductor is placed near a strong long bar magnet (Fig. 144).

How will the conductor arrange itself if current is passed through it from the top to the bottom?

460. Currents are passed through two free rectilinear conductors arranged at right angles as shown in Fig. 145.

How will the interaction of the magnetic fields of the currents change the position of the conductors relative to each other?

461. A rectilinear current I_2 is passed along the axis of a circular current I_1 (Fig. 146).

With what force are the currents interacting?

462. A soft spiral spring hangs freely. The lower end of the spring is immersed in a cup of mercury. The spring and the cup are connected to a d-c source as shown in Fig. 147.

What will happen to the spring after the circuit is closed by a switch S?

463. A beam of positively charged particles moves with a velocity v into a uniform magnetic field perpendicularly to the lines of force of this field (only one particle is shown in Fig. 148).

Along what path will the particles move in such a magnetic field?

464. An infinite rectilinear energized conductor AB has near it a movable uniform rectilinear conductor CD of finite length the whole of which lies on one side of AB and in a plane passing through AB (Fig. 149).

What will happen to the conductor CD if current is passed through it in the direction indicated by the arrow?

465. Current is passed along the conductor CD from point D to point C (see the previous problem).

How will the conductor CD move in this case?

466. Two vertical circular conductors with approximately equal diameters are arranged in mutually perpendicular planes as shown in Fig. 150.

How will the conductors behave if a current is passed through them in the directions indicated by the arrows?

467. An energized wire ring is freely suspended from soft infeed conductors as shown in Fig. 151. A horizontal magnet is brought close to the ring.

What will happen to the ring in this case?

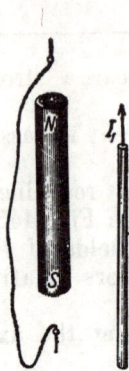

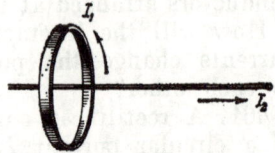

Fig. 144   Fig. 145   Fig. 146

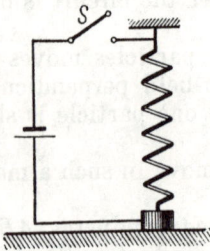

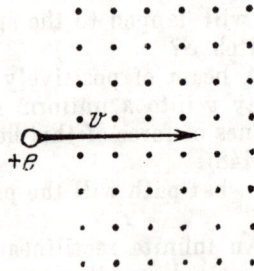

Fig. 147   Fig. 148

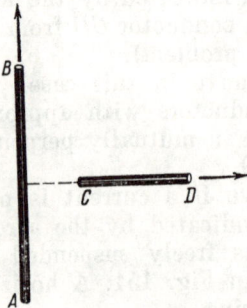

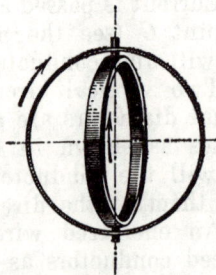

Fig. 149   Fig. 150

468. An energized ring (see the previous problem) is arranged in the middle of a magnet.

What will happen to the ring if the direction of current is reversed in it?

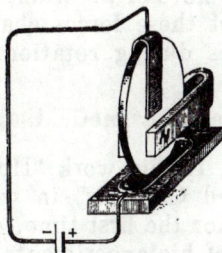

Fig. 151   Fig. 152

469. A copper disk is secured on a horizontal axis and placed between the poles of a strong magnet so that the north pole of the magnet is arranged on the right (Fig. 152). The bottom of the disk is immersed in a cup of mercury.

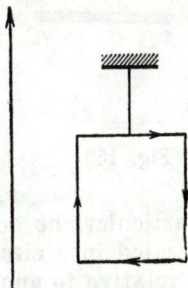
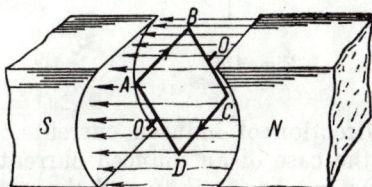

Fig. 153   Fig. 154

The axis of the disk and the cup are connected to a d-c source.

What will happen to the disk when the circuit is closed?

470. A light rectangular frame is suspended from a thread near an infinite rectilinear conductor with current passing through it (Fig. 153).

How will the frame behave if current is passed through it in the direction indicated by the arrows?

471. A rectangular frame with current passing along it is arranged in a uniform magnetic field so that its axis is perpendicular to the lines of force of the magnetic field (Fig. 154). Indicate the direction of the forces exerted on the sides of the frame *BC* and *DA*. Show how the magnitude of these forces changes as the position of the frame changes during rotation.

28. Electromagnetic Induction

472. In his work "How To Determine the Direction of Induced Currents" in which Lenz's famous rule was laid down for the first time, Academician H.F.E. Lenz describes some of his experiments which he carried out to determine

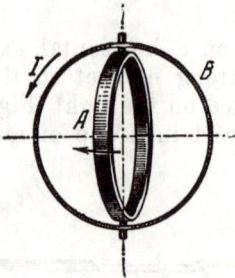

Fig. 155

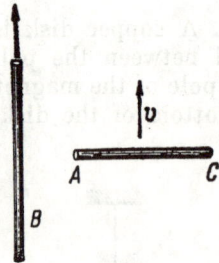

Fig. 156

the direction of induced currents. In particular, he considers the case of an induced current generated in a circular conductor when it is turned through 90° relative to another circular conductor with current passing along it (Fig. 155).

Determine the direction of current in a movable conductor *A* if it is transferred from a position perpendicular to the circuit *B* to one parallel to it as indicated by the arrow.

473. A rectangular conductor *AC* of finite length is perpendicular to an infinite rectilinear current *B* (Fig. 156). The conductor *AC* moves along metal guidelines parallel to itself in the direction of current *B*.

Indicate the direction of currents induced in the conductor AC when its direction of motion coincides with that of the current B. How will the induced current be directed if the conductor AC moves in the opposite direction?

474. Determine the directions of induced currents in the following experiment performed by Lenz.

A permanent magnet is placed along the magnetic meridian. A rectilinear conductor is arranged parallel to the magnet first above it and then under it. The magnet is

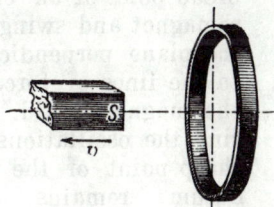

Fig. 157

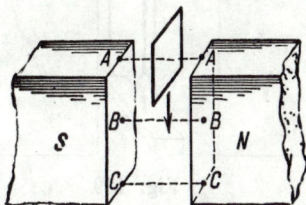

Fig. 158

rapidly turned through 90° first with its north pole to the east and then to the west.

475. A copper disk is placed between the poles of magnets as shown in Fig. 152. A galvanometer is connected instead of a storage battery to the electric circuit shown in the diagram.

In what direction will the induced current flow when the disk rotates: (1) clockwise; (2) counter-clockwise?

476. Two rectilinear parallel conductors are moved towards each other. A current I flows through one of them.

What is the direction of the current induced in the other conductor? What is the direction of induced current when the conductors are drawn apart?

477. The south pole of a magnet is removed with a certain velocity from a metal ring as shown in Fig. 157.

Determine the direction of the induced currents in the ring.

478. A small rectangular wire frame falls freely in the space between the wide poles of a sufficiently strong electromagnet (Fig. 158)

Show the direction of the currents induced in the frame
when the middle of the frame passes through the positions
A, B and C. How will the frame move in these sections?

479. A small pendulum consisting of a metal thread,
a ball and a sharp point immersed in a cup of mercury

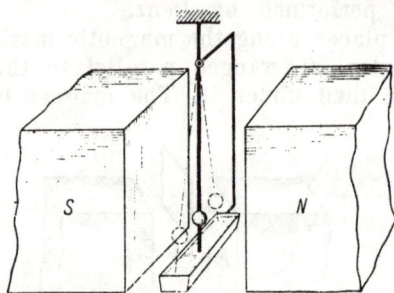
Fig. 159

(Fig. 159) makes part of
an electric circuit. The
pendulum is placed in
the space between the
broad poles of an elect-
romagnet and swings in
the plane perpendicular
to the lines of force of
the magnetic field. Du-
ring the oscillations the
sharp point of the pen-
dulum remains im-
mersed in mercury.

How will the magnetic field effect the motion of the
pendulum? What is the direction of the currents in the
circuit of the pendulum?

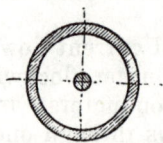
Fig. 160

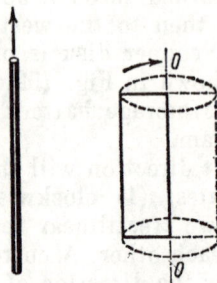
Fig. 161

480. A copper wire connected to a closed circuit is surrounded by a thick iron shell (Fig. 160) and introduced
together with the shell into the space between the poles of
an electromagnet. The iron shell acts as a magnetic screen
for the wire.
Will an e.m.f. be induced in the wire?

481. An aircraft flies along the meridian. Will the potentials of the ends of its wings be the same?

Will the potential difference change if the aircraft flies in any other direction with the same velocity?

482. A rectangular wire frame rotates with a constant velocity around one of its sides parallel to a current-carrying rectilinear conductor nearby (Fig. 161).

Indicate the positions in which the maximum and the minimum e.m.f.s will be induced in the frame.

483. Two circular conductors are perpendicular to each other as shown in Fig. 162.

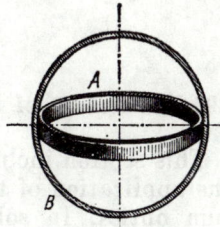

Fig. 162

Will a current be induced in the conductor A if the current is changed in the circuit B?

Chapter IV

OPTICS

29. The Nature of Light

This section includes a number of problems which require the application of the simplest relations of wave and quantum optics. In solving these problems, attention should also be paid to the change in individual magnitudes (wavelength and velocity) characterizing a light wave moving from one medium to another. It is difficult to understand the ratio $c = \lambda v$ if the nature of these changes and their physical meaning are not taken into account.

Before solving these problems it is recommended to refresh your knowledge of the subject from a text-book.

484. The velocity of light c and the length of a light wave λ are related to the frequency of oscillations v by the ratio

$$c = \lambda v$$

Determine the change in the wavelength of red rays during the passage from vacuum to glass if the refractive index of glass is $n = 1.5$ and the frequency of the red rays is $v = 4 \times 10^{14}$ s^{-1}.

485. The refractive index of any substance is equal to the ratio of the velocity of light propagation in vacuum to the velocity of light propagation in the given medium. It was found that the refractive index of one type of glass is equal to $n_1 = 1.50$ for red rays and to $n_2 = 1.54$ for violet rays.

Determine the velocities of propagation of these rays in glass.

486. P. A. Cerenkov has found experimentally that when an electron moves in some medium with a constant velocity exceeding the velocity of light propagation in this medium it will begin to emit light.

Determine the minimum velocity to which the electron should be accelerated to produce such an emission when the electron moves in a medium with a refractive index $n = 1.5$.

487. Explain the phenomenon of the coloured bands seen on thin films of oil on the surface of water.

488. If a thin soap film is arranged vertically the coloured horizontal interference bands move downwards and at the same time change their width. After some time a rapidly growing dark spot appears at the top of the film which bursts shortly afterwards.

Indicate what causes the motion of the bands and explain the origin of the dark spot.

489. How will the pattern of Newton's rings change if the space between a lens and a plane glass is filled with liquid whose refractive index is higher than that of the lens, but less than that of the glass?

490. "Antireflection Optics" which was developed by Academicians I.V. Grebenshchikov, A.A. Lebedev and A.N. Terenin is widely employed in present-day optical instruments to reduce the loss of light due to reflection from the surfaces of lenses. This method is based on the following phenomenon: if the surface of glass is coated with a thin transparent film whose refractive index is less than that of the glass and whose thickness is equal to a quarter of a wavelength of the incident light, the intensity of light reflected from such a plate will be zero and all of the light will pass through the plate.

Consider the interaction of the light beams reflected from the upper and lower surface of this film and explain why the surface of the glass ceases to reflect the light after the film is put on.

Why must the thickness of the film be equal to a quarter of the wavelength of incident light?

Why must the refractive index of the film be less than that of the glass?

491. Experiments show that the luminous flux is a flux of separate photons or light quanta. Each photon has an energy $E = h\nu$ where $h = 6.62 \times 10^{-27}$ erg·s is Planck's constant and ν is the frequency of the light wave.

Determine the energy of the photons emitted by a yellow

sodium flame if the frequency of the yellow line of sodium is $\nu = 5 \times 10^{13}$ s⁻¹.

492. When an electron was transferred in a hydrogen atom from one stable level to another a quantum of light was emitted with a frequency $\nu = 4.57 \times 10^{14}$ s⁻¹.

Determine the change in the energy of the electron in the atom due to this emission.

493. The great Russian physicist P.N. Lebedev established in his experiments that light exerts on bodies of ray

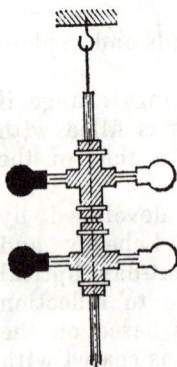

Fig. 163

absorptivity a pressure numerically equal to all the energy which the light brings in one second divided by the velocity of light (all magnitudes are in the cgs system).

What force would the sunrays exert on the Earth if they were entirely absorbed by the earth surface? In normal incidence, the sunrays supply 1.94 cal to each square centimetre of the Earth's surface every minute.

494. Lebedev's device was used to measure the pressure exerted by light on the wings of a light suspension shown in Fig. 163. Each wing has two circles one of which is darkened.

Find the force with which the luminous flux acts on the darkened circle in Lebedev's experiments if this flux supplies an energy of 1.5 cal per minute per each square centimeter of the illuminated surface. The diameter of the circle is 5 mm. Assume that all light is completely absorbed by the circle.

495. Prove that the force exerted by the light from the Sun on any body diminishes in proportion to the square of the distance of this body from the Sun.

30. Fundamentals of Photometry

496. A book can easily be read with an illumination of 50 lx. At what height should a lamp of 50 cd be hanging above a table to provide good illumination of its surface which lies directly under the lamp?

497. The width of the aperture of a cinema projector is 1.2 cm and that of the screen is 2.4 m.

How much stronger will the illumination of the aperture in the projector be than that of the screen? What should the illumination of the aperture be if the minimum permissible illumination of the screen is 4 lx?

498. A desk-lamp of height $h = 30$ cm stands on a table (Fig. 164).

Determine the illumination at a point on the table surface a distance $a = 60$ cm from the lamp. The luminous intensity of the lamp is 25 cd.

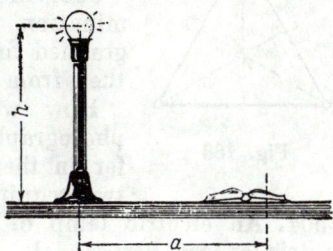

Fig. 164

499. At what distance should the posts for street lamps be installed so that the illumination on the ground at the point lying halfway between two posts is not less than 4/15 lx? The height of the posts is $h = 12$ m. The luminous intensity of the lamps is $I = 300$ cd. Assume that a noticeable illumination is provided only by the two lamps on either side.

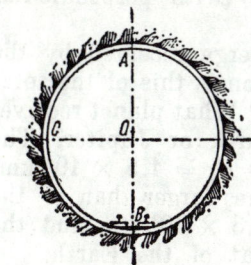

Fig. 165

500. During fitting jobs in a subway an electric lamp is secured at the top point of the tunnel A (Fig. 165). What is the ratio between the illuminations produced by the lamp at the lowest point B and those at the point C lying at the level with the horizontal cross section of the tunnel? The luminous intensity of the lamp is the same in all directions.

501. A lamp of 400 cd is installed in a narrow-film cinema projector.

What illumination can be produced by this projector on a screen 3 m² in area if only 0.3 per cent of the light emitted by the lamp falls on the screen?

502. Three point sources of light are arranged at the vertices of an equilateral triangle. A small plate is placed in the centre of the triangle perpendicular to its plane and parallel to one of its sides (Fig. 166).

Determine the illumination of this plate if the intensity of each source of light is I and the length of the side of the triangle is l.

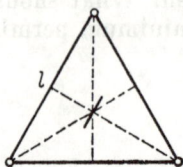

503. In constant conditions of illumination a certain object is photographed first from a large distance and then from a small distance.

How will the illuminations of the photographic plates in the camera differ in these two cases? Which of the two requires a longer exposure?

Fig. 166

504. An electric lamp of 100 cd consumes 0.5 W of electric energy per candela.

Determine the efficiency η of this lamp if the mechanical equivalent of light is equal to 0.00161 W/lu. Calculate the quantity of light in ergs emitted by the lamp every second.

505. The sunrays which reach the earth surface bring in every minute an energy approximately equal to 1.94 cal per 1 cm^2 of the terrestrial surface (with perpendicular incidence).

Determine the total amount of energy received by the entire terrestrial surface. What fraction is this of the total energy of light emission from the Sun? What planet receives more energy from the Sun—the Earth or Jupiter? The distance from the Earth to the Sun is $R_1 = 1.5 \times 10^8$ km, the distance to Jupiter R_2 is 5.20 times larger than to the Earth, the radius of the Earth is 6.3×10^3 km and the radius of Jupiter is 11.14 times that of the Earth.

31. The Laws of Rectilinear Propagation and Reflection of Light

Together with the problems on the position and the size of an image produced by various optical systems, Secs 31-34 include many problems involving calculation of the conditions when an observer can see these images.

These problems require a clear understanding of the meaning of auxiliary rays in geometrical optics used to construct images. It is equally important to know the methods for determining the rays that actually form these images. This will considerably facilitate the solution of such problems, for example, as the construction of an object positioned at some distance from a flat mirror, or of the image of a large object in a small lens or in a lens half covered by an opaque screen, and determining the position of an observer's eye for simultaneous viewing several images produced by optical systems.

In Secs 32-34 pay attention to the rules used to find graphically the focus of the rays in a beam that has passed through an optical system (for example, Problems 555-557). In solving these problems, study the specific uses of the equations of spherical mirrors and lenses for calculating the position of the images produced by systems with converging beams.

The problems in the sections that follow should be solved in the order in which they are presented because many of them are based on the results of previous problems.

506. How should a point source, a flat object and a screen be placed for the outline of the shadow on the screen to be similar to that of the object?

507. An electric lamp is placed into a frosted glass sphere of radius 20 cm and is suspended at a height of 5 m above the floor. A ball of radius 10 cm is held under the lamp at a height of 1 m.

Determine the dimensions of the shadow and half-shadow cast by the ball. At what height should the ball be placed for the shadow on the floor to disappear? What will the dimensions of the half-shadow be in this case? What should the diameter of the ball be for the dimensions of its shadow to be the same irrespective of the distance from the ball to the floor?

508. The following simple method can be used to compare the luminous intensity of two sources: a thick rod D and sources S_1 and S_2 some distance away are placed in front of a semi-opaque screen AB (Fig. 167). The sources are so arranged that the half-shadows AO and OB are of the same luminance.

In what directions should the sources be moved so that the half-shadows cast by them are in contact all the time? What patterns will be observed when the sources are shifted in any other directions?

509. The image of an object is obtained using a box with a small aperture (Fig. 168). The depth of the box $EC = 20$ cm, the distance to the object $CD = 20$ cm and the diameter of the aperture C is $d = 1$ mm.

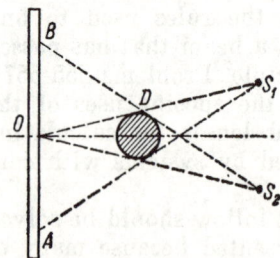

Fig. 167

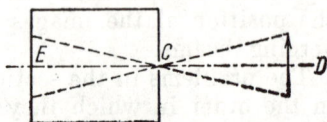

Fig. 168

Can the parts of an object 2 mm in size be distinguished on the image in these conditions?

510. What will the shape of a light spot be if the dimensions of the mirror are small and those of the source are large?

511. In one of his notes M.V. Lomonosov poses the following question: "Any colour if moistened with water becomes deeper. Why?" The colour of the surfaces of bodies that can be impregnated with water does indeed grow darker and richer after moistening.

Explain this phenomenon.

512. One of the expressions of the laws of propagation of light is Fermat's principle asserting that light always propagates along the shortest paths. Consider the following case: light is emitted from a source A (Fig. 169), then reflected from a mirror and reaches a point B. Prove that the path ACB as determined by the law of reflection is the shortest of all possible paths of the ray.

513. Two pins A and B arranged as shown in Fig. 170 are stuck in front of a mirror. What arrangement of the images of these pins will be seen by an observer in different viewing positions? In what position of the eye will the image of the pins be superimposed on each other?

514. An object $O'O$ and a mirror AC are placed as shown in Fig. 171. Construct the image of this object in the mirror. Where should the eye be placed to observe the image of the entire object?

515. A desk-lamp is placed in front of a mirror. What will be the change in the distance between the lamp and its image if the mirror is drawn 5 cm away from the lamp?

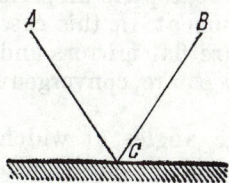

Fig. 169

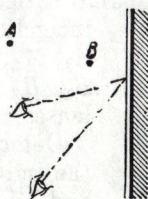

Fig. 170

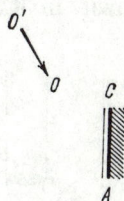

Fig. 171

516. A man stands in front of a mirror and looks at himself with one eye. What place should be covered in the mirror so as to keep the image of the other eye out of vision?

517. A ball is placed on a horizontal table. At what angle to the plane of the table should a mirror be placed to have the image of the ball moving vertically when the ball is brought towards the mirror?

518. A light ray is incident on a mirror. The mirror is turned through 1° about the axis lying in the plane of the mirror perpendicular to the ray.

Through what angle α will the reflected ray be turned in this case? What distance x will the light spot move on a screen set perpendicularly to the reflected ray at a distance $l = 5$ m from the mirror?

519. A mirror 1 m high hangs on a wall. A man stands a distance of 2 m away from the mirror. What is the height of the portion of the opposite wall in the room that can be seen by the man in the mirror without changing the position of his head? The wall is 4 m from the mirror.

520. Determine graphically the positions of the eye when an observer can simultaneously see in a flat mirror of finite dimensions the image of a point and a section of a straight line placed with respect to the mirror as shown in Fig. 172.

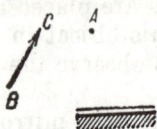

Fig. 172

521. When M.V. Lomonosov was attempting to increase the incendiary power of lenses he designed the device, shown in Fig. 173, and called it the catoptric-dioptric incendiary instrument. In this case A_1, A_2, A_3, A_5 are flat mirrors and B_1, B_2, B_3, B_4, B_5 are convergent lenses.

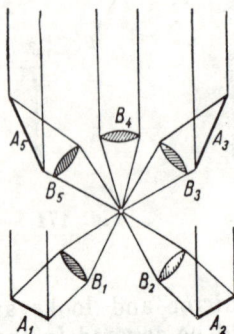

Fig. 173

Determine the angles at which the mirrors should be positioned and the minimum dimensions of these mirrors that will ensure the equality of the luminous fluxes incident on each lens. The diameter of the lenses is d and the optical axes of the lenses B_1, B_2, B_3, B_5 form angles of $\pm 45°$ with the direction of the primary beam.

522. A point source of light and its two images produced by two mirrors lie at the vertices of an equilateral triangle.

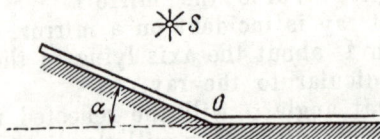

Fig. 174

Determine the position of the mirrors with respect to the source and the angle between them.

523. Prove that a source and its two images in mirrors

arranged at an angle α to each other (Fig. 174) lie on a circle. Show the position of the centre of this circle.

524. Two mirrors are situated at an angle of α to each other (Fig. 174) and a source of light is placed in front of them. Where should the eye of an observer be placed to see both images formed by the mirrors simultaneously?

32. Spherical Mirrors

525. Prove that for spherical mirrors the product of the distances of the object and the image to the principal focus is always equal to the square of the principal focal length.

526. The distance from a glowing point to the principal focus of a concave mirror is $p = 16$ cm and the distance from the image to the principal focus is $q = 100$ cm.

Find the principal focal length of the mirror.

527. Prove that the ratio of the length of the image formed by a concave mirror to the length of the object is equal to the ratio of their distances to the mirror.

528. An object is placed at a distance of 1 m from a concave mirror. Its image is one third the size of the object itself. Determine the position of the image, the radius of curvature of the mirror and its principal focal length.

529. The image produced by a concave mirror is one quarter the size of the object. If the object is moved $b = 5$ cm closer to the mirror the image will only be half the size of the object.

Find the principal focal length of the mirror.

530. The principal focal length of a concave mirror is f and the distance from the object to the principal focus is p.

What is the ratio of the size of the image to the size of the object?

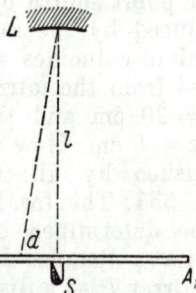

Fig. 175

531. A small concave mirror L is suspended from a thread in a mirror galvanometer to read the angles of turn (Fig. 175). A scale AA_1 is placed at a distance $l = 1$ m from the mirror and a lamp S is adjusted underneath the scale.

What should the focal length of the mirror be to obtain on the scale the real image of the aperture in the lamp? To what distance d will the image be shifted on the scale if the mirror is turned through a small angle φ?

532. A concave mirror forms the real image of a point source lying on the optical axis at a distance of 50 cm from the mirror. The focal length of the mirror is 25 cm. The mirror is cut in two and its halves are drawn a distance of 1 cm apart in a direction perpendicular to the optical axis (Fig. 176).

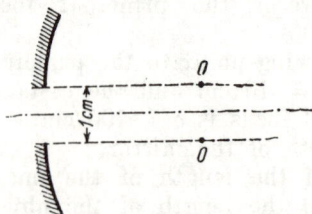

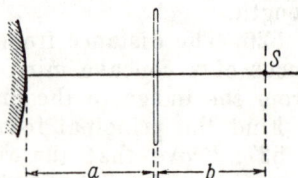

Fig. 176   Fig. 177

How will the images formed by the halves of the mirror be arranged?

533. A thin flat glass plate is placed in front of a convex mirror. At what distance b from the plate (Fig. 177) should a point source of light S be placed so that its image produced by the rays reflected from the front surface of the plate coincides with the image formed by the rays reflected from the mirror? The focal length of the mirror is $F = 20$ cm and the distance from the plate to the mirror $a = 5$ cm. How can the coincidence of the images be established by direct observation?

534. The focal length of a concave mirror can roughly be determined by the following method: place a needle A at a distance d from the mirror (Fig. 178), then place a flat mirror P at a distance a from the concave mirror and a second needle B at a distance b from the flat mirror.

Move the mirror P to match the virtual images A and B of both needles formed by the concave and flat mirrors. Knowing values of a, b and d corresponding to the coincidence of the images, determine the focal length of the mirror. Can these images be observed by the eye at the same time?

535. A screen S is placed a distance $b = 5$ cm from a circular convex mirror as shown in Fig. 179. An object KP of height $h = 3$ cm is arranged a distance $a = 5$ cm rom the screen.

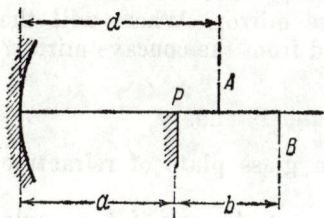

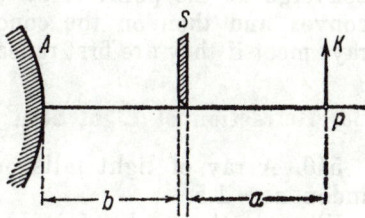

Fig. 178   Fig. 179

Where must an observer position himself to see the image of the entire object? What are the maximum dimensions of the object (with the given arrangement of the object, the mirror and the screen) for the mirror to reproduce an image of the entire object? The diameter of the mirror is $d = 10$ cm.

536. At what distance from one's face should a pocket convex mirror 5 cm in cross section be held to see all of the face if the focal length of the mirror is 7.5 cm and the length of the face is 20 cm?

537. The internal surface of the walls of a sphere is specular. The radius of the sphere is $R = 36$ cm. A point source S is placed a distance $R/2$ from the centre of the sphere and sends light to the remote part of the sphere.

Where will the image of the source be after two reflections—from the remote and the nearest walls of the sphere? How will the position of the image change if the source sends light to the nearest wall?

538. A point source of light S is placed on the major optical axis of a concave mirror at a distance of 60 cm.

At what distance from the concave mirror should a flat mirror be placed for the rays to converge again at the point S having been reflected from the concave mirror and then from the flat one? Will the position of the point where the rays meet change if they are first reflected from the flat mirror? The radius of the concave mirror is 80 cm.

539. Convex and concave mirrors have the same radii of curvature R. The distance between the mirrors is $2R$.

At what point on the common optical axis of the mirrors should a point source of light A be placed for the rays to converge at the point A after being reflected first on the convex and then on the concave mirror? Where will the rays meet if they are first reflected from the concave mirror?

33. Refraction of Light at a Plane Boundary

540. A ray of light falls on a glass plate of refractive index $n = 1.5$.

What is the angle of incidence of the ray if the angle between the reflected and refracted rays is 90°?

541. A pile 4 m high driven into the bottom of a lake protrudes by 1 m above the water.

Determine the length of the shadow of the pile on the bottom of the lake if the sunrays make an angle of 45° with the water surface. The refractive index of water is 4/3.

542. A swimmer observes from under the water a luminous object above his head at a distance of 75 cm above the water surface.

What is the visible distance of the object above the water surface? The refractive index of water $n = 4/3$.

543. A point source of light is arranged at a height h above the surface of water. Where will the image of this source in the flat mirror-like bottom of a vessel be if the depth of the vessel full of water is d?

544. What is the apparent distance from the surface of water to the image formed in Problem 543 by a mirror if the observer is standing in air and views the image vertically downwards?

545. One face of a prism with a refractive angle of 30° is coated with silver. A ray incident on another face at an angle of 45° is refracted and reflected from the silver-coated face and retraces its path.

What is the refractive index of the prism?

546. A coin lies on the bottom of a vessel filled with water to a depth of 40 cm.

At what height should a small electric lamp be placed above the water surface so that its image produced by the rays reflected from the water surface coincides with the image of the coin formed by the refracted rays?

How can the coincidence of the images of the lamp and the coin be established by direct observation? The observation is made along a vertical line.

547. The basic section of a prism is an equilateral triangle. A ray is incident on the prism perpendicular to one of its faces.

What will the path of this ray be for various refractive indices of the prism?

548. When bright sources of light are photographed, thick photographic plates exhibit around the images of the sources haloes whose internal boundary is sharp and whose external one is diffused.

Explain the origin and nature of the haloes. Determine the refractive index of the glass plate if its thickness is $d = 3.74$ mm and the radius of the sharp boundary of the halo around the image of a point source is $a = 4.48$ mm.

549. The perpendicular faces of a right isosceles prism are coated with silver.

Prove that the rays incident at an arbitrary angle on the hypotenuse face will emerge from the prism parallel to the initial direction.

550. In his notes on physics M.V. Lomonosov offers the ollowing observation for explanation: "Wet paper is more ransparent than crushed glass." Explain these phenomena.

34. Lenses and Composite Optical Systems

551. When observed from the Earth the angular diameter of the solar disk is $\varphi = 32'$.

Determine the diameter of the image of the Sun formed by a convergent lens with a focal length $f = 0.25$ m.

552. Where should an object be placed for a thin lens to produce its erect image in full size?

553. A narrow beam of light passing through an aperture in a screen S as shown in Fig. 180 is incident on a convergent lens.

Construct the path of the ray after it emerges from the lens. The position of the foci of the lens is known.

554. A converging beam of rays passes through a round aperture in a screen as shown in Fig. 181. The apex of the beam A is at a distance of 15 cm from the screen.

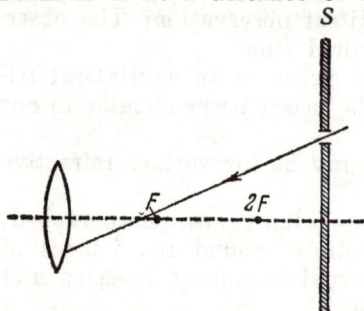

Fig. 180

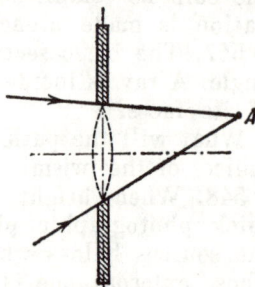

Fig. 181

How will the distance from the focus of the rays to the screen change if a convergent lens is inserted in the aperture with a focal length of 30 cm? Plot the path of the rays after the lens is fitted.

555. A converging beam of rays is incident on a diverging lens. Having passed through the lens the rays intersect at a point 15 cm from the lens. If the lens is removed the point where the rays meet will move 5 cm closer to the mounting that holds the lens.

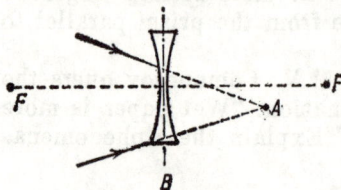

Fig. 182

Find the focal length of the lens.

556. The rays of a converging beam meet at a point A. A diverging lens is placed in their path in the plane B (Fig. 182).

Plot the position of the point where the rays meet after passing through the lens. The position of the principal foci FF is known.

557. In what position of the eye and for what distance between a point source and a convergent lens can an observer simultaneously see this source lying on the optical axis of the lens and its image produced by the lens? The focal length of the lens is f and its diameter is d.

558. The focal length of a convergent lens is 10 cm, the distance of an object from the front focus is 5 cm and the linear dimension of the object is 2 cm.

Determine the size of the image.

559. An image of a bright square is obtained on a screen with the aid of a convergent lens. The distance between the square and the lens is 30 cm. The area of the image is four times larger than that of the square.

Determine the position of the image and the focal length of the lens.

560. Photographs of the ground are taken from an aircraft flying at an altitude of 2,000 m by a camera with a focal length of 50 cm.

What will the scale of the photographs be? How will the scale change if the aircraft flies at an altitude of 1,000 m?

561. The size of the film in the camera in the previous problem is 18×18 cm. What area can be photographed by this camera at any one time?

562. A convergent lens forms on a screen an image of a lamp magnified to twice its normal size. After the lens has been moved 36 cm closer to the screen it gives an image diminished by a factor of two.

Find the focal length of the lens.

563. What are the smallest details of an object that can be observed separately with the naked eye at a distance of 2 km? The minimum angle of vision of the eye is $\varphi = 1'$.

564. A thin convexo-convex lens is placed on a flat mirror.

Where should a point source of light be arranged so that its image produced by this system is real and coincides with the source itself?

565. An optical system consists of a convergent lens with a focal length of 30 cm and a flat mirror placed at a distance $b = 15$ cm from the lens.

Determine the position of the image formed by this system if an object is at a distance $a_1 = 15$ cm in front of the lens.

Plot the path of the rays in this case.

566. Plot the image of an object in an optical system consisting of a convergent lens and a flat mirror arranged in the focal plane of the lens. The object is in front of the lens and between the focus and the double focal length of the lens.

What will the size of the image be if the object is positioned arbitrarily?

567. Determine the position of the image produced by an optical system consisting of a concave mirror with a focal length of 10 cm and a convergent lens with a focal length of 20 cm. The distance from the mirror to the lens is 30 cm and from the lens to the object 40 cm. Plot the image.

568. A convergent and a diverging lenses having focal lengths of 30 and 10 cm, respectively, are arranged at a distance of 20 cm from each other.

Where should a source of light be placed for this system to emit a beam of parallel rays?

569. Plot the image of an object formed by a system of two convergent lenses. The focal length of the first lens is 9 cm and of the second 15 cm. The second lens is in the focal plane of the first lens. The object is at a distance of 36 cm from the first lens.

Calculate the distance a_2 of the image from the second lens.

570. A plano-parallel plate is cut as shown in Fig. 183, and the lenses thus obtained are slightly drawn apart.

Fig. 183

How will a beam of parallel rays change after passing through this system if the beam is incident: (a) from the side of the convex lens? (b) from the side of the concave lens? How will the behaviour of the beam depend on the distance between the lenses?

ANSWERS AND SOLUTIONS

Chapter I

MECHANICS

1. Rectilinear Uniform Motion

1. (1) at a distance of 8.5 m; (2) at a distance of 21.5 m.

Solution. (1) The time of propagation of the sound to the man in the opera house is $t_1 = \dfrac{S_1}{v}$ where S_1 is the distance from the stage and v is the velocity of sound.

The time of propagation of the radio waves to the listener is $t_2 = \dfrac{S_2}{c}$ where S_2 is the distance from the opera house to the receiver and c is the velocity of propagation of the radio waves.

If the listener and the man at the opera hear the sounds at the same time, then $t_1 = t_2$ and $\dfrac{S_1}{v} = \dfrac{S_2}{c}$ or $S_1 = S_2 \dfrac{v}{c}$.

(2) $S_4 = S_3 - \dfrac{S_2 v}{c}$ where $S_3 = 30$ m and S_4 is the distance from the listener to the radio receiver.

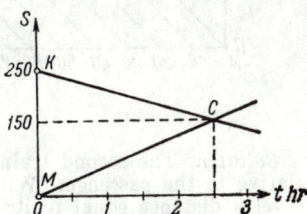

Fig. 184

2. The cars will meet after 2.5 hours at a distance of 150 km from M (Fig. 184).

3. Eleven cars (Fig. 185).

Solution. Assume that the man left B one hour after all the other cars set off. The motion of his car is depicted by the straight line BC. The lines *2, 3, 4,* etc., show the motion of the cars coming from A in 50, 40, 30, etc., minutes before the man has set off in his car.

The lines *8, 9, 10,* etc., show the motion of the cars leaving A after 10, 20, 30, etc., minutes after the man has departed from B. Obviously, the number of the cars which the man meets en route will be equal to the number of the points of intersection with the straight line BC.

4. $S = 510$ m; $u = 850$ m/s.

Solution. Since the velocity of light is many times greater than that of sound in the air, t_1 may be assumed as being equal to the time of flight of the shell and t_2 to the sum of the times of flight of the shell and the propagation of sound from the place where the shell bursts to the gun. For this reason the time of propagation of sound will be $t_2 - t_1$ and the shell range $S = v(t_2 - t_1)$, where v is the velocity of sound; the velocity of the shell is $u = \dfrac{S}{t_1} = \dfrac{v(t_2 - t_1)}{t_1}$

5. $t = 6$ s.

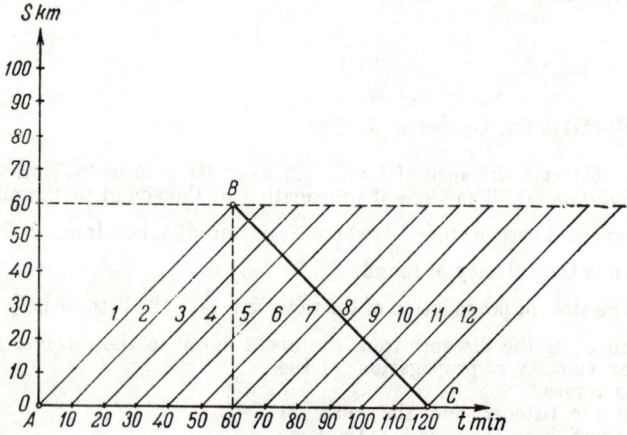

Fig. 185

Solution. The second train will travel with a speed $v = v_1 + v_2$ relative to the passenger. With this motion the oncoming train will travel a distance equal to its length in a time

$$t = \frac{l}{v_1 + v_2}$$

6. $v = 36$ km/hr.

Solution. If v is the speed of the electric train relative to the earth its velocity relative to the train coming in the opposite direction will be $2v$ and may be expressed through the length l and the time t of passage of the oncoming train, i.e., $2v = \dfrac{l}{t}$ where $l = 16.5 \times 10 + 10 \times 1.5 + 20 = 200$ m.

7. A factor of 1.07 more time is required on the river than on the lake.

Solution. The time of motion on the river upstream is

$$t_1 = \frac{S}{v_2 - v_1}$$

where $S = 1$ km.

The time of motion downstream is $t_2 = \dfrac{S}{v_2 + v_1}$.

The total time of motion on the river (up and down) is

$$t = t_1 + t_2 = \frac{2Sv_2}{v_2^2 - v_1^2}$$

The time of motion on the lake (up and down) is $t_3 = \frac{2S}{v_2}$.

The ratio of the times of motion is

$$\frac{t}{t_3} = \frac{v_2^2}{v_2^2 - v_1^2} = 1.07$$

Fig. 186 illustrates the plots of the motions: I—motion in stagnant water; II—motion on the river; t_3 and t are the respective times of motion for the two cases.

8. $S_1 = 2.1$ km.

Solution. Moving downstream the launch will cover, relative to the water, a distance

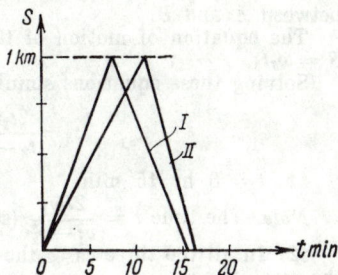

Fig. 186

$$S' = v_2 t_2 = \frac{v_2}{v_2 + v_1} S = 0.8 \text{ km}$$

(see the solution to Problem 7).

Upstream

$$S'' = v_2 t_1 = \frac{v_2}{v_2 - v_1} S \approx 1.3 \text{ k}m$$

The total distance covered by the launch relative to the water will be

$$S_1 = S' + S'' = 2.1 \text{ km}$$

9. $t_3 = 45$ s.

Solution. The equations of motion for the three cases specified in the problem are

$$S = v_1 t_1, \quad S = v_2 t_2, \quad S = (v_1 + v_2) t_3$$

where S is the length of the escalator; v_1—its velocity; v_2—the velocity of the passenger on the stationary escalator; t_1—the time of ascent of the passenger standing on the moving escalator; t_2—the time it takes him to up the stationary escalator; t_3—the time needed to arrive at the top when the passenger walks up the moving escalator.

Solving these equations we get

$$t_3 = \frac{t_1 t_2}{t_1 + t_2} = 45 \text{ s}$$

10. $t_3 = 12$ hours.

Solution. The equations of motion of the launch from A to B and from B to A are

$$S = (v_1 + v_2) t_1 \quad \text{and} \quad S = (v_1 - v_2) t_2$$

where $t_1 = 3$ hours is the time of motion downstream; $t_2 = 6$ hours is the time of motion upstream; v_1 is the velocity of the launch relative to the water; v_2 is the velocity of the river current and S is the distance between A and B.

The equation of motion of the launch with its engine cut off is $S = v_2 t_3$.

Solving these equations simultaneously for t_3 we obtain

$$t_3 = \frac{2 t_1 t_2}{t_2 - t_1} = 12 \text{ hr}$$

11. $t = 6$ hr 15 min.

Note. The time $t = \frac{2Sv_1}{v_1^2 - v_2^2}$ (see the solution to Problem 7).

12. In all the three cases the launches will meet the ring-buoy at the same time.

Solution. The velocity of the current affects the motion of both launches and the ring-buoy similarly and cannot change their mutual positions. This velocity may therefore be disregarded and the motion of the launches and the ring-buoy only considered relative to the water.

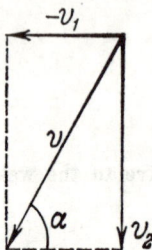

Fig. 187

The distances traversed by the launches relative to the water in the time t before they turn will be $S_1 = v_1 t$ and $S_2 = v_2 t$.

Returning to the ring-buoy with the original velocities v_1 and v_2 the launches should obviously spend the same time to cover the distances S_1 and S_2 to the ring-buoy as was spent when they steamed away from it.

13. $\alpha = 71°35'$.

Solution. The drop will move relative to the pipe in a vertical direction with a velocity v_2 and in a horizontal direction with a velocity v_1 in the opposite direction to the motion of the cart. The total velocity of the drop v relative to the pipe will be equal to the geometrical sum of the velocities v_1 and v_2 (Fig. 187).

For the drops to move parallel to the walls of the pipe the direction of the velocity vector v should coincide with the axis of the pipe. This will occur if

$$\tan \alpha = \frac{v_2}{v_1} = 3, \quad \alpha = 71°35'$$

14. $\beta = 18°30'$.

Solution. The direction of the weather vane will coincide with the direction of the air motion relative to the ice-boat. Since the ice-boat moves with a speed v, the total velocity w of the air relative to the ice-boat will be equal to the geometrical sum of the two velocities v and u (Fig. 188).

The velocity w will form an angle α with the line of motion of the ice-boat such that

$$\tan \alpha = \frac{u}{v} = 2$$

The angle between the plane of the sail and the weather vane will be

$$\beta = \alpha - 45° = 63°30' - 45° = 18°30'$$

15. $l = 200$ m; $u = 20$ m/min; $v = 12$ m/min; $\alpha = 36°50'$.

Solution. In both cases the motion of the boat is composed of its motion relative to the water and its motion together with the water relative to the banks.

First case (Fig. 189). The boat moves along the river with a velocity v and covers during the crossing a distance downstream of

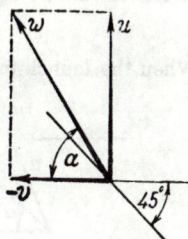

Fig. 188

$$l_1 = vt_1 \tag{1}$$

The boat moves across the river with a velocity u and traverses a distance of

$$l_2 = ut_1 \tag{2}$$

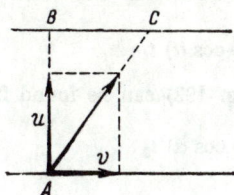

Fig. 189

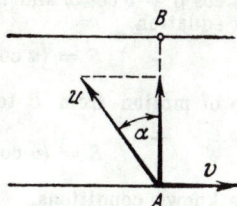

Fig. 190

Second case (Fig. 190). The velocity of the boat along the river is zero, i.e.,

$$u \sin \alpha = v \tag{3}$$

The velocity across the river is equal to $u \cos \alpha$, and the distance l_2 covered during the crossing will be

$$l_2 = u \cos \alpha t_2 \tag{4}$$

Solving the system of the four equations (1), (2), (3) and (4) we obtain

$$l = \frac{t_2 S}{\sqrt{t_2^2 - t_1^2}}, \quad u = \frac{l}{t_1}, \quad v = \frac{S}{t_1}, \quad \alpha = \text{arc} \sin \frac{v}{u}$$

16. $u = 8$ m/s; $\beta \approx 12°$.

Solution. As in the previous problem the velocities of the current and of the launch should be resolved into components along the line AB and perpendicularly to it (Fig. 191). In order that the moving launch is always on the straight line AB the components of the velocity of the current and of the launch in the direction perpendicular to AB should be equal, i.e.,

$$u \sin \beta = v \sin \alpha \qquad (1)$$

When the launch moves from A to B its velocity relative to the banks

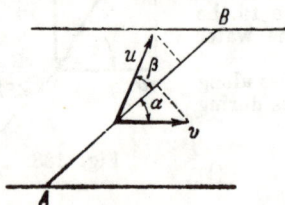

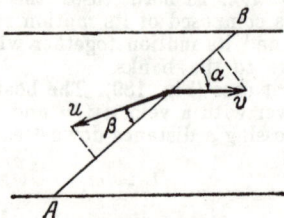

Fig. 191   Fig. 192

will be $u \cos \beta + v \cos \alpha$ and the time of motion will be determined from the equation

$$S = (u \cos \beta + v \cos \alpha)\, t_1 \qquad (2)$$

The time of motion from B to A (Fig. 192) can be found from the equation

$$S = (u \cos \beta - v \cos \alpha)\, t_2 \qquad (3)$$

From the known conditions,

$$t_1 + t_2 = t \qquad (4)$$

Solving the system of the four equations we find

$$\beta = \text{arc cot } \frac{S + \sqrt{S^2 + v^2 t^2 \cos^2 \alpha}}{vt \sin \alpha} \approx 12°$$

$$u = v\frac{\sin \alpha}{\sin \beta} \approx 8 \text{ m/s}$$

17. $u = 40$ km/hr.

Solution. All the points on the wheel rim simultaneously perform two motions: translational, with the entire bicycle, and rotational, around the wheel axis. The total velocity of each point will be the sum of the linear velocities of the translational and rotational motions. If the wheel of the bicycle moves without sliding the linear velocity of the rotational motion of the wheel rim will be equal in magnitude to the velocity of the translational motion of the bicycle. These velocities are opposite at the point A (Fig. 193). The total velocity of the point A will therefore be equal to zero. At the point B the velocities of the translational and rotational motion will be directed one way, and the total velocity of the point B will be equal to $2v$, i.e., to 40 km/hr.

18. The bobbin will roll in the direction of motion of the end of the thread with a velocity of $u = \dfrac{R}{R-r}\, v$.

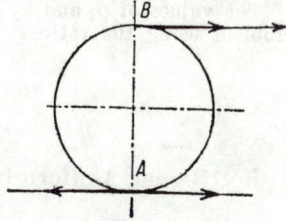

Fig. 193

Solution. The displacement of the thread end depends on two things: the movement of the bobbin axis and the change in the length of the thread during winding (or unwinding). It is clear that the motions of the end of the thread due to these causes will always be in opposite directions. If, for example, the bobbin moves to the right the motion of its axis will cause the thread end to move to the right and to the left due to the thread winding.

Since $r < R$, the change in the length of the thread during one full revolution will always be less than the motion of the bobbin axis during the same time.

If one adds these motions, the end of the thread should always be moving in the same direction as the axis of the bobbin. During one full revolution T the axis of the bobbin will be displaced to the right by a distance $2\pi R$ and the length of the thread will be reduced by $2\pi r$. If the velocity of the axis is $u = \dfrac{2\pi R}{T}$ the velocity with which the length of the thread diminishes will be $\dfrac{2\pi r}{T} = \dfrac{2\pi R}{T}\,\dfrac{r}{R} = \dfrac{r}{R}\,u$. The velocity of motion of the thread end will be equal to the difference between these velocities, i.e., $v = u - \dfrac{r}{R}\,u$.

Hence,

$$u = \frac{R}{R-r}\, v$$

The axis of the bobbin moves faster than the end of the thread.

19. The bobbin moves in the direction of motion of the thread end with a velocity $u = \dfrac{R}{R+r}\, v$.

Note. (See the solution to the previous problem.) The axis of the bobbin moves at a slower speed than the end of the thread.

20. $v_1 = 1.1$ m/s; $v_2 = 0.5$ m/s.

Solution. In the first case the velocity of one body relative to the other will be

$$u_1 = v_1 + v_2 \tag{1}$$

and in the second case

$$u_2 = v_1 - v_2 \tag{2}$$

Solving the system of equations (1) and (2) we get

$$v_1 = \frac{u_1 + u_2}{2}, \quad v_2 = \frac{u_1 - u_2}{2}$$

The values of u_1 and u_2 can be found from the conditions of the problem using the ratios

$$u_1 = \frac{S_1}{t_1}, \quad u_2 = \frac{S_2}{t_2}$$

2. Rectilinear Uniformly Variable Motion

21. $a = \frac{S_2 - S_1}{t^2} = 2.5$ m/s^2; $v_0 = \frac{3S_1 - S_2}{2t} = 1$ m/s.

22. $g \approx 973$ cm/s^2.
Note. Calculate the value of g for each path.

23. The distance from the fourth drop to the roof is $\frac{H}{16} = 1$ m; the distance between the 4th and 3rd drops $\frac{3H}{16} = 3$ m; between the 3rd and the 2nd $\frac{5H}{16} = 5$ m and from the 2nd to the 1st it is $\frac{7H}{16} = 7$ m.

24. $S = 27$ m; $v = 9$ m/s.

25. The motion is uniformly retarded up to the point B and uniformly accelerated after the point B. At the moment that corresponds to the point B the body stops and then the direction of its velocity is reversed.

The initial velocity $v_0 = 7$ m/s and the acceleration $a \approx 0.64$ m/s^2. The equation of the path is $S = 7t - 0.32t^2$.

26. $h = 14.7$ m.

27. $t = \frac{l}{g\tau} + \frac{\tau}{2}$.

Solution. If the time of fall of the first body is t, that of the second will be $t - \tau$ and the equations of motion of both bodies will take the form

$$H_1 = \frac{gt^2}{2} \quad \text{and} \quad H_2 = \frac{g(t-\tau)^2}{2}$$

Hence,

$$l = H_1 - H_2 = gt\tau - \frac{1}{2}g\tau^2$$

and the required time is $t = \frac{l}{g\tau} + \frac{\tau}{2}$.

28. $h \approx 57$ m; $t \approx 3.4$ s.

Solution. The equations for the lengths of paths AC and AB (Fig. 194) traversed by the body from the start of fall will be

$$AC = h = \frac{gt^2}{2} \quad \text{and} \quad AB = \frac{h}{2} = \frac{g(t-1)^2}{2}$$

where t is the time of fall from A to C.

Solving these equations gives us the required values of t and h.

Second method. Let us consider the equations for the paths AB and BC.

The equation for AB is

$$\frac{h}{2} = \frac{gt_1^2}{2}$$

where t_1 is the time of motion of the falling body from A to B.

For BC

$$\frac{h}{2} = v_0 t_2 + \frac{gt_2^2}{2}$$

where $v_0 = \sqrt{2g\dfrac{h}{2}}$ is the velocity of the body at

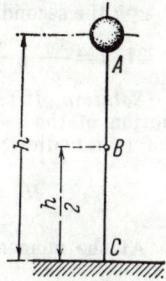

Fig. 194

B and $t_2 = 1$ is the time of motion from B to C.

The total time of fall is $t = t_1 + t_2 = t_1 + 1$.

By solving these equations we can obtain the values of h and t.

29. $v_0 = \dfrac{H+h}{2H}\sqrt{2gH}$; $h_{max} = \dfrac{(H+h)^2}{4H}$.

Solution. The path traversed by the first body before it meets the second is

$$H = \frac{gt^2}{2}$$

and by the second body before it meets the first is

$$h = v_0 t - \frac{gt^2}{2}$$

After a simultaneous solution of these equations

$$v_0 = \frac{H+h}{2H}\sqrt{2gH}$$

Hence,

$$h_{max} = \frac{v_0^2}{2g} = \frac{(H+h)^2}{4H} \quad (h_{max} > h)$$

When $H = h$ we have: $v_0 = \sqrt{2gh}$; $h_{max} = h$.

30. $t = \dfrac{\sqrt{2gH} - \sqrt{2gh}}{g}$; $v_0 = \sqrt{2gh}$.

Solution. The time the body takes in falling from A to B is $t_1 = \sqrt{\dfrac{2H}{g}}$. The time of rise of the body from C to the highest point is $t_2 = \sqrt{\dfrac{2h}{g}}$. The required time $t = t_1 - t_2 = \dfrac{\sqrt{2H} - \sqrt{2h}}{g} = \dfrac{\sqrt{2gH} - \sqrt{2gh}}{g}$.

If $H > h$, the second body should be thrown after some delay; when $H = h$, the bodies should be thrown simultaneously; when $H < h$ the second body should be thrown before the first begins to fall.

31. $t = \dfrac{v_0}{g} + \dfrac{\tau}{2}$.

Solution. If t is the time of motion of the first body the time of motion of the second will be $t - \tau$ and the equations of motion of the two bodies will take the form

$$H_1 = v_0 t - \frac{gt^2}{2} \quad \text{and} \quad H_2 = v_0(t - \tau) - \frac{g(t - \tau)^2}{2}$$

At the moment the bodies meet, $H_1 = H_2$ and

$$t = \frac{2v_0 + g\tau}{2g}$$

32. $t = \dfrac{v_0}{g} + \dfrac{1}{g}\sqrt{2H_0 g + v_0^2}; \quad v = \sqrt{2gH_0 + v_0^2}$.

Solution. Since the load is initially at an altitude H_0 and has an initial velocity v_0 directed upwards, the equation of motion of the load will be

$$H = H_0 + v_0 t - \frac{gt^2}{2}$$

and the magnitude of velocity at any moment will be determined by the equation

$$v = v_0 - gt$$

During the descent to the earth, $H = 0$. Inserting this value for H in the first equation, we find the time of descent t and use this time to find the velocity when the body reaches the ground from the second equation.

34. $t = \sqrt{\dfrac{H_0}{2g}}; \quad h_1 = \dfrac{3}{4} H_0$.

Solution. The velocity of the first ball at the moment it strikes the plate will be $v_0 = \sqrt{2gH_0}$. Since the impact is elastic, the ball will begin to rise after the impact with a velocity of the same magnitude v_0. During the time t the first ball will rise to a height

$$h_1 = v_0 t - \frac{gt^2}{2}$$

During this time the second ball will move down from a point A a distance

$$h_2 = \frac{gt^2}{2}$$

At the moment the balls meet, $h_1 + h_2 = H_0$. Hence,

$$t = \frac{H_0}{v_0} = \sqrt{\frac{H_0}{2g}}$$

35. (1) $v = g\tau$; (2) $v = -v_0 + g\tau$.
Solution. In the first case the velocity of the first body at any moment relative to the earth is

$$v_1 = v_0 - gt$$

The velocity of the second body relative to the earth is

$$v_2 = v_0 - g(t - \tau)$$

The required velocity of the second body relative to the first will be

$$v = v_2 - v_1 = g\tau$$

The velocity v is directed upwards both during the ascent and descent of both bodies.

During the ascent the distance between the bodies diminishes uniformly and during the descent it increases uniformly.

36. $t = 10$ s; $l_1 = 100$ m.

The distance between the motor-cyclists uniformly diminishes with time according to the law

$$l = S - t(v_1 + v_2)$$

and becomes zero after 10 s (Fig. 195).

Solution. If the distance from the point where they meet to the point A is l_1 and to the point B is l_2, then

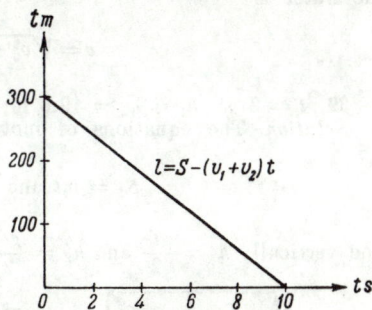

Fig. 195

$$l_1 = v_1 t - \frac{at^2}{2}, \qquad l_2 = v_2 t + \frac{at^2}{2}$$

and

$$S = l_1 + l_2$$

or $S = v_1 t + v_2 t = t(v_1 + v_2)$.
Hence,

$$t = \frac{S}{v_1 + v_2}, \quad l_1 = \frac{v_1 S}{v_1 + v_2} - \frac{a}{2} \frac{S^2}{(v_1 + v_2)^2}$$

3. Curvilinear Motion

37. In all three cases the body will have the same time of descent. The motion of the car only affects the magnitude of the horizontal components of the velocity and the acceleration of the body and does not affect the nature of its motion along the vertical.

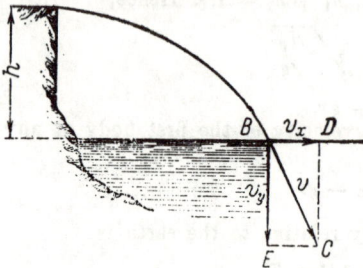

Fig. 196

38. $v = \sqrt{v_0^2 + 2gh}$.

Solution. The bullet takes part simultaneously in two motions: uniform motion in a horizontal direction with a constant velocity equal to the initial velocity v_0 and in free fall vertically. These two motions are added to produce the resultant motion in a parabola. Assume that B is the point where the bullet lands (Fig. 196); BC is the vector of the bullet velocity as it strikes the water; BD is the horizontal component of the velocity vector v equal to v_x; and BE is the vertical component equal to v_y.

Since $v_x = v_0$ and $v_y^2 = 2gh$ the velocity of the bullet striking the water is

$$v = \sqrt{v_0^2 + 2gh}$$

39. $t = 2$ s; $h_1 = h_2 = 19.6$ m; $S_2 = 15$ m.
Solution. The equations of motion of the bodies horizontally

$$S_1 = v_1 t \quad \text{and} \quad S_2 = v_2 t$$

and vertically $h = \dfrac{gt^2}{2}$ and $h_2 = \dfrac{gt^2}{2}$.

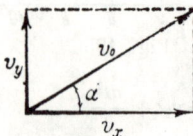

Fig. 197

Since it is given that the times of flight are the same and equal to $t = \dfrac{S_1}{v_1} = 2$ s, then $h_1 = h_2$ and $S_2 = v_2 t = 15$ m.

40. $t = 100$ s; $S = 88.7$ km.

Solution. The components of the shell velocity at the initial moment in the horizontal and vertical directions will be (Fig. 197):

$$v_x = v_0 \cos \alpha \quad \text{and} \quad v_y = v_0 \sin \alpha$$

The equation of motion of the shell horizontally is $S = v_x t$, and

vertically

$$H = v_y t - \frac{gt^2}{2}$$

We are given that the point where the shell falls is at the same height as the point of projection, i.e., at the point of fall $H = 0$.

Inserting the value of $H = 0$ into the equation of motion in the vertical direction we can find the time of flight of the shell from the point of projection to the point of landing: $t = \frac{2v_y}{g}$ (the second root of the equation $t = 0$ determines the moment of projection).

Inserting the value of t into the first equation we can determine the range of flight

$$S = \frac{2v_x v_y}{g} = \frac{2v_0^2}{g} \sin\alpha\cos\alpha = \frac{v_0^2}{g}\sin 2\alpha$$

41. $\alpha = 45°$.

Note. See the solution to Problem 40.

42. $\dfrac{H_1}{H_2} = \tan^2\alpha$.

43. $\alpha = \dfrac{1}{2}\arcsin\dfrac{gl}{v_0^2}$.

Solution. If $l < S_{max}$, there are two angles α_1 and α_2 for which the range will be l for the given initial velocity v_0. This result can be obtained directly from the equation of the range (see the solution to Problem 40) and from the well-known trigonometrical ratio:

$$\sin 2\alpha = \sin(180° - 2\alpha) =$$
$$= \sin 2(90° - \alpha)$$

With the given initial velocity v_0 the range l will be the same for the angles of throw $\alpha_1 = \alpha$ and $\alpha_2 = 90° - \alpha$.

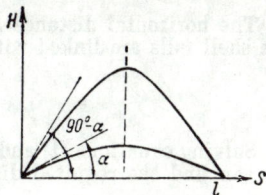

Fig. 198

There are always two trajectories for any one range of flight (Fig. 198).

The gently sloping trajectory corresponding to the angle α is known as "grazing", and the steep trajectory corresponding to the angle $(90° - \alpha)$ is called "curved".

44. $h_{max} = \dfrac{v_0^2 \sin^2\alpha}{2g} = 2{,}187$ m.

Solution. The minimum safe altitude is determined by the maximum elevation of the shells. The equation of motion of the shell in a vertical direction is

$$h = v_1 t - \frac{gt^2}{2}$$

where $v_1 = v_0 \sin \alpha$ (see the solution to Problem 40). The vertical component of the velocity of the shell at any moment is $v_y = v_1 - gt$.
At maximum elevation $v_y = 0$ and therefore the time of ascent is

$$t = \frac{v_1}{g} \text{ and } h_{max} = \frac{v_1^2}{g} - \frac{gv_1^2}{2g^2} = \frac{v_1^2}{2g} = \frac{v_0^2 \sin^2 \alpha}{2g} = 2{,}187 \text{ m}$$

45. $\alpha \approx 76°$.
Note. See the solutions to Problems 40 and 44.
46. $l = \dfrac{2v_0^2}{g \cos^2 \alpha} \sin \alpha \cos 2\alpha = \dfrac{2}{3} \dfrac{v_0^2}{g}$.

Solution. The curvilinear motion of the shell in a parabola can be resolved into two rectilinear motions in the horizontal and vertical directions. The motion of the shell is considered from the point A (see Fig. 8).
The initial velocities will be:
horizontally $v_1 = v_0 \cos \beta$;
vertically $v_2 = v_0 \sin \beta$.
The equations of motion of the shell will be:
horizontally

$$s = v_1 t = v_0 t \cos \beta \tag{1}$$

vertically

$$h = v_2 t - \frac{gt^2}{2} = v_0 t \sin \beta - \frac{gt^2}{2} \tag{2}$$

The horizontal distance S and the height h of the point B where the shell falls are linked with the length $AB = l$ by the ratio

$$\left. \begin{array}{l} S = l \cos \alpha \\ h = l \sin \alpha \end{array} \right\} \tag{3}$$

Solving equations (1) and (2) simultaneously and utilizing ratio (3) we can find the required distance

$$= \frac{2v_0^2}{g} \frac{(\sin \beta \cos \alpha - \cos \beta \sin \alpha) \cos \beta}{\cos^2 \alpha} \tag{4}$$

It is given that $\beta = 2\alpha$. Thus transforming the equation (4) we get

$$l = \frac{2v_0^2 \sin \alpha \cos^2 \alpha}{g \cos^2 \alpha}$$

4. Rotational Motion of a Solid Body

47. $v \approx 0.8$ cm/s; $\omega = 0.00175$ s^{-1}.
48. $v \approx 233$ m/s; $a \approx 1.7$ cm/s^2.

49. $\omega = 1$ s^{-1}; $a_1 = \dfrac{a}{R} \sqrt{R^2 + 4S^2} = 20.1$ cm/s^2,

Solution. At any moment the linear velocity of the points on the pulley is equal to that of the weight, i.e.,

$$v = \sqrt{2aS}$$

After the weight has moved a distance S_1 the velocity will be equal to 20 cm/s.

The angular velocity is

$$\omega = \frac{v}{R} = 1 \ \text{s}^{-1}$$

The total acceleration of the point A will be composed of the acceleration a and the centripetal acceleration equal to $\frac{v^2}{R}$ (Fig. 199):

$$a_1 = \sqrt{a^2 + \frac{4a^2 S^2}{R^2}} = \frac{a}{R}\sqrt{R^2 + 4S^2}$$

50. $v \approx 7.9$ km/s.

Note. With the conditions specified in the problem the centripetal acceleration during the motion of the body around the Earth should be equal to the acceleration of free fall.

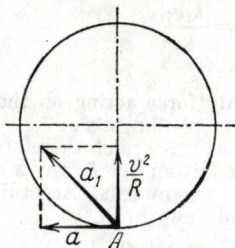

Fig. 199

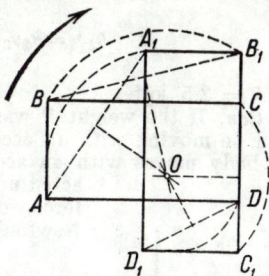

Fig. 200

51. The centre of rotation is 62.5 cm from the line AB and 12.5 cm from the line AD.

Note. When the top of the table is turned from the position $ABCD$ to the position $A_1 B_1 C_1 D_1$ (Fig. 200) the point A passes to the point A_1, B to B_1, etc. The lines AA_1 and BB_1 will be the chords of the arcs along which the points A and B move when the top is turned. The centre of rotation will lie at the point of intersection of the perpendiculars drawn from the middle of these chords.

5. Dynamics of the Rectilinear Motion of a Point

52. $F = 1,250$ dynes.

53. $v_0 = 7.56$ m/s.

Solution. If the weight of the stone is $P = mg$, the force of friction will be $F = kP = kmg$.

The acceleration acquired by the stone under the action of this force can be determined from the equation $kmg = ma$ and the initial velocity from the ratio $v_0 = \sqrt{2aS} = \sqrt{2kgS} = 7.56$ m/s.

54. $S = 25.6$ m.

Note. See the solution to Problem 53.

55. $F \approx 43.05$ kgf.

56. 1 km/hr.

Solution. Since the power of the engine is the same in both cases, the following relation should hold

$$N = F_1 v_1 = F_2 v_2 \tag{1}$$

where F_1 and v_1 are the tractive force of the engine and the speed of the tractor on the icy road; F_2 and v_2 are the tractive force and the speed over the ledger road.

Since at constant speed the work done by the tractive force of the engine is only expended in both cases to overcome the forces of friction,

$$F_1 = k_1 P \text{ and } F_2 = k_2 P \tag{2}$$

where P is the weight of the sledge.

It follows from (1) and (2) that

$$k_1 v_1 = k_2 v_2 \text{ and } v_2 = \frac{k_1 v_1}{k_2}$$

57. $F = 2.5$ kgf.

Solution. If the weight P was the only force acting on the body it would be moving with an acceleration $g = 9.8$ m/s².

The body moves with an acceleration $a > g$ and therefore it is acted upon, in addition to P, by a certain force directed downwards. According to Newton's second law,

$$P + F = \frac{P}{g} a$$

and

$$F = \frac{P}{g} a - P = P\left(\frac{a}{g} - 1\right)$$

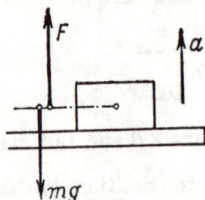

Fig. 201

58. $F = m(g + a)$.

Solution. The weight will move in the same manner as the support with an acceleration a. The weight is acted upon by the force of gravity mg (Fig. 201) and the force of reaction of the support F which will be equal to the pressure exerted by the weight on the support. According to Newton's second law,

$$F - mg = ma$$

hence

$$F = m(g + a)$$

59. $a = 4.9$ m/s^2.

Solution. The tension in the thread will diminish if the point O moves with an acceleration a directed downwards. In this case the tension in the thread T can be determined from the equation of motion of the ball, $mg - T = ma$. For T to be equal to $\dfrac{mg}{2}$ the acceleration should be

$$a = \frac{mg - T}{m} = \frac{g}{2} = 4.9 \text{ m/s}^2$$

60. $F_1 = 1{,}770$ kgf; $F_2 = 1{,}500$ kgf; $F_3 = 1{,}230$ kgf.

Solution. The accelerations of the lift are determined graphically and are: $a_1 = \dfrac{v}{t_1} = 1.8$ m/s^2 during the first two seconds; $a_2 = 0$ between the second and tenth seconds and

$$a_3 = -\frac{v}{t_1} = -1.8 \text{ m/s}^2$$

during the last two seconds.

The equations of Newton's law for each of these cases are written thus

$$F_1 - P = \frac{P}{g} a_1, \quad F_2 - P = 0, \quad F_3 - P = \frac{P}{g} a_3$$

where F_1, F_2, F_3 are the tensions in the cable during the respective intervals of time.

61. *Solution.* Each weight is acted upon by two forces: the force of gravity mg and the tension in the spring f (Fig. 202). According to Newton's second law, $mg - f = ma$ or $f = m(g - a)$. The tension in the springs will be different depending on the magnitude and direction of the acceleration a.

1. When the system is at rest, $a = 0$; $f = mg$, and the tension in each spring is equal to the weight attached to it.

2. The system falls freely, i.e., $a = g$; $f = 0$. The springs are not deformed or stretched. All the weights are at one level.

62. $F = 80$ kgf.

Solution. If the parachutist descends with a constant velocity v the resultant of all the forces on him is zero, i.e., $P - F = 0$ where F is the air resistance. Therefore, $F = P = 80$ kgf.

Fig. 202

63. $F = m\left(\dfrac{v_0}{t} - g\right) = 8{,}800$ dyn.

Solution. The equation of Newton's second law for a rising body is $mg + F = ma$ where F is the mean value of the air resistance.

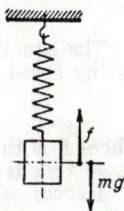

It follows from the equation of motion of a uniformly retarded body with a finite velocity that

$$a = \frac{v_0}{t_1}$$

Hence,

$$F = ma - mg = m\left(\frac{v_0}{t_1} - g\right)$$

Note. In actual fact, the air resistance is not constant and is proportional at low velocities to the velocity of the body. At high velocities the resistance increases in proportion to higher powers of the velocity.

64. At the beginning of the squatting motions $F < mg$ and at the end $F > mg$.

Solution. When the man begins to squat he relaxes the muscles in his legs and allows his body to "fall" with a certain acceleration a

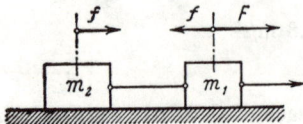

Fig. 203

directed downwards and the pressure on the platform of the balance F becomes such that $mg - F = ma$ or $F = mg - ma$ (i.e., $F < mg$). At the end of squatting the man increases the tension in the muscles of his legs, thus increasing the pressure on the platform and creating the acceleration a directed upwards which is necessary to compensate for the velocity acquired during squatting. In this case the second law equation will take the form $F - mg = ma$ and the pressure will be $F = mg + ma$ (i.e., $F > mg$).

65. $F = 34$ kgf.

Solution. The acceleration of the table during speed-up is

$$a = \frac{v}{t} = 2 \text{ m/s}^2$$

The equation of Newton's second law for the motion of the table during speed-up is

$$F - f_{fr} = Ma$$

where F is the force produced by the mechanisms of the machine and $f_{fr} = kMg$ is the force of friction.

Hence,

$$F = f_{fr} + Ma = 34 \text{ kgf}$$

66. $a = 200$ cm/s²; $f = 6 \times 10^4$ dyn; $F_{max} \approx 1.7 \times 10^6$ and 2.5×10^6 dyn.

Solution. To determine the tensions, write the equations of Newton's second law for each body separately. Both masses move with the same accelerations a. The forces F and f (Fig. 203) act on m_1 and only one force f on m_2. The second law equations for the masses m_1 and m_2 will take the form

$$F - f = m_1 a, \quad f = m_2 a$$

The solution of these equations gives us the required values

$$a = \frac{F}{m_1 + m_2} \quad \text{and} \quad f = \frac{m_2 F}{m_1 + m_2}$$

67. $f_1 = \frac{3}{4} F; \quad f_2 = \frac{1}{2} F; \quad f_3 = \frac{1}{4} F.$

Solution. Force F will cause the entire system to move with an acceleration a. The equations of Newton's second law for each block will be

$$F - f_1 = ma, \quad f_1 - f_2 = ma, \quad f_2 - f_3 = ma, \quad f_3 = ma$$

where f_1, f_2, f_3 are the tensions in the threads (Fig. 204).

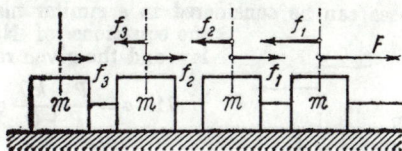

Fig. 204

By solving these equations it is possible to calculate all the tensions as well as the acceleration a with which the system will move.

68. *Solution.* It is difficult to start a heavy railway train when the couplings between the freight-cars are tensioned. In this case the traction of the locomotive has to impart an acceleration to the whole train at once. If the train is first backed up, the couplings between the cars will be slackened and the locomotive can with the same pull impart much larger accelerations first to the nearest car and then, successively, to all the other cars (see Problem 68).

69. *Solution.* If before the motion begins all the couplings in the train are tensioned, the break may occur in the couplings of the cars closest to the locomotive. The tension in these couplings should be greatest since it is intended to produce an acceleration for the greater mass of the cars behind all at once (see Problem 68).

If all the couplings between the cars are first slackened the break may occur in any part of the train depending on the ratios of the tensions in the couplings between separate cars.

70. The dynamometer will show a force:

(1) $f_n \approx f = 1$ kgf; (2) $f_n \approx F = 2$ kgf; and

(3) $f_n = \frac{F + f}{2} = 1.5$ kgf.

Solution. In all three cases the system will move with some acceleration a in the direction of the larger force and the dynamometer will show the bonding force f_n acting between the weights. To find f_n, it is necessary to write the equation of Newton's second law separately for each weight. For the first case (Fig. 205).

$$F - f_n = Ma, \quad f_n - f = ma$$

Hence,

$$a = \frac{F-f}{M+m}$$

and

$$f_n = F - \frac{M}{M+m}(F-f)$$

Since $m \ll M$ and $\frac{M}{M+m} \approx 1$ it may be assumed that

$$f_n \approx f$$

The other cases can be considered in a similar manner utilizing the equations of Newton's second law and the given ratios of masses.

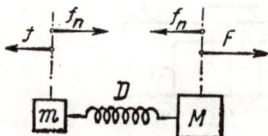

Fig. 205

71. $a = \dfrac{P-kQ}{P+Q}g;$

$f = \dfrac{PQ}{P+Q}(1+k).$

Solution. The bodies P and Q move with accelerations of equal magnitude a. The body P is acted upon by the force of gravity and the tension in the thread f, and the body Q by the tension in the thread and the force of friction $f_1 = kQ$.

The equation of Newton's second law for the motion of each body will be

$$P - f = \frac{P}{g}a, \qquad f - kQ = \frac{Q}{g}a$$

The solution of these equations determines the values of a and f

$$a = \frac{P-kQ}{P+Q}g \quad \text{and} \quad f = \frac{PQ}{P+Q}(1+k)$$

72. $a = \dfrac{mg}{2M+m};$

$T = \dfrac{2M(M+m)}{2M+m}g;$

$f = \dfrac{2Mm}{2M+m}g, \quad F = 2T$

Solution. All the bodies in the system move with accelerations of equal magnitude a (Fig. 206).

The left-hand weight M is acted upon by the force of gravity Mg and the tension in the thread T, and the right-hand weight by the force of gravity Mg, the pressure of the small weight f and the tension in the thread T. The small weight m is acted upon by the force of gravity mg and the pressure f exerted by the weight M.

For each of the three masses the equations of Newton's second law will be

$$T - Mg = Ma$$
$$Mg + f - T = Ma$$
$$mg - f = ma$$

The solutions of these equations determine the values of a, T and f.

The pressure on the axis of the pulley will be equal to twice the tension in the threads $F = 2T$.

73. $t = \sqrt{\dfrac{h(P_1 + P_2)}{(P_2 - P_1)g}} \approx 0.6$ s.

Note. The acceleration of the weights can be found from the equations of Newton's second law (see the solution to Problem 72) and will be $a = \dfrac{P_2 - P_1}{P_1 + P_2}g$, and the

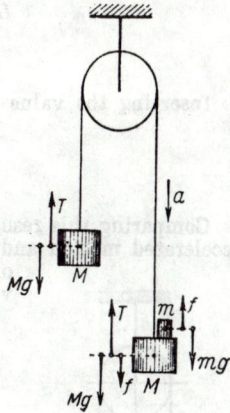
Fig. 206

time of motion from the kinematic equations of uniformly accelerated motions from rest will be

$$t = \sqrt{\frac{h}{a}}$$

74. The centre of gravity moves down with an acceleration

$$j = \frac{(P_1 - P_2)^2}{(P_1 + P_2)^2}g$$

Solution. After a time t each weight will be displaced from the initial position by a distance $S = \dfrac{at^2}{2}$ where $a = \dfrac{P_1 - P_2}{P_1 + P_2}g$ (see the solution to Problem 72).

In this case the centre of gravity of the system should obviously move down a certain distance L from the initial position towards the larger weight (Fig. 207). Upon determining the centre of gravity, the distances of the centre of gravity from the weights should be inversely proportional to the magnitudes of these weights, i.e.,

$$\frac{S + L}{S - L} = \frac{P_1}{P_2}$$

or

$$L = S \frac{\frac{P_1}{P_2} - 1}{1 + \frac{P_1}{P_2}} = \frac{P_1 - P_2}{P_1 + P_2} S$$

Inserting the value $S = \frac{at^2}{2}$, we get

$$L = \frac{P_1 - P_2}{P_1 + P_2} \times \frac{at^2}{2}$$

Comparing this result with the formula for the path of uniformly accelerated motion and then inserting the values of the acceleration of the weights we find that the centre of gravity should move down with an acceleration

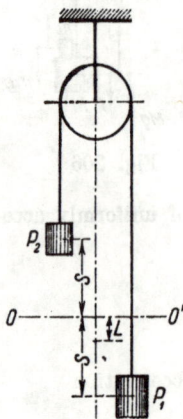

Fig. 207

$$j = \frac{P_1 - P_2}{P_1 + P_2} a = \left(\frac{P_1 - P_2}{P_1 + P_2}\right)^2 g$$

The magnitude of the acceleration of the centre of gravity is less than that of each weight separately.

75. In the first case the system moves with an acceleration $a = 9$ cm/s² and the force of friction between the block and the cart is $f = 180$ gf.

In the second case the acceleration of the block is $a_1 = 7.5$ m/s² and that of the cart $a_2 = 0.25$ m/s²; the force of friction is $f = 0.5$ kgf.

Solution. First case. The maximum force of friction at rest, $f_{fr} = kmg = 0.5$ kgf, is larger than the force F applied to the block. For this reason the force F cannot make the block slide along the cart. The entire system will move as a single whole with a total acceleration a, and the force of friction should be determined as the magnitude of the bonding force from the equation of Newton's second law. The second law equations for the block and the cart will be

$$F - f_{fr} = ma, \quad f_{fr} = Ma$$

hence

$$a = \frac{F}{M + m} = 9 \text{ cm/s}^2, \quad f_{fr} = \frac{MF}{M + m} = 180 \text{ gf}$$

Second case. The maximum force of friction f_{fr} is less than the force F. For this reason the force F will cause the block to slide along the cart. The block and the cart will have different accelerations a_1 and a_2. The force of friction will have its maximum value $f_{fr} = kmg = 0.5$ kgf during motion.

The equations of Newton's second law for the cart and the block
are written as

$$F - kmg = a_1 m$$
$$kmg = Ma_2$$

Hence,

$$a_1 = \frac{F - kmg}{m} = 7.5 \text{ m/s}^2$$

$$a_2 = \frac{kmg}{M} = 0.25 \text{ m/s}^2$$

76. The thread will be perpendicular to the inclined surface
the whole time the cart is rolling down.

Solution. The cart will roll down with an acceleration $a = g \sin \alpha$.
For the ball to have the same acceleration the resultant of the
forces of gravity and tension in the thread which are applied to the ball (Fig. 208) should be directed parallel to
the inclined surface and equal to $F = ma = mg \sin \alpha$.
But, this is possible only when the thread is perpendicular to the inclined surface.

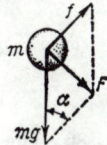

Fig. 208

77. $k = \dfrac{F \sqrt{l^2 - h^2}}{Pl - Fh}$; $f_{fr} = F \dfrac{\sqrt{l^2 - h^2}}{l}$.

Solution. The log moves without acceleration and
therefore the force of friction is equal to the horizontal
component of the force F, i.e.,

$$f_{fr} = F \frac{\sqrt{l^2 - h^2}}{l}$$

The normal pressure will be $N = P - F_y = P - F \dfrac{h}{l}$.

The coefficient of friction $k = \dfrac{f_{fr}}{N} = \dfrac{F \sqrt{l^2 - h^2}}{Pl - Fh}$.

Changing the point of application of the force F only changes the
point of application of the normal pressure, but does not change its
magnitude. For this reason the force of friction will have the same
value as in the first case.

78. In the second case.

Note. The normal pressure of the wheelbarrow on the ground (see
Fig. 209) is $N = P - F \sin \alpha$ in the first case and $N' = P + F \sin \alpha$
in the second (F is the force applied by the man).

Since $N < N'$ the man has to overcome a greater force of friction
$f = kN'$ in the second case.

79. $F = 269$ kgf.

Solution. The acceleration of the cart during braking will be
$a = \dfrac{v_0}{t}$ and directed up the slope. The cart is also acted upon by the
tension in the cable F and the force of friction $f = kN = kMg \cos \alpha$

in the same direction. The component of the force of gravity $Mg \sin \alpha$ is directed down the inclined surface. The equation of Newton's second law for the cart is

$$F + f - Mg \sin \alpha = Ma$$

Therefore,

$$F = M (a + g \sin \alpha) - f \approx 269 \text{ kgf}$$

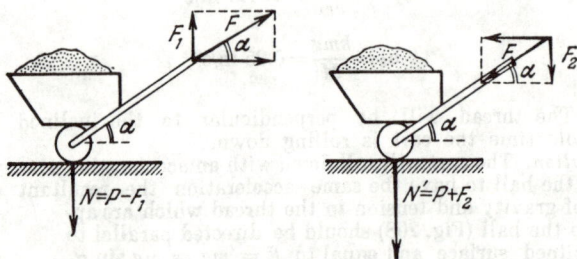

Fig. 209

80. The ball will be deflected forward and assume a perpendicular position to the inclined surface.

Solution. As the cart runs onto the inclined surface the cart acquires an acceleration a in the opposite direction to its motion. The point of suspension lags behind the ball in its retarded motion. The accelerations of the ball and the cart will become the same when the thread holding the ball is directed along a vertical line to the inclined surface (see the solution to Problem 76).

6. Power Impulse. Momentum

81. $-2mv$; $F = \dfrac{2mv}{t}$.

Solution. By Newton's second law, the impulse received by the ball upon impact against the wall will be

$$Ft = mv_2 - mv_1$$

where mv_2 is the momentum of the ball after impact and mv_1 is the momentum before impact.

Since the impact reverses the direction of the vector of momentum (Fig. 210) while preserving its magnitude, the vector of the momentum change and, therefore, the vector of the impulse will be $2mv$ and directed away from the wall. The force exerted by the ball on the wall is $F = \dfrac{2mv}{t}$ where t is the time of impact.

82. $-mv$.

Note. The velocity of the ball after the impact is $v_2 = 0$ (see Problem 81).

83. $2mv \sin \alpha$. The vector of the momentum change is directed away from the wall.

Solution. The vector OA (Fig. 211) shows the momentum of the ball before impact and the vector OB the momentum after impact. The vector AB shows the change in the momentum of the ball. If the vectors OA and OB are resolved into components perpendicular and

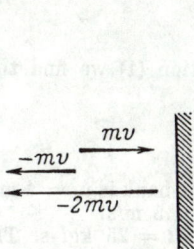

Fig. 210

Fig. 211

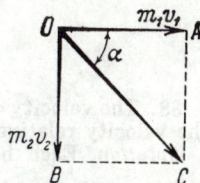

Fig. 212

parallel to the wall it will obviously follow from the equality of the angles α and the magnitudes of the vectors OA and OB that the change in the momentum is caused only by the change in the direction of the component perpendicular to the wall, and is equal to $2mv \sin \alpha$.

84. $\sqrt{(m_1v_1)^2 + (m_2v_2)^2} \approx 1,700 \dfrac{\text{g} \cdot \text{cm}}{\text{s}}$.

The sum of the momenta of the balls is depicted by the vector OC (Fig. 212) which makes an angle $\alpha = 45°$ with OA and OB.

85. $m = \dfrac{Ft}{\Delta v} = 98.1$ kg.

86. $F = 102$ tons.

Solution. The momentum imparted to the train during time t by the tractive force of the locomotive will be Ft and by the force of friction $-kPt$. By Newton's second law,

$$Ft - kPt = \frac{P}{g} v.$$

Hence,

$$F = \frac{Pv}{gt} + kP.$$

87. $t \approx 1$ s.

Solution. The force exerted by the body on the surface is $N = P \cos \alpha$, the force of friction $F_1 = kN = kP \cos \alpha$ and the resultant force of gravity acting along the inclined surface is $F = P \sin \alpha$.

According to Newton's second law,

$$(F - F_1)\, t = \frac{P}{g}\, v \tag{1}$$

where v is the velocity of the body at the end of descent and t is the time of descent. Since the initial velocity is zero,

$$l = \frac{at^2}{2} = \frac{vt}{2}$$

hence $v = \dfrac{2l}{t}$.

Inserting the calculated value of v in equation (1) we find that

$$t = \sqrt{\frac{2l}{g\,(\sin\alpha - k\cos\alpha)}}.$$

88. The velocity of the first boat relative to the bank is $v_1 = 1$ m/s. The velocity relative to the second boat is $v = 1.5$ m/s.

Solution. Each boat receives a momentum $Ft = 25$ kgf·s. This imparts to the first boat a velocity $v_1 = \dfrac{Ft}{m_1}$ relative to the bank and to the second boat a velocity $v_2 = \dfrac{Ft}{m_2}$. The velocity of the first boat relative to the other is $v = v_1 + v_2$.

Assuming approximately that $g = 10$ m/s² we get

$$v_1 = 1 \text{ m/s}, \quad v_2 = 0.5 \text{ m/s and } v = 1.5 \text{ m/s}$$

The problem can also be solved if the accelerations of the boats are calculated from Newton's second law. The velocities can then be calculated from the equations of uniformly accelerated motion.

89. The balloon will descend with a velocity $u = \dfrac{mv}{M+m}$.

Solution. Since the sum of the momenta of the bodies in the system is zero before the man begins to climb the ladder the ascent of the man must cause the balloon to descend with a velocity u such that the sum of the momenta of the balloon and the man is equal to zero as before.

The velocity of the man relative to the earth will be $w = v - u$. His momentum will be mw and that of the balloon Mu. The sum of the momenta of the man and the balloon will be

$$m\,(v - u) - Mu = 0$$

Hence,

$$u = \frac{mv}{M+m}$$

90. *Solution.* The combined centre of mass of the carts before motion will lie on the straight line OO (Fig. 213). By definition the distances of the carts l_1 and l_2 to their centre of mass should at any

moment of time t be inversely proportional to the masses of the carts, i.e.,

$$\frac{l_1}{l_2} = \frac{m_2}{m_1}$$

The distances covered by the carts during the time t will be

$$S_1 = v_1 t \text{ and } S_2 = v_2 t$$

i.e.,

$$\frac{S_1}{S_2} = \frac{v_1}{v_2}$$

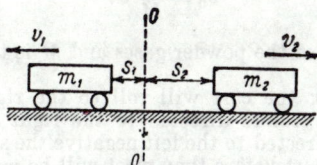

Fig. 213

The velocities imparted to the carts by the action of the compressed spring will, by Newton's second law, be equal to

$$v_1 = \frac{F\tau}{m_1} \quad \text{and} \quad v_2 = \frac{F\tau}{m_2}$$

Therefore,

$$\frac{S_1}{S_2} = \frac{v_1}{v_2} = \frac{F\tau}{m_1} : \frac{m_2}{F\tau} = \frac{m_2}{m_1} = \frac{l_1}{l_2}$$

and the distances of the carts from the straight line OO satisfy the same ratio as the distances from the centre of gravity, i.e., the centre of gravity of the carts is always on the straight line OO.

This result can also be obtained directly from the law of conservation of momentum which gives in this case

$$m_1 v_1 = m_2 v_2 \quad \text{or} \quad \frac{v_1}{v_2} = \frac{m_2}{m_1}$$

91. $v_1 = \dfrac{m_1 v_0 + m_2 v_0 - m_2 v_2}{m_1} = -12.5 \text{ m/s}$

Solution. The sum of momenta of the fragments from the grenade is $m_1 v_0 + m_2 v_0$ before the burst and $m_1 v_1 + m_2 v_2$ after the burst. Since the change in the momenta of the fragments is caused only by the internal forces it should follow from the law of conservation of momentum that

$$m_1 v_0 + m_2 v_0 = m_1 v_1 + m_2 v_2$$

hence

$$v_1 = \frac{m_1 v_0 + m_2 v_0 - m_2 v_2}{m_1} = -12.5 \text{ m/s}$$

The minus sign in the velocity shows that after the burst the smaller fragment begins to move in the opposite direction to the initial motion of the grenade.

92. $S = \left(\dfrac{m}{M} \right)^2 \dfrac{u^2}{g} \sin 2\alpha = 360$ m.

Note. The range of the projectile will be $S = \dfrac{v_0^2}{g} \sin 2\alpha$ (see the solution to Problem 40). The initial velocity of the projectile is determined from the law of conservation of momentum and is

$$v_0 = \frac{m}{M} u$$

where m is the mass of the powder gases and M is the mass of the projectile.

93. $u = 33$ cm/s; the cart will roll to the right.

Solution. If the vectors directed to the right are assumed to be positive and those directed to the left negative the sum of the momenta of the ball and the cart before they meet will be $mv_1 - Mv_2$ and after they meet, $mu + Mu$, or

$$u = \frac{mv_1 - Mv_2}{M + m} = 0.33 \text{ m/s}$$

94. $v_3 \approx 2$ m/s; $v_N = \dfrac{Nmv}{M - Nm}$; the velocity at the end of the first second $u \approx 49$ km/hr.

Solution. Denoting the velocity of the rocket by v_1 after the ejection of the first portion of gas, by v_2 after the second portion, by v_3 after the third and by v_N after the N-th portion and utilizing the law of conservation of momentum we obtain:

for the velocity of the rocket after the ejection of the first portion of gas

$$(M - m) v_1 - mv = 0 \quad \text{or} \quad v_1 = \frac{mv}{M - m}$$

after the second portion

$$(M - m) v_1 = (M - 2m) v_2 - mv \quad \text{or} \quad v_2 = \frac{2mv}{M - 2m}$$

after the third portion

$$(M - 2m) v_2 = (M - 3m) v_3 - mv \quad \text{or} \quad v_3 = \frac{3mv}{M - 3m}$$

The velocity of the rocket after the N-th ejection is

$$v_N = \frac{Nmv}{M - Nm}$$

95. $v_2 = \dfrac{2mv_0}{M - 2m} \approx 1$ m/s.

Note. See the solution to the previous problem.

96. $v_1 = \dfrac{m v_0 \cos \alpha}{M} \approx 3.5$ m/s.

Solution. In determining the velocity of recoil, consider only the horizontal component of the velocity of the cannon-ball, since the recoil caused by the vertical component of this velocity will be damped by the reaction forces of the earth.

The horizontal component of the velocity of the ball $v_x = v_0 \cos \alpha$. According to the law of conservation of momentum, we have: $M v_1 = m v_x$, hence

$$v_1 = \frac{m v_x}{M} = \frac{m v_0 \cos \alpha}{M}$$

97. $v = \dfrac{P \sqrt{2gh} \cos \alpha}{P + Q}$.

Note. See the solution to Problem 96.

7. Work. Energy. Power

98. $F = \dfrac{m^2 v^2}{2MS} \approx 1{,}250$ kgf.

Solution. At the moment of firing the velocity of the barrel u is determined from the law of conservation of momentum and will be equal to

$$u = \frac{mv}{M}$$

where m and M are the masses of the shell and the gun barrel. The kinetic energy $\dfrac{Mu^2}{2}$ imparted to the barrel at the moment of firing will be completely expended on the work against the braking force $A = FS$, i.e., the following equality will be true

$$\frac{Mu^2}{2} = FS$$

Hence,

$$F = \frac{Mu^2}{2S} = \frac{m^2 v^2}{2MS} \approx 1{,}250 \text{ kgf}$$

99. $F = \dfrac{m}{2S} (v_0^2 + 2gh) = 1{,}250$ kgf.

Solution. At the end of fall the kinetic energy of the body will be $E = \dfrac{m v_0^2}{2} + mgh$ where m is the mass of the body.

The mean resistance of the sand can be determined from the equation of the law of conservation of energy $FS = E$. Hence

$$F = \frac{E}{S} = \frac{mv_0^2}{2S} + \frac{mgh}{S} = 1{,}250 \text{ kgf}$$

The problem can also be solved with the aid of Newton's second law and by calculating the acceleration of the body as it penetrates into the sand.

The velocity of the body as it hits the earth is $v = \sqrt{v_0^2 + 2gh}$.

The acceleration of the body in the sand is $a = \dfrac{v^2}{2S} = \dfrac{v_0^2 + 2gh}{2S}$

and the sand resistance

$$F = ma = \frac{m}{2S}(v_0^2 + 2gh)$$

Since the weight mg is small compared with F, its action during the motion of the body in the sand is neglected.

100. $k = \dfrac{h}{S}$, $a_1 = \dfrac{gh}{\sqrt{l^2 + h^2}}\left(1 - \dfrac{l}{S}\right)$, $a_2 = -kg$.

Solution. The sledge at the top of the hill has a potential energy $E = mgh$. During motion this energy is expended on the work A_1 to overcome the forces of friction over the path DC and on the work A_2 to overcome these forces over the path CB, i.e.,

$$E = mgh = A_1 + A_2$$

The force of friction F_1 over the path DC

$$F_1 = kmg \, \frac{l}{\sqrt{l^2 + h^2}}$$

where l is the length of AC. The work will be

$$A_1 = F_1 DC = klmg$$

For the path CB the force of friction $F_2 = kmg$ and the work is

$$A_2 = F_2 CB = kmg(S - l)$$

Hence,

$$mgh = A_1 + A_2 = mgkS$$

and

$$k = \frac{h}{S}$$

The equation of Newton's second law for the motion of the sledge over the path DC will be

$$mg \, \frac{h}{\sqrt{l^2 + h^2}} - F_1 = ma_1$$

and therefore $a_1 = \dfrac{gh}{\sqrt{l^2 + h^2}} \left(l - \dfrac{l}{S} \right)$. Since $\dfrac{l}{S} < 1$, $a_1 > 0$ and the sledge will move over the path DC with a uniformly accelerated motion.

The acceleration over the path CB is $a_2 = -kg$ and the sledge moves with a uniformly retarded motion.

101. (1) When the coefficient of friction is constant the value of S will not change if the hill is more sloping.

(2) The sledge will not move. With an angle of inclination $\tan \alpha = \dfrac{h}{S} = k$, the force of friction equalizes the component of the force of gravity directed along the inclined surface.

102. The potential energy E_n of the parallelepiped in various positions will be:

$E_1 = 2mgl$ when it rests on the small side.

$E_2 = mgl$ when it rests on the middle side.

$E_3 = \dfrac{mgl}{2}$ when it rests on the large side.

The most stable position corresponding to the body's minimum potential energy will be in the last of the three cases.

103. $A \approx 375$ kgf-m.

Solution. The work done against the air resistance is equal to the loss of the kinetic energy of the bullet:

$$A = \frac{mv_0^2}{2} - \frac{mv^2}{2} = \frac{m}{2}(v_0^2 - v^2) \approx 375 \text{ kgf-m}$$

104. *Solution.* In the first case the boy throwing the stone does an amount of work

$$A = \frac{mv_1^2}{2}$$

If, in the second case, he throws the stone with the same force, he will do the same work but this work is now expended to impart kinetic energy to the stone and to the boy. Therefore,

$$\frac{mv_1^2}{2} = \frac{mv_2^2}{2} + \frac{Mu^2}{2} \tag{1}$$

where u is the velocity with which the boy moves.

By the law of conservation of momentum,

$$mv_2 = Mu \tag{2}$$

Solving these equations it is possible to find the velocity of the stone in the second case

$$v_2 = v_1 \sqrt{\frac{M}{M+m}}, \quad v_2 < v_1$$

and the velocity of the boy after he has thrown the stone

$$u = v_1 \sqrt{\frac{m^2}{M(M+m)}}$$

The velocity of the stone relative to the boy is

$$v = v_2 + u = v_1 \sqrt{\frac{M+m}{M}}, \quad v > v_1$$

Since the power $N = Fv$ and the stone moves faster relative to the boy in the second case than in the first ($v > v_1$), the boy should develop a greater power in the second case.

105. $v_1 = 1$ m/s; $A_1 = 15$ kgf-m; $A_2 = 37.5$ kgf-m; $N_1 = 10$ kgf-m/s and $N_2 = 25$ kgf-m/s.

Solution. In both cases the man imparts the same acceleration $a = \dfrac{F}{m_1}$ to the boat A and therefore the velocity of the boat A $\left(v_1 = at = \dfrac{F}{m_1} t = 1 \text{ m/s} \right)$ will be the same in both cases. In the first case the work done by the man is $A_1 = \dfrac{m_1 v_1^2}{2} = 15$ kgf-m and in the second case

$$A_2 = \frac{m_1 v_1^2}{2} + \frac{m_2 v_2^2}{2} = 37.5 \text{ kgf-m}$$

where $v_2 = \dfrac{F}{m_2} t$ is the velocity of the second boat by the end of the third second. The power developed by the man at the end of the third second in the first case is

$$N_1 = Fv_1 = 10 \text{ kgf-m/s}$$

and in the second

$$N_2 = F(v_1 + v_2) = 25 \text{ kgf-m/s}$$

if $N_2 > N_1$.

106. *Solution.* The velocity of the body will be less in the second case since the body's potential energy at a height h is expended in the first case to impart kinetic energy to the body alone, whilst in the second case it is used to impart kinetic energy to the body and the prism at the same time.

107. $\tan \beta = \dfrac{m+M}{M} \tan \alpha$.

Solution. Let us denote the velocity of the prism (Fig. 214) by u, the horizontal and vertical components of the load velocity v relative to the earth by v_x and v_y and the angle between the direction of motion of the load and the horizontal by β, assuming that

$$\tan \beta = \frac{v_y}{v_x} \tag{1}$$

Since the prism is acted upon in a vertical direction by the reaction of the support in addition to the load, the law of conservation of momentum may be applied only to the horizontal components of the velocity of the load and the prism when the behaviour of the "load-prism" system is considered. The velocities u and v_x will obviously be linked by the ratio

$$Mu = mv_x \tag{2}$$

Let the load be situated at the point A of the prism at a certain moment of time (Fig. 215). During the first second after this the prism

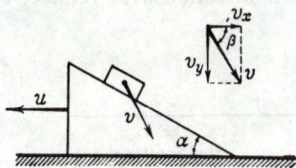

Fig. 214

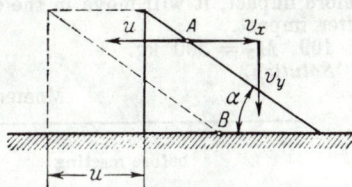

Fig. 215

has moved u cm to the left and the load has been displaced v_x cm horizontally to the right and by v_y cm vertically. All these displacements should be such as to return the load again to the prism at a certain point B. Therefore, the velocities u, v_x and v_y should satisfy the laws of conservation of energy and momentum and also the ratio

$$\frac{v_y}{u + v_x} = \tan \alpha \tag{3}$$

This ratio expresses the condition that the moving load is always located on the prism.

We find from (2) that $u = \dfrac{m}{M} v_x$.

Inserting the value of u into equation (3), utilizing (1) and performing simple transformations we get

$$\tan \beta = \frac{v_y}{v_x} = \frac{m + M}{M} \tan \alpha$$

As we would expect, $\tan \beta > \tan \alpha$ and $\beta > \alpha$.

The velocity of the load down the moving prism is directed at a larger angle to the horizontal than during descent from a stationary prism. Using the law of conservation of energy and knowing the height of the initial position of the load it is possible to calculate the velocities u and v.

108. After the impact the balls will exchange their velocities.

Solution. If the masses of the balls are denoted by m_1 and m_2 and the velocities after impact by x and y, we can obtain from the law of conservation of momentum

$$m_1v_1 + m_2v_2 = m_1x + m_2y \tag{1}$$

Applying the law of conservation of energy and assuming that the total kinetic energy of the balls does not change after the impact we may write

$$\frac{m_1 v_1^2}{2} + \frac{m_2 v_2^2}{2} = \frac{m_1 x^2}{2} + \frac{m_2 y^2}{2} \qquad (2)$$

Solving equations (1) and (2) simultaneously and using $m_1 = m_2 = m$, we get $y = v_1$ and $x = v_2$, i.e., perfectly elastic balls of equal mass will exchange their velocities after impact.

If the first ball moves from the left to the right with velocity v_1 before impact, it will move in the opposite direction with velocity v_2 after impact.

109. $M_2 = 300$ kg.

Solution.

Momentum

	before meeting	after meeting
First boat	$(M_1 + m)\, v$	$M_1 v$
Second boat	$- M_2 v$	$- (M_2 + m)\, v_2$

The momentum of the two boats before the load is shifted is equal to their momentum after the transfer of the load, i.e.,

$$(M_1 + m)\, v - M_2 v = M_1 v - (M_2 + m)\, v_2$$

Hence, $M_2 = \dfrac{m\,(v + v_2)}{v - v_2} = 300$ kg.

The energy of the boats before they meet is

$$E_1 = \frac{(M_1 + M_2 + m)\, v^2}{2}$$

and after reshifting the load the energy of the boats is

$$E_2 = \frac{M_1 v_1^2}{2} + \frac{(M_2 + m)\, v_2^2}{2}$$

The energy has diminished due to the transfer of a part of the energy into heat when the velocities of the load and the second boat become the same.

110. $N = \dfrac{mgh}{t} = 49 \times 10^{11}$ erg/s $= 490$ kW.

111. $F = 4{,}896$ kgf.

Solution. The useful power $N_2 = k N_1 = Fv$. Hence,

$$N_1 = \frac{Fv}{k} \quad \text{and} \quad F = \frac{N_1 k}{v} \approx 4{,}896 \text{ kgf}$$

112. The power $N = 4.2$ hp.

Solution. The force of friction F between the shoes and the shaft is determined from the equilibrium condition of the lever in the absorption dynamometer: the moment of the force F is equal to the moment of the force Q:

$$Fr = Ql$$

and hence

$$F = \frac{Ql}{r}$$

The velocity of the points on the surface of the shaft will be

$$v = 2\pi\nu r$$

where $\nu = \frac{n}{60}$ is the number of shaft revolutions per second

$$N = Fv = \frac{2Q\pi\nu l r}{r} = 2\pi Q\nu l \approx 4.2 \text{ hp}$$

113. $N = 11.8$ kgf-m/s.

114. The maximum power should be developed by the engine at the end of the take-off run and equal to $N = Fv$ where F is the tractive force of the propellers which, as is given in the problem, remains constant during the entire time of the run.

The force F is determined from the equation of Newton's second law for the take-off run:

$$F - kP = \frac{P}{g}a$$

The acceleration $a = \frac{v^2}{2S}$ and therefore

$$F = kP + \frac{Pv^2}{2gS}$$

and the power is

$$N = kPv + \frac{Pv^3}{2gS}$$

115. $N \approx 1$ hp.

Solution. The force of friction overcome during machining is $F_1 = kF$, the velocity of the rim of the stone is $v = \pi dn$ and the required power

$$N = F_1 v = kF \pi dn$$

116. $f \approx 490$ kgf; $F \approx 980$ kgf.

Note. The pulley will rotate under the action of a force equal to $F - f$. The velocity of the pulley rim is $v = 2\pi rn$ and the power $N = (F - f) 2\pi rn$. Since it is given in the problem that $F = 2f$, then

$$f = \frac{N}{2\pi rn} \quad \text{and} \quad F = \frac{N}{\pi rn}$$

8. Dynamics of a Point Moving in a Circle

117. $AO = \dfrac{ml}{M+m} = 25$ cm; $OB = 75$ cm.

Solution. The centripetal force acting on M will be $F_1 = \omega^2 Mx$ (Fig. 216). The force acting on m will be $F_2 = \omega^2 m \,(l - x)$.

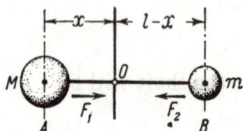

From the given conditions F_1 must be equal to F_2, i.e.,

$$\omega^2 Mx = \omega^2 m \,(l - x)$$

or

$$x = AO = \frac{ml}{M+m}$$

Fig. 216

These expressions also determine the distances from the balls to the centre of gravity of the system. The tensions in the threads are the same when the centre of rotation coincides with the centre of gravity of the system.

118. $\omega = \sqrt{\dfrac{g}{r}} = 7$ s^{-1}.

Solution. The balls will be in equilibrium when the centripetal force acting on the ball B is equal to the weight of the ball A, i.e., when $r\omega^2 m = mg$. Hence, $\omega = \sqrt{\dfrac{g}{r}}$. The equilibrium will be unstable.

119. $v_0 \geqslant \sqrt{gR}$.

Solution. The velocity of the washer v_0 should be such that the parabolic path it takes under the force of gravity can pass outside the hemisphere, only touching it at the upper point A (Fig. 217).

When the washer moves along a parabola its vertical acceleration at the point A will be g and the centripetal acceleration for motion in a circle of radius R with a velocity v_0 will be $\dfrac{v_0^2}{R}$.

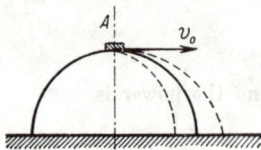

Fig. 217

If $g \leqslant \dfrac{v_0^2}{R}$ the curvature of the parabola will be less than the curvature of the surface of the hemisphere and the parabola will be outside the hemisphere, i.e., the washer will not slide over the hemisphere at velocities v_0 when $v_0 \geqslant \geqslant \sqrt{gR}$.

120. $a = \dfrac{4\pi^2 R}{T^2} = 0.033$ m/s^2 (T is the time for one complete revolution of the Earth).

The reduction in the weight of bodies on the equator caused by the rotation of the Earth comes approximately to 0.0034 of the force of attraction.

121. $n = \dfrac{\sqrt{2gh}}{2\pi R}$; $p = gh = \dfrac{\omega^2 R^2}{2}$.

Solution. (1) If the particles of water emerge from the pump with
velocity v they can rise to such a height h at which all their kinetic
energy will pass into potential energy, i.e., the following will always
be true:

$$v^2 = 2gh$$

Assuming that the velocity of the water particles is equal to the linear
velocity of the ends of the pump vanes it is possible to determine the
number of revolutions n of the pump

$$n = \frac{v}{2\pi R} = \frac{\sqrt{2gh}}{2\pi R}$$

(2) When equilibrium is established and the water rises in the pipe
to the maximum height, the pressure at the exit of the pump will
become equal to the weight of the water column of
height h, i.e.,

$$p = gh = \frac{v^2}{2} = \frac{\omega^2}{2} R^2$$

where $\omega = 2\pi n$ is the angular velocity of the water
particles in the pump.

Inside the pump, during motion from the axis to
the ends of the vanes, the pressure will grow in proportion to the square of the distance to the axis.

(3) To calculate the centripetal force, let us separate a thin layer of water between the cylinders of
radii R and r (Fig. 218). The thickness of the layer
$S = R - r$ should be small enough for the velocities

Fig. 218

of all the particles of this layer to be regarded as identical. Each
element of the water volume supported on 1 cm² of the surface of the
internal cylinder r will be acted upon by a force equal to the pressure
difference

$$F = P_1 - P_2 = \frac{\omega^2 R^2}{2} - \frac{\omega^2 r^2}{2} = \frac{\omega^2}{2}(R^2 - r^2)$$

As the mass of the water in this volume is $m = dS \times 1 = R - r$
(where $d = 1$ is the density of the water) and assuming (since S is
small) that $R + r = 2R$, we get

$$F = \frac{\omega^2}{2}(R + r)(R - r) = \frac{m\omega^2}{2}(R + r) \approx m\omega^2 R$$

i.e., the pressures are distributed in a centrifugal pump so that the
pressure difference acting on each layer is enough to produce the required centripetal accelerations of the water particles present in this layer.

122. $F_{fr} = \dfrac{4\pi^2 R P n^2}{g} = 0.08$ kgf; $\omega = \sqrt{\dfrac{kg}{R}} = 2.2\ \dfrac{1}{s}$.

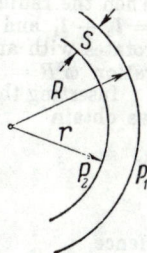

Solution. The centripetal acceleration for a moving load is only provided by the force of friction and in the first case

$$F_{fr} = m\omega^2 R = 4\pi^2 Rmn^2 = \frac{4\pi^2 RPn^2}{g}$$

The load will begin to slide with that angular velocity at which the centripetal force becomes equal to the maximum force of friction at rest, i.e., when

$$kP = m\omega^2 R$$

or

$$\omega = \sqrt{\frac{kP}{mR}} = \sqrt{\frac{kg}{R}}$$

123. $R = \dfrac{l_0 f_0}{f_0 - m\omega^2}$; $F = \dfrac{m\omega^2 f_0 l_0}{f_0 - m\omega_0^2}$.

Solution. Assume that the length of the cord has increased by l_1 cm Then the radius of the circle along which the ball will move is $R = l_0 + l_1$ and the tension in the cord is $F = f_0 l_1$. When the ball rotates with an angular velocity ω it will have a centripetal acceleration $\omega^2 R = \omega^2 (l_0 + l_1)$ and by Newton's second law $F = m\omega^2 R$.

Inserting the values of F and $\omega^2 R$ in Newton's second law equation we obtain

$$f_0 l_1 = m\omega^2 (l_0 + l_1)$$

or

$$l_1 = \frac{m\omega^2 l_0}{f_0 - m\omega^2}$$

Hence,

$$R = l_0 + l_1 = \frac{l_0 f_0}{f_0 - m\omega^2}$$

and

$$F = f_0 l_1 = \frac{m\omega^2 f_0 l_0}{f_0 - m\omega^2}$$

124. $F_1 = P$; $F_2 = P - \dfrac{Pv^2}{gR}$; $F_3 = P + \dfrac{Pv^2}{gR}$.

Solution. The car is acted upon in the vertical direction by two forces: the weight P and the reaction of the support F.

(1) When the car runs over a horizontal flat bridge there are no accelerations in the vertical direction and the sum of the forces acting on the car in this direction should by Newton's second law be equal to zero

$$P - F_1 = 0 \text{ or } F_1 = P$$

(2) When the car runs over a convex bridge a centripetal acceleration will act vertically downwards and therefore

$$P - F_2 = \frac{mv^2}{R}$$

or

$$F_2 = P - \frac{Pv^2}{gR}, \qquad F_2 < P$$

i.e., the pressure exerted by the car on the bridge is less than the weight of the car.

(3) Similarly, if the car crosses a concave bridge it will have an acceleration directed upwards and the pressure can be determined from the equation

$$F_3 - P = \frac{mv^2}{R}$$

$$F_3 = P + \frac{mv^2}{R} = P + \frac{Pv^2}{gR}$$

$$F_3 > P$$

The pressure on the bridge is larger than the weight of the car.

125. $F_1 = 4P$; $F_2 = 6P$.

Solution. At the highest point of the loop the weight P and the reaction of the support acting on the pilot are both directed downwards (Fig. 219).

The pilot's centripetal acceleration $\frac{v^2}{R}$ is also directed downwards.

According to Newton's second law,

$$F_1 + P = \frac{mv^2}{R}$$

or

$$F_1 = \frac{Pv^2}{gR} - P = 307 \text{ kgf} \approx 4P$$

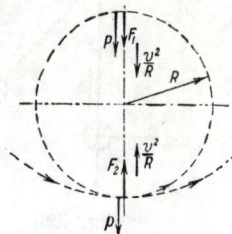

Fig. 219

At the lower point of the loop the acceleration $a = \frac{v^2}{R}$ and the force F_2 are directed upwards. The equation of Newton's second law will have the form

$$F_2 - P = \frac{mv^2}{R}$$

and the force is

$$F_2 = P + \frac{Pv^2}{gR} = 457 \text{ kgf} \approx 6P$$

126. $F = 3mg = 3P$.

Solution. The pendulum passes through the equilibrium position moving along the arc of a circle of radius l with a velocity v. At this moment the bob of the pendulum will possess a centripetal acceleration $a = \dfrac{v^2}{l}$ directed upwards. This acceleration is provided by the joint action of the force of gravity and the tension in the thread (Fig. 220). By Newton's second law,

$$F - mg = m\frac{v^2}{l}$$

and hence

$$F = m\left(g + \frac{v^2}{l}\right)$$

The velocity v is determined from the law of conservation of energy and is

$$v = \sqrt{2gl}$$

and therefore

$$F = mg + \frac{mv^2}{l} = 3mg = 3P$$

where P is the weight of the bob. The thread must be able to support a load equal to three times the weight of the bob.

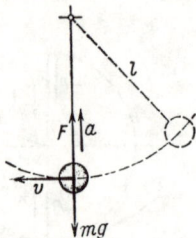

Fig. 220

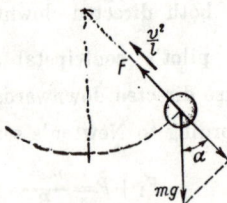

Fig. 221

127. $\alpha = 60°$.

Solution. Use Newton's second law to find the velocity when the bob passes through the position of equilibrium (see the solution to Problem 126)

$$v^2 = \frac{(F - mg)\,l}{m} = gl$$

From the equation of the law of conservation of energy, $\dfrac{mv^2}{2} = mgh$, it is possible to find the height from which the bob dropped: $h = \dfrac{v^2}{2g} = \dfrac{l}{2}$ and

$$\cos\alpha = \frac{h}{l} = \frac{1}{2}$$

128. $\alpha \approx 48°11'$.

Solution. In any intermediate position the ball is acted upon along the thread by the tension in the thread F and the component of the force of gravity $mg\cos\alpha$ (Fig. 221). The acceleration of the ball

$\frac{v^2}{l}$ (where $v^2 = 2gl \cos \alpha$) will be in the same direction. Therefore (see the solution to Problem 126),

$$F - mg \cos \alpha = \frac{2mgl}{l} \cos \alpha = 2mg \cos \alpha$$

Knowing that $F = 2mg$, we obtain

$$\cos \alpha = \frac{F}{3mg} = \frac{2}{3}$$

129. $\omega = 5.4$ rad/s; $S \approx 4.24$ m.

Solution. The tension in the thread will be greater when the stone passes through the bottom point of the circle. The equation of Newton's second law at this moment will be $F - mg = m\omega^2 l$. Hence, the angular velocity at which the thread is broken will be

$$\omega = \sqrt{\frac{F - mg}{ml}}$$

The velocity of the stone at the moment the thread is broken will be directed horizontally and equal to

$$v = \omega l = l \sqrt{\frac{F - mg}{ml}}$$

The range of the stone is $S = vt$ where $t = \sqrt{\frac{2(h-l)}{g}}$ is the time of free fall from the height $(h - l)$ and therefore

$$S = \omega l \sqrt{\frac{2(h-1)}{g}} =$$
$$= l \sqrt{\frac{2(h-l)(F-mg)}{mgl}}$$

130. $H = \frac{2R}{3}$.

Solution. For the body to lie on the surface of the hemisphere the

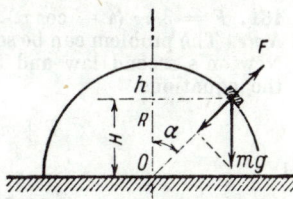
Fig. 222

sum of the forces acting on it at any point in the direction of the radius should be enough to produce the centripetal acceleration $\frac{v^2}{R}$. The velocity of the body at any point is determined from the ratio $v^2 = 2gh$, where h is the vertical distance of the body from the top of the hemisphere. The body is acted upon along the radius of the hemisphere by the reaction of the support F and the component of the force of gravity $mg \cos \alpha$ (Fig. 222). Hence,

$$mg \cos \alpha - F = \frac{mv^2}{R} = \frac{2mgh}{R}$$

As the body moves, the acceleration $\frac{v^2}{R}$ is constantly growing but the force F diminishing faster than $mg \cos \alpha$ provides the increase in the resultant necessary to build up the higher acceleration.

At a certain point the force F will become zero and a further growth in the acceleration $\frac{v^2}{R}$ will no longer be provided by the forces acting on the body. It is precisely at this moment that the body will be detached from the hemisphere.

Thus, the condition for the body to be detached from the hemisphere is $F = 0$ or

$$mg \cos \alpha = \frac{2mgh}{R}$$

Considering that

$$\cos \alpha = \frac{R-h}{R}$$

we find that the body will be detached at a distance from the top equal to

$$h = \frac{R}{3}$$

Hence,

$$H = \frac{2}{3} R$$

131. $F = 3mg (1 - \cos \alpha)$.

Note. The problem can be solved similarly to Problems 129 and 130. Newton's second law and the law of conservation of energy give us the equations

$$F + mg \cos \alpha = \frac{mv^2}{R}$$

and

$$v^2 = gR (3 - 2 \cos \alpha)$$

Hence,

$$F = mg (3 - 2 \cos \alpha - \cos \alpha) = 3mg (1 - \cos \alpha)$$

132. $F = 3mg (1 + \cos \beta)$.

133. $H_1 = \frac{5}{3} R$; $H_2 = \frac{50}{27} R$.

Solution. The height at which the ball will be detached from the chute is determined in the same way as in Problem 130 on the basis of Newton's second law and is equal to

$$H_1 = \frac{5}{3} R$$

The ball will move from the point C (Fig. 223) in a parabola with initial velocity

$$v_0 = \sqrt{2gh_1} = \sqrt{\frac{2gR}{3}}$$

directed at an angle α which can be determined from the equation

$$\cos \alpha = \frac{R - h_1}{R} = \frac{2}{3}$$

At the maximum elevation of the parabola the velocity of the ball will be equal to the horizontal component of velocity v_0, i.e.,

$$v_x = v_0 \cos \alpha =$$
$$= \frac{2}{3} \sqrt{\frac{2gR}{3}} = \sqrt{\frac{8gR}{27}}$$

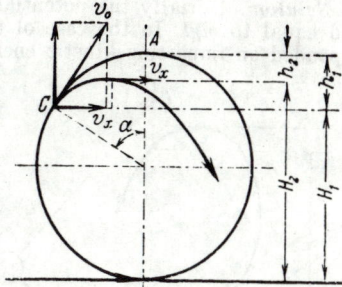

Fig. 223

It follows from the law of conservation of energy that at this moment the ball should be at such a distance h_2 along the vertical from the point A that $v_x^2 = 2gh_2$. Hence,

$$h_2 = \frac{v_x^2}{2g} = \frac{4}{27} R$$

and

$$H_2 = 2R - h_2 = \frac{50}{27} R$$

134. $H_1 = \frac{25}{27} l$.

Note. Up to the height $H_1 = \frac{5}{6} l$ (Fig. 224) the ball will move over an arc of a circle of radius $\frac{l}{2}$. After this, the ball will move in a parabola up to the height $H_2 = \frac{25}{27} l$. This problem is solved in the same way as Problem 133.

135. $h_1 = \frac{3}{5} l$.

Solution. The centripetal acceleration of the ball at the upper point C (Fig. 225) of a circle of radius h_2 should be not less than the acceleration of the force of gravity, i.e., $\frac{v^2}{h_2} \geqslant g$. The minimum velocity at the point C should be

$$v = \sqrt{2g\,(l - 2h_2)}$$

and therefore

$$5h_2 = 2l \quad \text{or} \quad h_2 = \frac{2}{5}\,l$$

136. The ball suspended on the rigid thread will have a higher velocity.

Solution. Initially the potential energy of both balls is the same and equal to mgl. In the case of the rigid thread all this energy is expended on imparting kinetic energy to the ball. As the ball passes

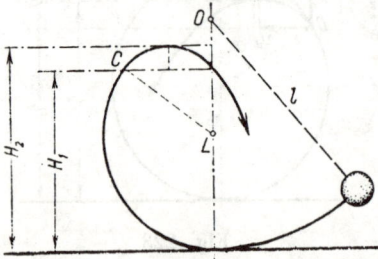

Fig. 224

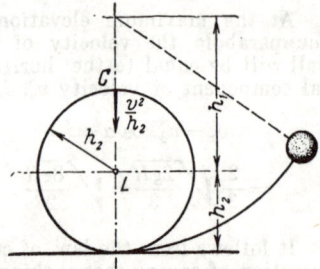

Fig. 225

through the point of equilibrium its velocity will be determined in this case on the basis of the law of conservation of energy from the ratio

$$mgl = \frac{mv_1^2}{2}, \quad v_1 = \sqrt{2gl}$$

For the ball suspended on the rubber cord only a part of its potential energy is changed into kinetic energy, the rest being changed into the potential energy of deformation of the rubber cord.

Therefore, $\dfrac{mv_2^2}{2} < mgl$ and $v_2 < v_1$.

137. $v_1 = \sqrt{2gl}$; $v_2 = \sqrt{\dfrac{12gl}{5}} = 2\sqrt{\dfrac{3gl}{5}}$.

Solution. In the first case the law of conservation of energy gives us

$$\frac{2mv_1^2}{2} = 2mgl, \quad v_1^2 = 2gl$$

In the second case the initial store of energy of the mass C will be $\dfrac{mv_2^2}{2}$ and of the mass B

$$\frac{m}{2}\left(\frac{v_2}{2}\right)^2 + mg\,\frac{l}{2}$$

After deflection the total store of energy of both masses is equal to $2mgl$.

It follows from the law of conservation of energy that

$$\frac{mv_2^2}{2} + \frac{mv_2^2}{8} + mg\frac{l}{2} = 2mgl$$

and therefore

$$v_2^2 = \frac{12}{5}gl, \quad v_2 = \sqrt{\frac{12}{5}gl}$$

138. $\tan\alpha = \dfrac{v^2}{gR}$ and $\alpha = 16°42'$.

Solution. The cyclist is acted upon by three forces (Fig. 226): his weight mg applied through the centre of gravity, the normal pressure (reaction of support) $N = mg$ directed vertically upwards and applied through the point A and the force of friction F_{fr} directed towards the centre of the circle along which the cyclist rides. The force of friction F_{fr} takes a value such that, when added to the normal pressure N, it produces the force AB directed along the line OA passing through the centre of gravity, and, when added to the force mg, produces the resultant $F = F_{fr}$ which is directed horizontally and is great enough to provide the centripetal acceleration $\dfrac{v^2}{R}$ of the cyclist. The resultant F of the forces mg, N and F_{fr} may also be expressed by the weight and the angle of inclination α of the cyclist.

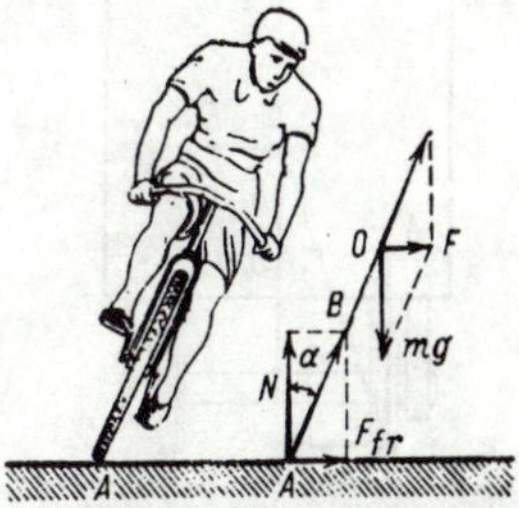

Fig. 226

According to Newton's second law, $F = mg\tan\alpha = \dfrac{mv^2}{R}$ and therefore $\tan\alpha = \dfrac{v^2}{gR}$, $\alpha = 16°42'$.

139. $R = \dfrac{v^2}{kg} = 21.8$ m; $\tan\alpha = k$; $\alpha = 16°42'$.

Solution. The resultant of all the forces applied to the bicycle is equal to the force of friction F_{fr} (see the solution to the previous problem).

Since the maximum force of friction is $F_{fr} = kmg$, the minimum radius of curvature will be $R = \dfrac{v^2}{kg}$. The maximum angle at which the bicycle must be inclined can be determined from the condition

$$F_{fr} = mg\tan\alpha, \quad \tan\alpha = k$$

140. $v_{max} = 31.3$ m/s.

Solution. When the railway carriage runs on horizontal rails along a curve the pressure exerted on the outer rail will always be larger than on the inner one. This difference of pressures will be increased as the speed of the carriage increases. When the carriage runs at the maximum permissible speed the entire pressure of the carriage is applied to the rail A —the outer rail relative to the centre of curvature.

The rail A produces two forces: the normal pressure $N = mg$ and the lateral force F. Together with the force of gravity, these forces provide the necessary accelerations of the carriage.

Two different cases are possible:

(a) The carriage runs along the curve with a speed slightly less than the critical speed. In this case the centripetal acceleration $\frac{v^2}{R}$

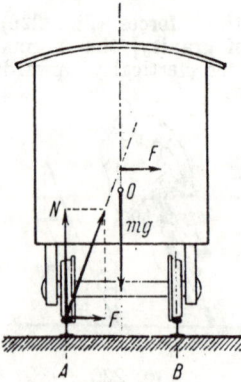

Fig. 227

and the force F are small. The point of application of the resultant of all the three forces lies above the centre of gravity O (Fig. 227). The resultant F not only produces the centripetal acceleration but also tends to turn the carriage clockwise around the centre of gravity and press it again to the rail B. The movement of the carriage along the curve will be stable.

(b) The speed v is larger than the critical speed, the force F is high and the point of application of the resultant lies below the centre of gravity. The resultant will turn the carriage anti-clockwise around the centre of gravity. The carriage will tend to topple over and stable motion at this speed is impossible.

The maximum possible speed of the carriage along the curve will obviously correspond to the case when the point of application of the resultant of all the forces coincides with the centre of gravity of the carriage, i.e., when

$$\frac{F}{mg} = \frac{l}{2h}, \qquad \frac{mv^2}{mgR} = \frac{l}{2h}$$

$$v = \sqrt{\frac{lgR}{2h}} = 31.3 \text{ m/s}$$

141. When the longitudinal gradient is measured the spirit level will only show correct readings if the train moves uniformly.

If the transverse gradient is measured the readings of the spirit level will only be true when the train moves in a straight line.

142. $F \approx 5.025$ kgf.

Solution. The load suspended from a spring balance in a carriage running along a curve is acted upon by two forces: its weight P and the tension in the spring F (Fig. 228). The resultant of these two forces produces the centripetal force $\frac{mv^2}{R}$ directed horizontally. It

follows from the drawing that

$$F^2 = P^2 + \left(\frac{mv^2}{R}\right)^2$$

Hence,

$$F = \sqrt{P^2 + \left(\frac{mv^2}{R}\right)^2} \approx 5.025 \text{ kgf}$$

143. $\alpha \approx 22°$; $F \approx 320$ kgf.

Solution. When the aircraft makes a turn in a horizontal plane,

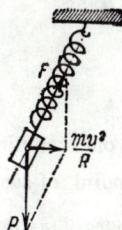

Fig. 228

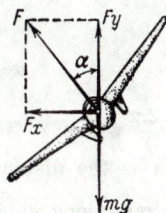

Fig. 229

the horizontal and vertical components of the lift F should be related by the following ratios (Fig. 229):

$$F_x = F \sin \alpha = \frac{mv^2}{R}, \qquad F_y = F \cos \alpha = mg$$

from which we get

$$\tan \alpha = \frac{v^2}{gR}$$

and

$$F = \sqrt{F_x^2 + F_y^2} = \sqrt{\left(\frac{mv^2}{R}\right)^2 + (mg)^2}$$

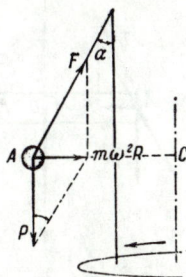

Fig. 230

144. $\omega \approx 8$ s^{-1}.

Solution. The centripetal acceleration of the ball is caused by the joint action of its weight P and the tension F in the thread (Fig. 230). The drawing shows that

$$m\omega^2 R = P \tan \alpha = mg \tan \alpha$$

where

$$R = r + l \sin \alpha$$

from which we get

$$\omega = \sqrt{\frac{g \tan \alpha}{R}}$$

or

$$\omega = \sqrt{\frac{g \tan \alpha}{r + l \sin \alpha}} = 8 \text{ s}^{-1}$$

145. $T = 2\pi \sqrt{\dfrac{h}{g}}$.

Solution. The centripetal force $m\omega^2 R$ required to move the ball along a circle of radius $R = l \sin \alpha$ may be expressed in terms of the force of gravity (see the solution to Problems 142-144 and Fig. 230):

$$mg \tan \alpha = m\omega^2 l \sin \alpha$$

from which

$$\omega^2 = \frac{g}{l \cos \alpha}$$

Since $\omega = \dfrac{2\pi}{T}$ where T is the time for one complete revolution and $l \cos \alpha = h$ is the distance from the point of suspension to the surface of the circle along which the ball moves, $T = 2\pi \sqrt{\dfrac{h}{g}}$. This expression corresponds to the formula describing the period of a theoretical pendulum of length h.

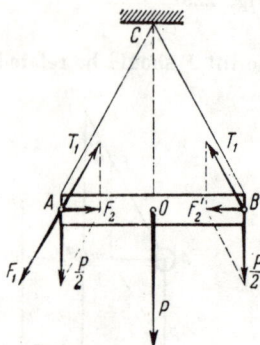

Fig. 231

9. Statics

146. $R = 0$.

148. $T_1 = \dfrac{Pl}{\sqrt{4l^2 - L^2}} = 10$ kgf; $F_2 = \dfrac{PL}{2\sqrt{4l^2 - L^2}} = 6$ kgf.

Solution. The weight of the rod P acting through the centre of gravity of the rod may be replaced by two equal forces $\dfrac{P}{2}$ applied at the ends of the rod.

In the first case (Fig. 231) the force $\dfrac{P}{2}$ applied to the rod at the point A should be resolved into two components: F_1—in the direction of the extension of the rope AC, and F_2—acting along the rod and directed towards the centre of gravity of the rod. As the triangle of forces and the triangle AOC are similar we get for the tension in the rope T_1 and the force F_2:

$$T_1 = \frac{Pl}{2\sqrt{l^2 - \dfrac{L^2}{4}}} = \frac{Pl}{\sqrt{4l^2 - L^2}} = 10 \text{ kgf}$$

$$F_2 = \frac{\frac{P}{2} \times \frac{L}{2}}{\sqrt{l^2 - \frac{L^2}{4}}} = \frac{PL}{2\sqrt{4l^2 - L^2}} = 6 \text{ kgf}$$

The force F_2 and the force F_2' applied at the point B compress the rod with a force of 6 kgf.

In the second case the tension in the rope will be the same as in the first case. The forces F_2' and F_2 will extend the rod AB with a force of 6 kgf.

149. At $\alpha > 120°$.

150. $Q = 200$ kgf.

Note. The magnitude of the force is determined from the similarity of triangles OCB and OKM (Fig. 232) and is equal to $Q = \frac{Fl}{4S}$.

151. $T = \frac{P}{2} \cos \alpha$. When α changes from 0 to 90° the tension in the rope T diminishes from $\frac{P}{2}$ to zero.

Note. The magnitude of the force T is determined from the condition of equilibrium of the board. The sum of the moments of the forces T and P with respect to the point A should be equal to zero, i.e., $Tl = P\frac{l}{2}\cos\alpha$ where $l = AB$ is the length of the board; hence, $T = \frac{P}{2}\cos\alpha$.

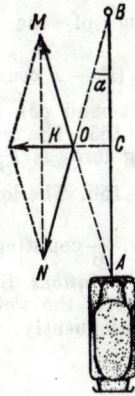
Fig. 232

152. The weight of the beam is $Q = 300$ kgf.

Solution. The weight of the overhanging end of the beam equal to $\frac{Q}{4}$ acts through the point O (Fig. 233). The equation of the moments of the forces with respect to the point C will be

$$\frac{3}{4}Q \times \frac{3}{8}l = \frac{1}{4}P + \frac{Q}{4} \times \frac{l}{8}$$

(where l is the length of the beam) and therefore $Q = P$.

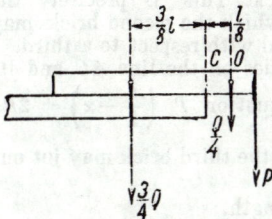
Fig. 233

153. $Q = \sqrt{P_1 P_2} = 3.2$ kgf.

Solution. Let us denote the length of the arms of the balance beam by l_1 and l_2. The equations of the moments are:

for the first weighing, $Ql_1 = P_1 l_2$
for the second weighing, $P_2 l_1 = Ql_2$.

We find from the two equations

$$Q^2 = P_1 P_2 \quad \text{or} \quad Q = \sqrt{P_1 P_2}$$

154. The left-hand pan will move down.

Solution. The moment of the force of gravity is $M_1 = P\dfrac{l}{2}$. The moment of the force F with which the man pulls the rope is $M_2 = F\dfrac{l}{4}\cos\alpha$; the force of pressure exerted by the man on the pan is $P - F\cos\alpha$ and the moment of this force $M_3 = (P - F\cos\alpha)\dfrac{l}{2}$.

The sum of the moments of the forces acting on the right-hand arm of the beam of the balance is $M_2 + M_3 = \dfrac{Fl\cos\alpha}{4} + (P - F\cos\alpha)\dfrac{l}{2}$. Obviously, $M_1 > M_2 + M_3$ and therefore the left-hand pan will move down.

155. The tensioning force is $P_x = P\cos\alpha \approx 86.6$ kgf. The deflecting force is $P_y = P\sin\alpha = 50$ kgf.

156. The length of the overhanging edges of the bricks will be $\dfrac{l}{2}$, $\dfrac{l}{4}$, $\dfrac{l}{6}$ counting from the top brick.

Solutions. Since the bricks are homogeneous the point of application of the weight of each brick will lie half way along its length. Consequently, the first top brick will still be in equilibrium with respect to the second when its centre of gravity is arranged above the edges of the second brick, i.e., the maximum length of the free edge of the first brick will be $\dfrac{l}{2}$.

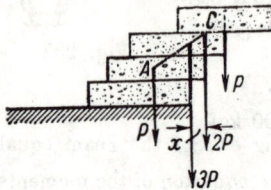

Fig. 234

The centre of gravity of the first and second bricks taken together will be at a distance $\dfrac{l}{4}$ from the edge of the second brick. This is precisely the length by which the second brick may be displaced with respect to a third.

The centre of gravity of three bricks lies on the line AC and its position can be determined from the equation $P\left(\dfrac{l}{2} - x\right) = 2Px$ (Fig. 234) from which we get $x = \dfrac{l}{6}$, i.e., the third brick may jut out over a fourth by not more than $\dfrac{1}{6}$ of its length.

157. The equilibrium will be disturbed, but can be restored by applying to the right-hand end of the beam a force $F = \dfrac{P}{4}$ equal to the weight of the part cut off.

158. *Solution.* The magnitude of the force F can be found from the equation of the moments of the forces relative to the bottom of the ladder

$$Ph \tan \alpha = \frac{Fl}{2} \cos \alpha, \quad F = \frac{2Ph}{l} \times \frac{\sin \alpha}{\cos^2 \alpha}$$

159. The force required in the second case is half that required in the first.

160. $F = 1.4$ kgf.

Solution. For the block to be in equilibrium on the inclined surface the force of friction $f_{fr} = kN$ should be equal to the component of the weight directed along the inclined surface (Fig. 235)

$$P_2 = P \frac{h}{l} = f_{fr}$$

The normal pressure $N = F + P \dfrac{\sqrt{l^2 - h^2}}{l}$. Inserting the values of N, P_2 and f_{fr} into the condition for equilibrium we get

$$k \left(P \frac{\sqrt{l^2 - h^2}}{l} + F \right) = \frac{h}{l} P$$

$$F = \frac{1}{k} \left(\frac{h}{l} P - \frac{kP}{l} \sqrt{l^2 - h^2} \right)$$

161. $F = \dfrac{Ph}{4l} = 50$ kgf.

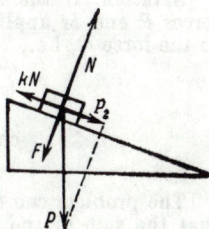

Fig. 235

Solution. In order to raise the log to the height h each rope should be pulled up a distance $2l$. On the basis of the "golden rule" of mechanics $Ph = 2 (F \times 2l)$, where Ph is the work done by the force of gravity and $F \times 2l$ is the work done by the force of tension in one rope. Therefore, $F = \dfrac{Ph}{4l}$.

The problem can also be solved considering the equilibrium of forces applied to the log.

162. $F = 2.5$ kgf.

Note. The force required to keep the differential winch in equilibrium can be determined from the principle of the moments or from the "golden rule" of mechanics.

From the equation of the moments

$$\frac{P}{2} r_2 + Fl = r_1 \frac{P}{2}$$

from which

$$F = \frac{P (r_1 - r_2)}{2l}$$

163. $h = 3.14$ m.

164. $F = \dfrac{P}{3}$.

Note. The force F can be determined by the "golden rule" of mechanics and from the condition of equilibrium of forces.

If the end B is attached a distance l from the centre of gravity of the log, the end C should be fastened a distance $2l$ from it. In this case the point of application of the resultant of the tensions F and $2F$ in the ropes will coincide with the centre of gravity and the rising log will be in a horizontal position.

165. $m_3 = (m_1 - m_2) \sin \alpha$; $N = (m_1 - m_2) g \cos \alpha$.

Solution. The body of mass m_1 is acted upon by its weight $P_1 = m_1 g$, the tensions in the threads $m_2 g$ and $m_3 g$ and the reaction N of the inclined surface.

The equations of equilibrium will have the form: $(m_1 - m_2) g \cos \alpha = N$ and $(m_1 - m_2) g \sin \alpha = m_3 g$ from which

$$m_3 = (m_1 - m_2) \sin \alpha, \quad N = (m_1 - m_2) g \cos \alpha$$

166. $Q = 15$ kgf; $\alpha \approx 56°$.

Solution. If the system is in equilibrium, the resultant of the forces P and M applied at the point A should be equal in magnitude to the force Q, i.e.,

$$Q = \sqrt{P^2 - M^2} \approx 15 \text{ kgf}$$

$$\cos \alpha = \frac{M}{P}, \quad \alpha \approx 56°$$

The problem can also be solved in a different manner. Considering that the sum of the projections of forces in any direction should be equal to zero we may write

$$P \cos \alpha = M, \quad P \sin \alpha = Q$$

from which Q and α can be determined.

167. $Q = \frac{P}{2}$. If the point A is shifted, the equilibrium will be disturbed. The weight P will go down and Q will go up.

Note. This result can easily be obtained from the "golden rule" of mechanics or when the sum of forces acting on the movable pulley is considered.

168. $Q = 3P = 9$ kgf.

Solution. For the system to be in equilibrium the moments of both

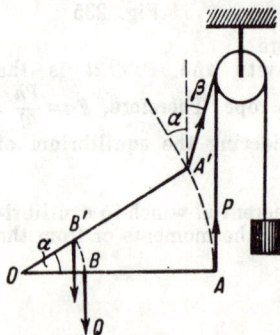

Fig. 236

forces P and Q should be the same, i.e., $M_1 = Pl = M_2 = Q \frac{l}{3}$ and therefore $Q = 3P$.

If the rod is deflected upwards from the position of equilibrium through a small angle α (Fig. 236), the moments of the forces Q and P

will no longer be the same. After the rod is turned, the moment of the force Q will be $M_2' = Q \dfrac{l}{3} \cos \alpha$.

Obviously, $M_2' < M_2$.

It is easy to see that this change in the moment M_2 is due only to the change in the direction of the rod.

When the rod is turned through the angle α the direction of the force P will also be changed by an angle β and so the moment of the force P after the rod turns will be $M_1' = Pl \cos (\alpha + \beta)$.

The value of M_1' is affected by both deflections (of the rod and the thread) in a similar way and the reduction in M_1 with a given deflection of the rod will therefore always be larger than the decrease in M_2. The resultant moment $M_2 - M_1 \neq 0$ will cause a clockwise rotation of the rod. The rod will tend to return to the horizontal position corresponding to a stable position of equilibrium.

By considering the change in the moments M_1 and M_2 when the rod is displaced downwards and the change in the direction of the force P it can be shown that if the rod is displaced downwards, it will tend to return to the position of equilibrium.

169. The centre of gravity lies in the middle of the bisector of the angle on whose vertex is situated the ball of mass $2m$.

170. The centre of gravity will be at a distance

$$x = \frac{Rr^2}{2(R^2 - r^2)}$$

from the point O.

Solution. The weight of the disk before the hole is cut out may be represented as the resultant of two forces: the weight of the cut-out portion and that of the remaining portion, each of which is applied through the centre of gravity of the respective part. This makes it possible to reduce the problem of finding the centre of gravity of the intricate figure left after the hole is cut out to resolving parallel forces and finding one of the components of the forces from the given resultant and the other component force.

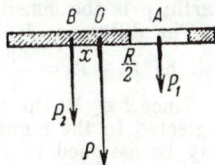

Fig. 237

The weight P of a uniform solid disk is proportional to R^2 and acts through the centre of the disk O. The weight P_1 of the cut-out portion of the disk is proportional to r^2 and acts through the centre of the hole A (Fig. 237).

The weight of the remaining portion P_2 equal to the difference $P - P_1$ acts through a certain point B at a distance x from O.

It follows from the rules for summation of parallel forces that the distances x and $\dfrac{R}{2}$ of the points of application of the forces P_1 and P_2 from the point O should satisfy the ratio

$$\frac{x}{\dfrac{R}{2}} = \frac{P_1}{P_2}$$

Knowing that

$$\frac{P_1}{P_2} = \frac{P_1}{P - P_1} = \frac{r^2}{R^2 - r^2}$$

we obtain

$$\frac{2x}{R} = \frac{r^2}{R^2 - r^2}$$

or

$$x = \frac{Rr^2}{2(R^2 - r^2)}$$

10. Universal Gravitational Forces

171. $\gamma = 6.86 \times 10^{-10} \dfrac{\text{m}^4}{\text{kgf} \cdot \text{s}^4}$.

172. The difference in the lengths of the threads should be equal to $l \approx 3$ m.

Solution. If the difference in the lengths of the threads is assumed to be equal to l and one of two identical loads is right on the terrestrial surface, the following expressions can be obtained for the forces of attraction acting on the loads by the Earth:

$$P_1 = \gamma \frac{Mm}{R^2}, \qquad P_2 = \gamma \frac{Mm}{(R+l)^2}$$

where $M = \dfrac{4\pi}{3} \rho R^3$ is the mass of the Earth, R is the radius of the Earth; ρ is the density of the Earth and m is the mass of the load.

The difference $P_2 - P_1$ will be equal to the weighing error and will be $P_1 - P_2 = \dfrac{4\pi}{3} \gamma \rho m R^3 \dfrac{2Rl + l^2}{R^2 (R+l)^2}$.

Since $l \ll R$, the term l^2 which is small compared to $2Rl$ may be neglected in the numerator of the formula obtained and $R + l \approx R$ may be assumed in the denominator.

We get

$$P_1 - P_2 = \frac{4\pi}{3} \gamma \rho m 2l$$

and therefore

$$l = \frac{3(P_1 - P_2)}{8\pi \gamma \rho m}$$

173. $F \approx 4.1 \times 10^{20}$ kgf.

Solution. Since it is necessary to determine the mean force of attraction, assume that the Earth rotates around the Sun in a circle of radius R. In this motion the centripetal acceleration of the Earth provided by the universal gravitation force will be

$$a = \frac{v^2}{R} = \frac{4\pi^2 R^2}{RT^2}$$

By Newton's second law,

$$F = Ma = \frac{4\pi^2 MR}{T^2}$$

where $M = \frac{4}{3}\pi r^3 \rho$ is the mass of the Earth.

Inserting the value of M we shall obtain the following expression for the force of attraction of the Sun:

$$F = \frac{16\pi^3}{3} \times \frac{r^3 R \rho}{T^2}$$

174. $\omega \approx 1.3 \times 10^{-3}$ s⁻¹.

Solution. The weight of the bodies on the surface of the Earth will become zero at that angular velocity of Earth's rotation ω for which the centripetal acceleration $\omega^2 r$ corresponding to this angular velocity is equal to the acceleration of free fall of the bodies g, i.e., when $\omega^2 r = g$, where r is the radius of the Earth.

Hence,

$$\omega = \sqrt{\frac{g}{r}} \approx 1.3 \times 10^{-3} \frac{1}{s}$$

The value of the required angular velocity can also be obtained directly from the law of universal gravitation and Newton's second law.

The gravitational force exerted on a body by the Earth is $F = \frac{4\pi}{3}\gamma \rho r m$ where ρ is the density of the Earth and m is the mass of the body.

When the weight of a body on the surface of the Earth becomes zero the equation of Newton's second law for a body rotating with the Earth with an angular velocity ω will have the form

$$\frac{4\pi}{3}\gamma \rho r m = m \omega^2 r$$

and therefore

$$\omega = 2\sqrt{\frac{\pi}{3}\gamma \rho} \approx 1.3 \times 10^{-3} \frac{1}{s}$$

(If the Earth rotates with an angular velocity smaller than the calculated value, the reaction of the support numerically equal to the weight of the body should also be introduced into the left-hand side of the equation of Newton's second law in addition to the universal gravitational forces.)

175. $M = \frac{\omega^2 R^3}{\gamma} \approx 2 \times 10^{27}$ tons where ω is the angular velocity of the Earth in its orbit; R is the distance from the Earth to the Sun and γ is the gravitational constant.

Note. To solve the problem write the equation of Newton's second law for the motion of the Earth around the Sun.

176. $g_1 - g_2 = \dfrac{8\pi}{3} \gamma \rho h \approx 7$ cm/s² where ρ is the density of the Earth and γ is the gravitational constant.

Note. The method of solution and the simplifications used are similar to these in Problem 172.

177. Larger in winter and smaller in summer (for the northern hemisphere).

Solution. When it is winter in the northern hemisphere the Earth in its motion around the Sun passes through the points in its orbit

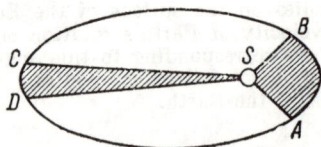

Fig. 238

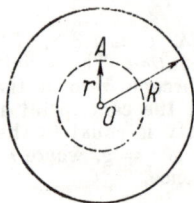

Fig. 239

lying near the perihelion. In summer the Earth passes through the sections of the orbit located in the aphelion. Since, by Kepler's laws the radius-vector connecting the Sun with the Earth should describe equal areas in equal intervals of time, the Earth should move with

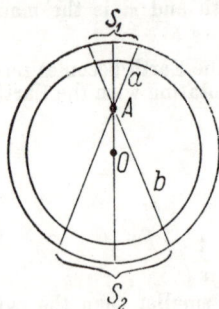

Fig. 240

a higher linear velocity in winter as it traverses the section AB of the orbit than in summer when it traverses the section CD (Fig. 238).

178. $F = \dfrac{4\pi}{3} \gamma \rho m r.$

Solution. When the body is at a distance r from the centre of the Earth which is smaller than the terrestrial radius R, the gravitational force exerted on the body by the Earth may be taken as the sum of two forces: the gravitational force produced by the sphere of radius r and the force created by the spherical layer enclosed between the spheres of radius R and r (Fig. 239).

Let us show that the force created by such a layer is equal to zero for all the points lying inside the sphere of radius r.

The force of attraction exerted by the spherical layer on the body placed at a certain point A (Fig. 240) will be the geometrical sum of the forces of attraction produced by the separate elements of the spherical layer. Let us compare the forces of attraction produced by the small elements S_1 and S_2 cut out from the layer in the form of similar cones with the vertex at the point A as shown in the diagram. Since the thickness of the layer is assumed to be everywhere the same, the volumes and, therefore, the masses of these elements will be proportional to the squares of their distances from the point A, i.e.,

$$\frac{m_1}{m_2} = \frac{a^2}{b^2}$$

The force of attraction created by the element S_1 is

$$f_1 = \gamma \frac{mm_1}{a^2}$$

where m is the mass of the body. The force produced by the element S_2 is

$$f_2 = \gamma \frac{mm_2}{b^2}$$

Since $\frac{m_1}{m_2} = \frac{a^2}{b^2}$ the ratio of these forces will be

$$\frac{f_1}{f_2} = \frac{m_1 b^2}{m_2 a^2} = 1$$

i.e., $f_1 = f_2$.

Reasoning similarly for any other two corresponding elements of the spherical layer we see that all of them compensate in pairs for each other. Thus, the resultant gravitational force produced by the spherical layer as a whole should be identically equal to zero for any point A lying inside a sphere of radius r.

Therefore, the force of attraction acting on the body moving inside the Earth will be equal to the force of attraction created by a sphere of radius equal to the distance of the body from the centre of the Earth. The magnitude of this force can be determined in the same way as the magnitude of the force acting on bodies on the terrestrial surface. If the density of the Earth is denoted by ρ and the mass of the body by m, then the force

$$F = \gamma \frac{m \frac{4}{3} \pi \rho r^3}{r^2} = \frac{4\pi}{3} \gamma \rho m r$$

i.e., when the body inside the Earth moves from the surface to the centre it is acted upon by a force of attraction which diminishes in proportion to its distance from the centre of the Earth.

11. Oscillations

179. $\Delta t = 2.7$ s.

Solution. The pendulum of an accurate clock should make $N = 24 \times 60 \times 60 \frac{1}{T_1}$ swings in twenty-four hours (T_1 is the period of the pendulum).

If after the clock has been moved the period of the pendulum becomes equal to T_2 the clock will lose

$$\Delta t = N \, (T_2 - T_1)$$

in twenty-four hours.

The period of the pendulum before the clock has been moved is

$$T_1 = 2\pi \sqrt{\frac{l}{g_1}}$$

where g_1 is the acceleration of the force of gravity in the basement.

The period of the pendulum after it is moved is

$$T_2 = 2\pi \sqrt{\frac{l}{g_2}}$$

where g_2 is the acceleration of the force of gravity in the upper storey of the University.

The ratio of the periods will be

$$\frac{T_1}{T_2} = \sqrt{\frac{g_2}{g_1}}$$

It follows from the law of universal gravitation that $\dfrac{g_2}{g_1} = \left(\dfrac{R}{R+h} \right)^2$
where R is the radius of the Earth and h is the height of the University building.

Hence,

$$T_2 = T_1 \frac{R+h}{R}$$

and

$$T_2 - T_1 = \frac{h}{R} \, T_1$$

The clock will lose

$$\Delta t = \frac{Nh}{R} \, T_1$$

in twenty-four hours.

180. $\dfrac{l_1}{l_2} = \dfrac{N_2^2}{N_1^2} = \dfrac{4}{9}$ (N_1 and N_2 are the numbers of oscillations of the pendula).

181. The pendulum will not swing.

182. $T = \dfrac{T_0}{\sqrt{\cos \alpha}}$.

Solution. When the cart rolls down, the pendulum simultaneously performs two motions: translational accelerated motion with the cart relative to the Earth and oscillatory motion with respect to the cart. The translational acceleration of the pendulum is caused by the component of the weight $mg \sin \alpha$ (Fig. 241) acting along the inclined surface.

With the conditions specified in the problem this component of the force of gravity cannot change the position of the pendulum with

respect to the cart (see Problem 181) and cannot therefore affect the
change in the period of the pendulum. The oscillations of the pendulum
with respect to the cart will be
brought about by the action
of the component of the weight
$mg \cos \alpha$ perpendicular to the
inclined surface, i.e., the pendulum will oscillate as if it
were acted upon by the force
of gravity $mg \cos \alpha$ and not mg.

The acceleration of free fall
that would correspond to this
value of the force of gravity
must be $g' = g \cos \alpha$.

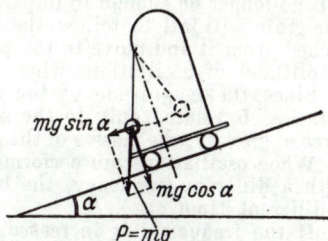

Fig. 241

Correspondingly, the period
of the pendulum on a cart moving with an acceleration should be

$$T = 2\pi \sqrt{\frac{l}{g'}} = 2\pi \sqrt{\frac{l}{g \cos \alpha}} = \frac{T_0}{\sqrt{\cos \alpha}}$$

where T_0 is the period of the pendulum on a stationary cart.

Thus, the period of the pendulum increases when the cart rolls
down the inclined surface.

183. *Solution.* When an oscillating body (e.g. a pendulum,
a weight on a spring, a sand grain on an oscillating membrane) passes
through the position corresponding to its maximum deflection from
the position of equilibrium, it has the maximum acceleration at that
moment. When the body approaches the position of equilibrium the
acceleration gradually decreases and becomes zero as it passes through
the position of equilibrium since the forces returning the body to the
position of equilibrium also become zero at this moment.

Since the time needed for the body to pass from the position of
equilibrium to the position of maximum deflection for the given period
of oscillation remains invariable at all amplitudes and the velocity
with which the body passes through the position of equilibrium increases as the amplitude increases, the accelerations of the body in the
extreme positions and the specified period of oscillation should also
increase as the amplitude increases. (Velocities of different magnitudes
should become zero at the same time.)

Therefore, the sand grains present at those points of the membrane
where the amplitude of oscillation is small will have smaller accelerations than the grains at the points with a greater amplitude of oscillation. At any moment the grains are accelerated by the joint action of
the weight mg and the pressure of the membrane f.

When during oscillations the grain passes with the membrane
through the uppermost position, the acceleration of the grain a has
its maximum value and is then directed downwards.

The equation of Newton's second law at this moment will take
the form: $mg - f = ma$.

When the amplitude is high enough, the acceleration a may become
numerically equal to the acceleration of the force of gravity and at

this amplitude the force f exerted by the grain on the membrane will become zero. As the amplitude continues to grow, the force of gravity will no longer be enough to impart an acceleration $a > g$ to the grain. The grain will fail to follow the motion of the membrane, will be detached from it and move to the points on the membrane with small amplitudes of oscillations where $a < g$.

Since the magnitude of the amplitude at which the grains are detached is related only to the magnitude of the acceleration of the force of gravity, the masses of the grains will not affect their behaviour.

When oscillations are performed with an invariable amplitude but with a different frequency, the body should cover the same path in a different time.

If the frequency is increased, the velocity with which the body passes through the position of equilibrium will grow, the time for the body to move from the position of equilibrium to the extreme position will diminish and therefore the accelerations of the body oscillating with a constant amplitude should increase in the extreme positions as the frequency of oscillation increases.

In the case of high-frequency oscillations the grains will begin to be detached at lower amplitudes than during oscillations of small frequency.

184. *Solution.* The hydrometer immersed in a liquid is acted upon by two forces: the weight mg and the buoyancy (Archimedes force) f, the magnitude of which depends on the volume of the immersed portion of the hydrometer. When the hydrometer is in equilibrium these two forces are equal.

Suppose the hydrometer is immersed in a liquid h cm deeper than the position of equilibrium, then the buoyancy is $Sh\rho$ larger than the weight and tends to return the hydrometer to the position of equilibrium. This force will impart an acceleration $a = \dfrac{\rho h S}{m}$ to the hydrometer. The hydrometer will begin to oscillate with an amplitude h.

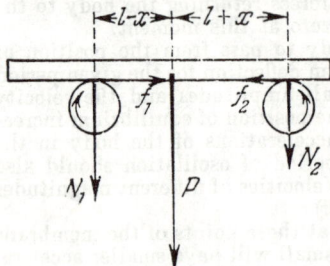

Fig. 242

It has been shown in the solution of Problem 183 that for the given amplitude of oscillation larger frequencies of oscillations correspond to larger accelerations when the oscillating body is deflected to the maximum.

When the mass of the hydrometer is increased its accelerations will diminish as will the frequency of oscillations. The frequency will also diminish when the diameter of the tube is reduced and will increase when the density of the liquid is increased.

185. The board will perform oscillatory motions.

Solution. Each roller will exert on the board forces of friction equal to $f_1 = kN_1$ and $f_2 = kN_2$ where N_1 and N_2 are the pressures of the board on the respective rollers.

The forces f_1 and f_2 are directed as shown in Fig. 242.

If initially the centre of gravity of the board is displaced a certain distance x from the middle line, the pressures N_1 and N_2 and therefore the forces f_1 and f_2 will not be equal to each other. Since the board can not move in a vertical direction,

$$N_1 = \frac{l+x}{2l} P$$

$$N_2 = \frac{l-x}{2l} P$$

i.e., $N_1 > N_2$ and therefore $f_1 > f_2$.

The resultant of the forces f_1 and f_2 will be $f = kP \dfrac{x}{l}$ directed towards the position of equilibrium.

The board will tend to go back to the position of equilibrium. Thus, the forces of friction will cause the board to oscillate.

12. Hydro- and Aerostatics

186. $h \approx 10.34$ m.

Note. The water will rise with the piston until the pressure produced by the weight of the water column becomes equal to the atmospheric pressure.

187. $P_0 = 21.5$ kgf/cm^2.

188. $F = 1.5$ kgf.

189. $P = 1.04$ kgf/cm^2.

190. $d = \dfrac{h_1}{h_2} d_0 = 0.83$ g/cm^3 (d_0 is the density of water).

191. $h = r$.

Solution. The pressure exerted on the separate elements of the side of the vessel (as measured by the height of the liquid column) changes from 0 to h in proportion to the distance of these elements from the free surface of the liquid. For this reason the total force of pressure on the side surface can be calculated from the mean pressure equal to $\dfrac{h}{2}$. The force of pressure on the side surface will be proportional to $2\pi rh \dfrac{h}{2}$, the force of pressure on the bottom will be proportional to $\pi r^2 h$. The required result can be obtained by equating these forces.

192. It will not.

Solution. The pressure in the tube at the level of the tap A will be below atmospheric pressure. Therefore, the atmospheric pressure will not allow the water to flow out when the tap is opened. Air will enter the tube through the tap until the atmospheric pressure is reached inside the tube and until the water sinks to the initial level.

193. 148.5 cm Hg.

194. $h \approx 85$ cm.

Solution. The water in the tube will rise until the pressure of the water column that is being formed equalizes the pressure produced by the piston.

The pressure exerted by the piston is

$$P = \frac{Q}{\pi (R^2 - r^2)} \approx 85 \text{ gf/cm}^2$$

The height of water column can be found from the equality

$$dgh = P$$

195. $P = 4$ cm Hg.

Solution. The heights of the layers of water and mercury h_1 and h_2 can be found from the ratios

$$h_1 + h_2 = h_0$$

and

$$h_1 \gamma_1 = h_2 \gamma_2$$

where γ_1 and γ_2 are the specific gravities of water and mercury.

The pressure in centimetres of mercury column can be found from the ratio

$$P = \frac{h_1 \gamma_1}{\gamma_2} + h_2 = 2h_2$$

196. $h \approx 3.7$ cm.

Solution. When the water is poured in, the mercury level will sink a distance h in the first vessel and rise by the same amount in the second vessel.

The pressure of the mercury column of height $2h$ thus formed will be equalized by the pressure built up by the column of water and the body floating in it, i.e., in the case of equilibrium, the following will hold

$$2\,dgh = \frac{P+p}{S}$$

where d is the density of mercury and P is the weight of water.

Hence, $h = \dfrac{P+p}{2gdS}$.

197. $h_1 = h_2\, \dfrac{d_2}{d_1} = 18$ cm.

198. $h_2 = 0.3$ cm; $h_1 = 4.8$ cm.

Solution. If the displacement of the mercury levels in the right- and left-hand vessels is denoted by h_1 and h_2 ($h_1 + h_2 = x$) and the pressure is measured in centimetres, the condition of equilibrium of the liquid will take the form

$$h_1 + h_2 = \frac{h_0 d_0}{d}$$

where d_0 is the density of water and d is the density of mercury. As liquid is incompressible

$$S_1 h_1 = S_2 h_2$$

where S_1 and S_2 are the cross-sectional areas of the vessels related, from the given conditions, by the ratio $S_2 = 16S_1$. The first equality determines the condition of equilibrium of the liquids in the tube and the second expresses the constancy of the volumes of mercury transferred from the left-hand limb to the right-hand one.

From these equations:

$$h_2 = \frac{h_0 d_0}{17d} \quad \text{and} \quad h_1 = \frac{16 h_0 d_0}{17d}$$

199. $h_2 \approx 0.6$ cm.

Solution. When water is poured in, the level of mercury in the narrow limb will sink to a height h_1 and in the broad one it will rise to a height $h_2 = \frac{h_1}{3}$. The height of the water column will be $l + h_1$ and the height of the mercury column equalizing the weight of the water column will be $h_1 + h_2$. Equilibrium will be established when the following ratio is observed

$$d_0 \, (l + h_1) = d \, (h_1 + h_2)$$

where d is the density of mercury and d_0 is the density of water.

Hence,

$$h_2 = \frac{l d_0}{4d - 3d_0}$$

200. The difference in the heights of mercury levels is $h_1 = 0.5$ cm.

Solution. Since we are given that both limbs have the same height the equal columns of kerosene above the water level may be ignored.

The mercury level in the limb containing water will obviously be below the mercury level in the other limb (since the specific gravity of kerosene γ_2 is smaller than that of water γ_0).

If the difference in the mercury levels in the two limbs is denoted by h, the condition of equilibrium of the liquids in the tube may be written as

$$h_0 \gamma_0 = h_1 \gamma_1 + (h_0 - h_1) \, \gamma_2$$

Hence,

$$h_1 = \frac{\gamma_0 - \gamma_2}{\gamma_1 - \gamma_2} \, h_0$$

201. 50 gf.
202. $V \approx 75$ dm^3.
203. $d \approx 1.5$ g/cm^3.
204. $V_1 = V \dfrac{\gamma_2 - \gamma}{\gamma_2 - \gamma_1}$; $V_2 = V \dfrac{\gamma - \gamma_1}{\gamma_2 - \gamma_1}$.

Solution. Let us denote the fraction of the volume of the ball in the upper liquid by V_1 and the fraction in the lower one by V_2. Then, $V = V_1 + V_2$.

Each of these parts of the ball is acted upon by the force of gravity $V_1 \gamma$ and $V_2 \gamma$ and the buoyance (Archimedes force) $V_1 \gamma_1$ and $V_2 \gamma_2$. Since the ball is in equilibrium on the boundary of the liquids, the sum of all these forces is equal to zero, i.e.,

$$(V_1 + V_2) \gamma = V_1\gamma_1 + V_2\gamma_2$$

Hence,

$$V\gamma = V_1\gamma_1 + (V - V_1) \gamma_2$$

or

$$V_1 = V \frac{\gamma_2 - \gamma}{\gamma_2 - \gamma_1}$$

Similarly,

$$V_2 = V \frac{\gamma - \gamma_1}{\gamma_2 - \gamma_1}$$

These formulas can be verified by the method of passage to the limit.

(1) Suppose that the specific gravity of the ball is equal to that of the upper liquid, i.e., $\gamma = \gamma_1$. Introducing $\gamma = \gamma_1$ into the expression for V_1 we get

$$V_1 = V \frac{\gamma_2 - \gamma_1}{\gamma_2 - \gamma_1} = V$$

i.e., the ball is in the upper liquid.

The same result will be obtained if $\gamma = \gamma_1$ is inserted in the expression for V_2

$$V_2 = V \frac{\gamma_1 - \gamma_1}{\gamma_2 - \gamma_1} = 0$$

(2) Suppose that the specific gravity of the ball is equal to that of the lower liquid, i.e., $\gamma = \gamma_2$. We get: $V_1 = 0$ and $V_2 = V$, i.e., the ball floats in the lower liquid

205. $\gamma = \dfrac{\gamma_1 + \gamma_2}{2} = 7.25$ gf/cm^3.

Note. Since $V_1 = V_2$ (see the solution to Problem 204), then

$$V \frac{\gamma_2 - \gamma}{\gamma_2 - \gamma_1} = V \frac{\gamma - \gamma_1}{\gamma_2 - \gamma_1}$$

or $\gamma_2 - \gamma = \gamma - \gamma_1$, from which $2\gamma = \gamma_2 + \gamma_1$ or $\gamma = \dfrac{\gamma_2 + \gamma_1}{2}$.

206. 0.19 of the volume.

Solution. It follows from the given condition that the weight of the body is $P = 0.25 \, V\gamma$ where V is the volume of the body and γ the specific gravity of mercury. If x is the volume of the body left in the mercury after the water is poured in, the condition of equilibrium of the body may be written in the form $x\gamma + (V - x) \gamma_0 = 0.25 \, V\gamma$ where γ_0 is the specific gravity of water. Therefore,

$$x = \frac{0.25\gamma - \gamma_0}{\gamma - \gamma_0} V = 0.19V$$

207. $d \approx 2.5$ g/cm^3.

208. $d = 1.5$ g/cm^3.
209. The pan with the piece of silver on it will move down.
210. $V = 13$ cm^3.
211. $V \approx 59$ cm^3.
212. $P \approx 10.9$ gf.
Note. If P is the weight of the mercury the following equality should hold

$$\frac{P}{\gamma_1} + \frac{P_1 - P}{\gamma_2} = \frac{P_1 - P_2}{\gamma_0}$$

where γ_0 is the specific gravity of water equal to unity.
213. $d = 1.8$ g/cm^3.
214. $\Delta U_1 = Vgh \, (d - d_0); \quad \Delta U_2 = 0$.
Solution. The body moving in water is simultaneously subjected to the force of gravity and hydrostatic forces. The work done by the hydrostatic forces, as well as the work done by the forces of gravity, does not depend on the path. We may therefore introduce the concept of the potential energy of a body acted upon by hydrostatic forces.

When the body is raised to a height h its potential energy will be increased by $Vdgh$ by the action of the forces of gravity and decreased by $-Vd_0gh$ by the action of the hydrostatic forces. The total change in the potential energy of the body will be

$$\Delta U_1 = Vgh \, (d - d_0)$$

If $d > d_0$, then $\Delta U_1 > 0$ and the energy of the body increases. If $d < d_0$, then $\Delta U_1 < 0$ and the energy of the body diminishes.

When the body moves up to the height h a volume of water V is displaced downwards by the same distance. In this case the potential energy of this volume in the field of the forces of gravity will diminish by Vd_0gh and the energy due to the hydrostatic forces will increase by Vd_0gh. Therefore, the total potential energy of the water will remain constant:

$$\Delta U_2 = 0$$

215. $P = P_1 + \gamma_0 \left(V - \frac{P_1}{\gamma_1} \right) = 440.6$ gf.
216. When the set of weights is made of material having the same density as the body being weighed.
217. $\gamma_1 = 1.94$ gf/l; $V = 1$l; $P_0 = 125$ gf.
Solution. The following ratios can be obtained for the specific gravities of air γ_0, carbon dioxide γ_1 and water γ_2

$$\gamma_0 = \frac{P_1 - P_0}{V}, \quad \gamma_1 = \frac{P_2 - P_0}{V}, \quad \gamma_2 = \frac{P_3 - P_0}{V}$$

Hence, the formulas for the weight and volume of the vessel and for the specific gravity of carbon dioxide are

$$P_0 = \frac{P_1 \gamma_2 - P_3 \gamma_0}{\gamma_2 - \gamma_0}, \quad V = \frac{P_3 - P_1}{\gamma_2 - \gamma_0}, \quad \gamma_1 = \frac{(P_2 - P_1)\,\gamma_2 + (P_3 - P_2)\,\gamma_0}{P_3 - P_1}$$

218. 79 kgf; 0.5 g/l.

219. The ratio between the volumes of water and alcohol should be 8 : 13.

Note. The density of the mixture can be found from the relationship

$$d_0 = \frac{V_1 d_1 + V_2 d_2}{K (V_1 + V_2)} \tag{1}$$

where V_1 and V_2 are the volumes of water and alcohol; d_1 and d_2 are their respective densities and $K = 0.97$ is the coefficient of reduction in the volume of the mixture.

The numerator and denominator in relationship (1) determine the mass and the volume of the mixture, respectively.

Hence the ratio of the volumes of water and alcohol is

$$\frac{V_1}{V_2} = \frac{K d_0 - d_2}{d_1 - K d_0}$$

220. 77.4 parts by volume of air are needed for 100 parts of carbon dioxide.

Solution. The specific gravity of the mixture should be such that the weight of five litres of it is equal to the weight of the ball and the air. The weight of the ball and the air is $\gamma_1 V + P$.

If W is the volume of the air in the mixture, the weight of the mixture will be $\gamma_1 W + \gamma_2 (V - W)$.

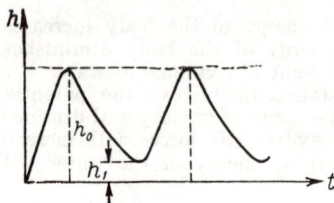

The condition of equilibrium of the ball may be written as

$$\gamma_1 V + P = \gamma_1 W + \gamma_2 (V - W)$$

Hence,

$$W = V + \frac{P}{\gamma_1 - \gamma_2} \approx 2.18 \, l$$

and

$$\frac{W}{V - W} = \frac{2.18}{2.82} \approx 77.4 : 100$$

Fig. 243

221. The water level will perform periodic oscillatory motions (Fig. 243).

Solution. At first the level of water will gradually rise to the height h_0.

After reaching the height h_0 some of the water will be drained through the siphon. As soon as the entire cross section of the top of the siphon pipe is filled with water, the water level will begin to drop since from the given conditions the velocity of the water flowing from pipe B is higher than from pipe A. The level will continue to sink until it reaches the height h_1 coinciding with the edge of pipe B. After this the process will be repeated.

Chapter II

HEAT AND MOLECULAR PHYSICS

13. Thermal Expansion of Bodies

222. The clock will lose $\tau = 8$ s.

Solution. A definite number N of oscillations of the pendulum will correspond to one full revolution of the hour-hand. If the clock is accurate, these N oscillations are performed in twenty-four hours. From the given conditions

$$N = \frac{24 \times 60 \times 60}{2\pi \sqrt{\dfrac{l_0}{g}}}$$

When the temperature changes by t degrees the length of the pendulum will be $l = l_0 (1 + \alpha t)$ and the period of oscillations of the pendulum will change by

$$T - T_0 = 2\pi \left(\sqrt{\frac{l}{g}} - \sqrt{\frac{l_0}{g}} \right) =$$

$$= \frac{2\pi}{g} \frac{l - l_0}{\sqrt{\dfrac{l}{g}} + \sqrt{\dfrac{l_0}{g}}} \approx \frac{\pi}{g} \frac{l - l_0}{\sqrt{\dfrac{l_0}{g}}} = \frac{\pi}{g} \frac{\alpha l_0 t}{\sqrt{\dfrac{l_0}{g}}}$$

The clock will gain or lose

$$\tau = N (T - T_0) = \frac{24 \times 60 \times 60}{2\pi \sqrt{\dfrac{l_0}{g}}} \frac{\pi}{g} \frac{\alpha l_0 t}{\sqrt{\dfrac{l_0}{g}}} = 12 \times 60 \times 60 \alpha t \text{ s}$$

in twenty-four hours.

223. $F = SE\alpha t = 3,465$ kgf.

Solution. If the rod were free, heating it by $t°$ would expand it by a length

$$l - l_0 = \alpha l_0 t$$

Since, from the given conditions the distance between the steel plates remains constant, the value $l - l_0$ will determine the compressive deformation of the rod caused by the heating.

According to Hooke's law, the force of pressure of the rod will be

$$F = \frac{SE}{l_0} (l - l_0) = SE\alpha t$$

224. $x = l_0 \alpha t \approx 0.02$ mm.

Solution. At 20°C the length of the 180 divisions of the vernier caliper is 180 mm. At 10°C the length of the 180 divisions will be

$$l = l_{20} (1 + \alpha t)$$

(t is the temperature difference), i.e., the length of the rod measured at 10°C will be $x = l_{20}\alpha t$ smaller than its actual length.

225. The increase in the diameter caused by heating of the workpiece is equal to $\alpha l_0 (t - t_0) = 38.5$ microns, i.e., it will exceed the permissible errors. Corrections should be introduced.

226. Iron cylinder 28.3 cm and copper cylinder 18.3 cm.

Solution. At any temperature the lengths of the iron and copper cylinders will be

$$l_1 = l_{01} (1 + \alpha_1 t), \quad l_2 = l_{02} (1 + \alpha_2 t) \qquad (1)$$

From the given conditions

$$l_1 - l_2 = 10 \text{ and } l_{01} - l_{02} = 10 \qquad (2)$$

It follows from (1) and (2) that

$$\frac{l_{02}}{l_{01}} = \frac{\alpha_1}{\alpha_2} \qquad (3)$$

The initial lengths of the cylinders should be inversely proportional to the coefficients of linear expansion.

It follows from (3) and (2) that

$$l_{01} = \frac{10\alpha_2}{\alpha_2 - \alpha_1}, \quad l_{02} = \frac{10\alpha_1}{\alpha_2 - \alpha_1}$$

227. $l_0 = l_1 \dfrac{1 + \alpha t}{1 + \beta t} = 757.3$ mm Hg.

Solution. Since, from the given conditions, the scale has been checked at 0°C, then $l_1 = 760$ graduations on the scale will correspond to the length of the mercury column

$$l_2 = l_1 (1 + \alpha t)$$

The column of mercury of height l_2 will set up a pressure $P = \gamma l_2$, where γ is the specific gravity of mercury at a temperature $t = 18$°C. At 0°C the same pressure will be built up by the mercury column of height l_0, such that $P = \gamma_0 l_0$.

Since $\gamma = \dfrac{\gamma_0}{1 + \beta t}$ the actual pressure expressed in millimetres of the mercury column will at 0°C be equal to

$$l_0 = \frac{\gamma}{\gamma_0} l_2 = l_1 \frac{1 + \alpha t}{1 + \beta t}$$

228. $V - V_0 = 1.14$ cm³.

Note. The change in the total volume of a body being heated does not depend on the presence of spaces inside the body and can be calculated from the usual formula for volume expansion

$$V = V_0 (1 + \beta t)$$

where β is the coefficient of volume expansion.

The volumes occupied by the vessel and the sphere will be the same at all temperatures. The change in volume on heating will be

$$V - V_0 = \beta V_0 t$$

229. $V_1 = \dfrac{\beta_1}{\beta_2} V_0 = \dfrac{3}{8} V_0.$

Note. See the solution to Problem 226.

230. $P = \gamma V_0 (\beta_2 - \beta_1) \approx 0.1$ gf.

Solution. The volume of the vessel at 0°C is

$$V_0 = \frac{700}{13.6} = 51.5 \text{ cm}^3$$

The volume of the vessel after heating by 1° is $V_1 = V_0 (1 + \beta_1)$. The volume of the mercury after heating is $V_2 = V_0 (1 + \beta_2)$. The volume and the weight of the mercury that flows out during heating will be

$$V_2 - V_1 = V_0 (\beta_2 - \beta_1)$$

and

$$P = \gamma V_0 (\beta_2 - \beta_1)$$

231. *Solution.* To answer these questions, consider the aerostatic pressure produced by the columns of air at points A and B in the mine (Fig. 244).

The total pressure at these points has three components: (a) the pressure of the air column lying above the level DD_1 and the same for the points A and B; (b) the pressure of columns CA and C_1B. These pressures will also be the same since the temperatures and therefore the densities of air are identical in these columns; (c) the pressures built up by columns CD and C_1D_1.

Assume that the temperature of the air in the mine which is given as constant is below the temperature outside in summer and above that temperature in winter.

If this is the case, the temperature of the air in summer in column CD will be higher

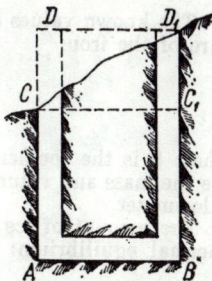
Fig. 244

and its density lower than in column C_1D_1. For this reason the pressure built up by column C_1D_1 in summer will be higher than the pressure created by column CD. A certain pressure difference will exist between points A and B which will disturb the equilibrium of the air in the mine and will cause it to flow from point B to point A. In summer the air will enter the mouth of the mine lying at a higher level and flow out from the mouth at a lower level.

In winter the density of air in column CD and the pressure built up by this column will be larger than the density of air and the pressure created by column C_1D_1 and the air will therefore move in the reverse direction from point A to point B.

232. *Solution.* In winter the air will enter the bottom gallery and flow out of the upper one. In summer the air will move in the reverse direction.

The direction of the air motion will be determined by the ratio of the pressures set up in the bottom gallery by the air columns AD and BC (Fig. 245).

In winter the density of air in column AD and the pressure created by it will be higher than the density of air and the pressure in column CB. For this reason the air will move from point A to point B.

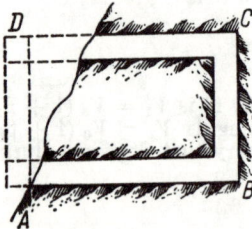

Fig. 245

14. Quantity of Heat. Heat Exchange

233. 0°C.

234. $M = \dfrac{mC}{q}\dfrac{(Vd_0 - m)}{\beta m} \approx 64$ g.

Solution. At the moment the piece of iron is placed in the calorimeter the density of the iron $d = \dfrac{m}{V}$ is related to its density at 0°C by the ratio $d = \dfrac{d_0}{1 + \beta t}$.

The known values d and d_0 can be used to determine the temperature of the iron:

$$t = \frac{d_0 - d}{\beta d} = \frac{Vd_0 - m}{\beta m}$$

where β is the coefficient of volume expansion of iron and m and V are the mass and volume of the iron at the moment it is placed in the calorimeter.

The amount of ice that melts can be found from the equation of thermal equilibrium:

$$M = \frac{mCt}{q}$$

where q is the latent heat of fusion of ice.

235. $q = \dfrac{t_2}{t_1} 100 = 533$ cal.

236. ~87 per cent of the original mass of water.

Solution. The heat necessary for evaporation can be obtained only from the latent heat of fusion liberated when the water freezes. Upon freezing of m_1 grams of water, $m_1 q_1$ calories of heat will be liberated (q_1 is the latent heat of fusion of ice) which will form the amount of vapour $m_2 = \dfrac{m_1 q_1}{q_2}$ where q_2 is the heat of evaporation at 0°C. If $m =$

$= m_1 + m_2$ is the mass of the water before pumping, the mass of the ice produced will be

$$m_1 = \frac{q_2}{q_1 + q_2}\, m$$

or ~ 87 per cent of the original mass of water.

15. The Gas Laws

237. $\dfrac{V}{T} = \dfrac{V_0}{T_0}$; see Fig. 246.

238. $\dfrac{P}{T} = \dfrac{P_0}{T_0}$; see Fig. 247.

239. See Fig. 248.

Solution. At any temperature a given mass of gas will create a pressure which will increase, as the volume of the vessel containing the gas decreases. When the gas is heated in the small vessel the pres-

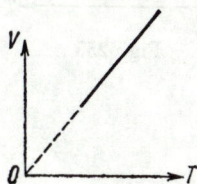

Fig. 246

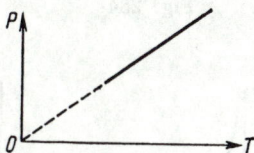

Fig. 247

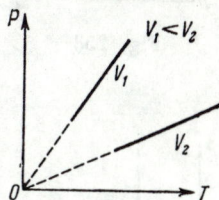

Fig. 248

sure will increase faster than during heating in the large vessel. The constant-volume line corresponding to the small volume will always form a larger angle with the X-axis on the plot (P, T) than the con-

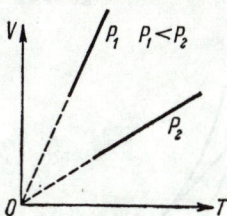

Fig. 249

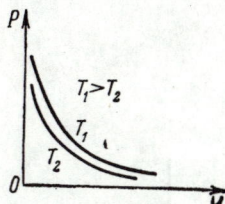

Fig. 250

stant-volume line that corresponds to the larger volume (Fig. 248).

240. See Fig. 249.

Solution. At a given temperature and a high pressure the gas will occupy a smaller volume than at a small pressure although at the

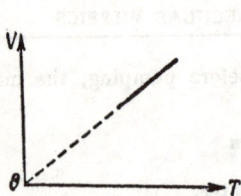
Fig. 251

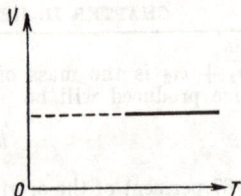
Fig. 252

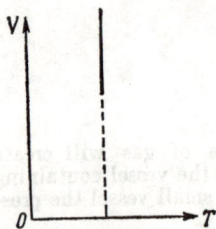
Fig. 253

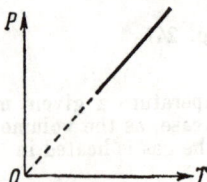
Fig. 254

Fig. 255

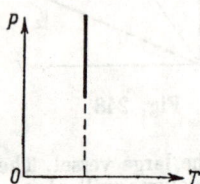
Fig. 256

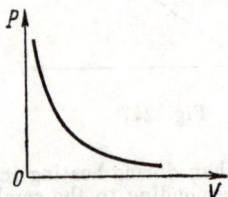
Fig. 257

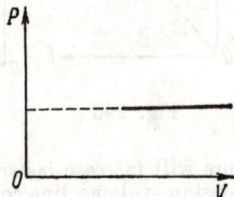
Fig. 258

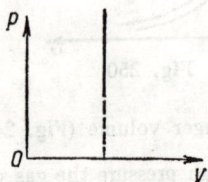
Fig. 259

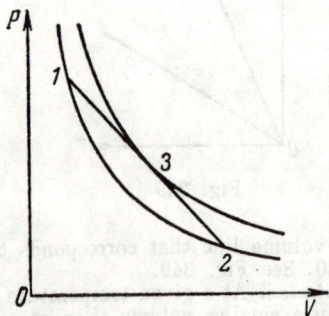
Fig. 260

same temperature. The higher the pressure at which the constant-pressure process occurs, the smaller the angle formed by the constant-pressure line with the X-axis on the plot (V, T) (Fig. 249).

241. See Fig. 250.

The constant-temperature lines corresponding to the lower temperatures arrange themselves on the PV plot closer to the origin of coordinates.

242. See Figs 251, 252, 253.

243. See Figs 254, 255, 256.

244. See Figs 257, 258, 259.

245. To determine the temperature of the gas at the initial point *1*, at the final point *2* and at a certain point *3*, draw constant-temperature lines (Fig. 260) through these points and determine the ratio of the temperatures at these points from the relative position of the constant-temperature lines. The gas is heated in the section *1-3* and cooled in the section *1-2*.

246. The gas expands during heating.

Solution. In order to determine the nature of change in the gas volume during heating, draw constant-volume lines on the drawing

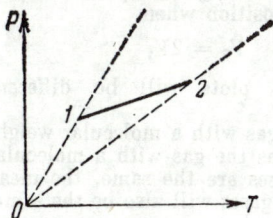

Fig. 261

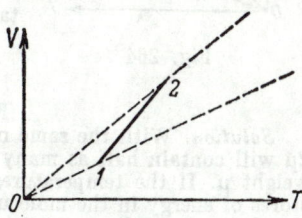

Fig. 262

passing through the initial and final points *1* and *2* (Fig. 261). Point *2* lies on the constant-volume line which is more sloping with respect to the X-axis than the constant-volume line passing through point *1* and therefore (see the solution to Problem 239) the gas occupies a larger volume at point *2* than at point *1*. Heating was conducted for an increasing volume of gas.

247. The pressure constantly diminishes.

Solution. In order to solve the problem, draw lines of constant pressure on which points *1* and *2* lie (Fig. 262). Point *1* lies on the constant-pressure line which forms a smaller angle with the X-axis

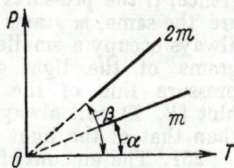

Fig. 263

than the constant-pressure line passing through point *2* and therefore (see the solution to Problem 240) the gas is present at point *1* at a larger pressure than at point *2*. Heating was conducted with a diminishing pressure of the gas.

248. See Fig. 263.

Solution. At any given temperature, $2m$ grams of gas will produce twice as great a pressure than m grams enclosed within the same volume.

The constant-volume line for $2m$ grams of gas will be at a larger angle with respect to the X-axis than the constant-volume line for m grams, and

$$\tan \beta = 2 \tan \alpha$$

249. 2/3 of the cylinder volume.

Solution. If P_1, V_1 and T_1 are the pressure, volume and temperature of m grams of gas and P_2, V_2 and T_2 are the pressure, volume and temperature of $2m$ grams of gas the following ratio will always hold:

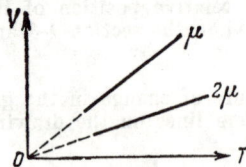

Fig. 264

$$\frac{P_2 V_2}{T_2} = 2 \frac{P_1 V_1}{T_1}$$

(see the solution to Problem 248).

From the given conditions, when the piston is in equilibrium, $T_1 = T_2$ and $P_1 = P_2$. Therefore, the piston should take such a position when

$$V_2 = 2V_1$$

250. The plots will be different (Fig. 264).

Solution. With the same masses, the gas with a molecular weight 2μ will contain half as many molecules as the gas with a molecular weight μ. If the temperatures of the gases are the same, the mean stores of energy in the molecules of both gases will also be the same. For the gases in these conditions to create the same pressure the number of impacts of the molecules per each cm^2 of the surface of the vessels should be the same too. This is only possible when the heavier gas occupies a smaller volume. Hence, if the pressures and temperatures are the same, m grams of the heavy gas always occupy a smaller volume than m grams of the light gas. The constant-pressure line of the heavy gas on the plot (V, T) will always be more sloping than that of the light gas.

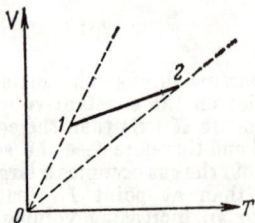

Fig. 265

251. The amount of gas has decreased.

Solution. In order to solve the problem, draw lines of constant pressure corresponding to the constant masses of the gas through points *1* and *2* (Fig. 265). The constant-pressure line on which point *1* lies is steeper than the line on which point *2* lies. Therefore (see the solution to Problem 248) the mass of the gas in state *1* is larger than in state *2*.

252. See Figs 266 and 267.

253. Two answers are possible: 1/610 or 1/360.

Solution. The coefficient of gas expansion α shows that the volume of gas is increased by 1° during heating with respect to the volume it occupied at 0°C on the temperature scale.

But 0°C on Delil's scale corresponds to the boiling point of water. For this reason, utilizing the usual definition of the coefficient of gas expansion all the changes in volume should be referred to the volume occupied by the gas at the boiling point of water.

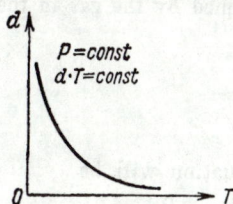

Fig. 266

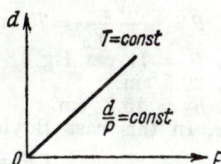

Fig. 267

Since 1 deg by Delil = $\frac{2}{3}$ by centigrade scale and $\alpha V_0 = \frac{1}{273} V_0 = \frac{1}{373} V_{100} = \alpha_1 V_{100}$, the coefficient of gas expansion on Delil's cale will be

$$\alpha_D = \frac{2}{3} \alpha_1 \approx \frac{1}{560}$$

and the equation of Gay-Lussac's law may be written as

$$V = V_0' (1 + \alpha_D t) \tag{1}$$

where V_0' is the volume occupied by the gas at 0° on Delil's scale and t is the temperature in Delil's degrees.

If the change in the volume of gas is referred, as before, to the volume occupied by the gas at the melting point of ice (i.e., as it is commonly done when measuring temperature on the centigrade scale) it will be necessary to:

(a) determine the coefficient of gas expansion as the number showing the increase in the volume of the gas when it is heated by 1° on Delil's scale with respect to the volume occupied by the gas at the temperature −150° Delil;

(b) assume the coefficient α_D' as equal to

$$\alpha_D' = \frac{2}{3} \alpha = \frac{2}{3} \frac{1}{273} \approx \frac{1}{410}$$

In this case the equation of Gay-Lussac's law will take the form

$$V = V_{-150} [1 + \alpha_D' (t + 150)] \tag{2}$$

It is easy to see that equations (1) and (2) always produce the same results when the volume of gas is calculated.

254. 21°C.

Solution. It follows directly from Gay-Lussac's law that

$$T_2 = \frac{V_2}{V_1} T_1 = \frac{110}{104} \times 278 \approx 295° \text{ abs}$$

where V_1 and V_2 are the volumes occupied by the gas in the device before and after heating.

255. $P = \dfrac{hV_2}{V_1 - V_2} = 75$ cm Hg.

256. $P = 71$ cm Hg.

257. 20.5 cm.

258. $h_2 = 15.8$ cm.

Note. In this case Boyle's law equation will be

$$l_1 P = h_2 (P + h_2 - l)$$

where l is the total length of the part of the tube projecting from the mercury.

259. 0.96 of the initial volume.

Note. After submergence the air in the glass will be under a pressure of $P + \dfrac{Q}{S}$.

260. $y = 600$ mm Hg; $x = 15$ cm.

Solution. The flow of mercury through the siphon will continue as long as the pressure built up by the mercury at point C inside the tube (Fig. 268) exceeds the atmospheric pressure.

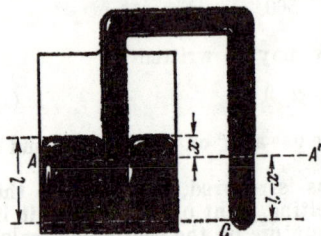

Fig. 268

Assume that the mercury level in the vessel has dropped by x cm and the pressure of the air in the vessel becomes y cm Hg.

The same pressure y will obviously be established also in the tube at the level AA' corresponding to the free surface of the mercury in the vessel.

The pressure P_1 produced by the mercury at point C at the exit from the tube will be formed from the pressure y and the pressure of the mercury column $A'C = l - x$, i.e., it will be equal to $P_1 = = y + l - x$ where l is the initial height of the mercury level in the vessel.

As the mercury level drops in the vessel, the pressure y and also P_1 will diminish, and at the moment the flow of mercury ceases P_1 will be equal to P_0, where P_0 is the atmospheric pressure. Hence, the air pressure in the vessel at this moment will be

$$y = P_0 - (l - x) \text{ cm Hg}$$

We are given that a pressure of P_0 and a volume of air proportional to l were recorded in the vessel at the initial moment. The volume of air at the moment the flow of mercury ceases will be proportional to $l + x$.

It follows from Boyle's law that

$$P_0 l = y\,(l + x)$$

or

$$P_0 l = [P_0 - (l - x)]\,(l + x)$$

Introducing the values given and solving the equation for x we can find the drop in the mercury level and the pressure in the vessel at the moment the flow of mercury ceases.

261. $x \approx 4.5$ cm.

Solution. Denoting the displacement of the mercury column by x, the length of the tube occupied by the gas in each of its halves when the tube is in a horizontal position by l_0 and the pressures of the gas in the upper and lower halves of the tube after it is placed vertically by P_1 and P_2, we can write the equations of the change in the state of gases in each half as follows:

$$l_0 P_0 = (l_0 + x)\,P_1$$
$$l_0 P_0 = (l_0 - x)\,P_2$$
$$P_2 = P_1 + h_0$$

The solution of these equations will give us the required result.

262. $x = l\dfrac{T - T_0}{T + T_0} = 2$ cm; $P = \dfrac{l}{l - x}\,P_0 = 1.05$ atm.

Solution. Knowing that the masses of the gas are equal and taking into account that after the piston is displaced by an amount x the pressures will be the same in both parts of the cylinder, we may apply Gay-Lussac's law and obtain the ratio

$$\frac{l - x}{T_0} = \frac{l + x}{T}$$

from which

$$x = l\,\frac{T - T_0}{T + T_0}$$

263. Up to 663°C.

Note. When solving the problem bear in mind that the pressure in the tube will be $(75 - 5)$ cm Hg before heating and $(75 + 5)$ cm Hg after heating.

264. $R \approx 1.9$ cal/deg $= 8.3 \times 10^7$ erg/deg.

Solution. One gram-molecule of any gas at $T_0 = 273°$ abs and a pressure of $P_0 = 1$ atm occupies a volume of $V_0 = 22.4$ litres. Therefore,

$$R = \frac{P_0 V_0}{T_0} = \frac{22.4}{273}\ l \cdot \text{atm/deg} = 0.82\ l \cdot \text{atm/deg}$$

The answer can be obtained by simply changing the dimensions for the different systems of units.

265. Less work is required to immerse the vessel with an opening.

Solution. During the whole time the vessels are submerged the one without an opening will be acted upon by a constant force $F_1 = dV$, where d is the specific gravity of the water and V is the volume of the vessel. As the other vessel is immersed the water will flow into it and compress the air it contains. Accordingly, the volume of the water displaced by this vessel and the buoyancy F_2 will diminish. Therefore, the work done against this force will at any moment be less than the work against the force F_1.

266. $Q = 1,904$ cal.

Solution. The final temperature of the gas is determined from Gay-Lussac's law

$$\frac{V_0}{T_0} = \frac{V}{T}$$

and the quantity of heat from the equation

$$Q = C_P \mu \, (T - T_0)$$

where μ is the molecular weight of oxygen.

267. $A = P \, (V - V_0) = R.$

Solution. The pressure acting on the gas is $P = \dfrac{G}{S}$. If heating the gas by $1°$ raises the piston to a height h the work done by the gas will be

$$A = Gh = PSh$$

But Sh is equal to the increment in the gas volume $(V - V_0)$ caused by the rising piston. Hence,

$$A = P \, (V - V_0)$$

The equation of state of an ideal gas gives us the following equations:

$$PV_0 = RT_0 \text{ and } PV = R \, (T_0 + 1)$$

whence $A = PV - PV_0 = R$.

268. $Q = 71$ cal.

Solution. The heat taken from the heater will be expended on increasing the temperature of the gas and doing work to raise the piston.

The heating will increase the volume of the gas to

$$V = \frac{T}{T_0} V_0 = 11.65 l$$

The work done by the gas in this expansion (see the previous problem) will be

$$A = P \, (V - V_0) = 20 \times 0.45 \text{ litre-atm} = 9 \text{ kgf-m} \approx 21 \text{ cal}$$

The quantity of heat used to heat the gas will be

$$Q = C_V (T - T_0) + A = 71 \text{ cal}$$

269. The heat supplied to the gas is expended on doing external work when the gas expands.

270. During expansion at constant pressure.

Note. For all volumes from V_0 to V_1 the gas pressure in the constant-pressure process will be larger than in the constant-temperature one (Fig. 269). Accordingly, the work done by the gas will also be larger in the constant-temperature process (see the solution to Problem 267).

271. The temperature of the gas will decrease because some of the internal energy of the gas is converted into the mechanical work during expansion.

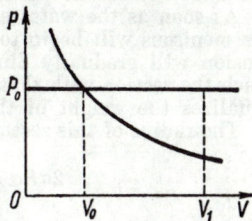

Fig. 269

16. Surface Tension

272. The surface tensions of the alcohols will be related to α of water as 7.2 : 13 and 13.2 : 13; $r \approx 0.2$ mm.

273. *Solution.* From the moment the filling begins to the moment of time A (Fig. 270) the water level will uniformly rise in the capillary tube (curve I) and remain at the same level in the broad tube (curve II).

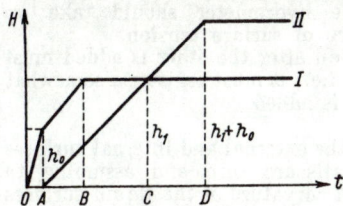

Fig. 270

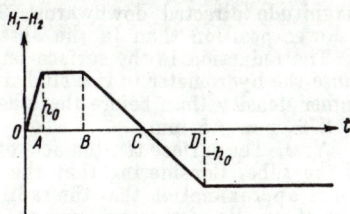

Fig. 271

The difference in the levels will constantly increase (Fig. 271). At the moment of time A the difference in the levels will reach

$$h_0 = \frac{2\alpha}{gr}$$

From this moment up to the moment of time B the levels in the capillary and broad tube will rise with the same velocities while the difference in the levels will remain constant and equal to h_0.

At the moment of time B the water level in the capillary tube will reach the end of the capillary and will stop at a height h_1 (Fig. 270).

From the moment B to the moment D the water level will continuously rise in the broad tube. The water level in the capillary will remain constant but the meniscus will change its shape from concave of radius r (at the moment B) to a flat one (at the moment C) and then to a convex one of radius r (at the moment D). The difference in the levels in the section BC will decrease to zero and in the section CD it will change its sign and will increase to h_0.

At the moment D the water will begin to flow out of the capillary tube and from this moment onwards all the levels will be constant.

The maximum height to which the water rises in the broad tube is $h_1 + h_0$. The maximum difference in the levels is h_0.

274. The perpetuum mobile will not operate and the water will not flow out of the funnel.

As soon as the water enters the funnel the radius of curvature of the meniscus will begin to increase and, correspondingly, the surface tension will gradually diminish. The water in the funnel will only reach the section with that radius R where the surface tension exactly equalizes the weight of the water column h.

The radius of this section can be determined from the ratio

$$2\pi R\alpha = \pi r^2 dgh \text{ or } R = \frac{dg\, hr^2}{2\alpha}$$

275. The action of surface tension should in principle have an effect on the position of the hydrometer.

In the case of the wetting agent the surface tension produces a resultant which is directed upwards and is applied to the particles of the liquid arranged near the hydrometer. By Newton's third law, the tube of the hydrometer should be acted upon by a force of the same magnitude directed downwards. The hydrometer should take up a lower position than in the absence of surface tension.

The reduction in the surface tension after the ether is added must cause the hydrometer to rise slightly, i.e., it must register a somewhat higher density than before the ether is added.

276. $r \approx 1.5$ mm.

Note. The surface tension acts on the external and internal surfaces of the tube. Considering that the walls are thin and assuming to a first approximation that the radii of curvature of the liquid surfaces near the walls of the capillary are the same in size both outside and inside the tube the forces acting on the internal and external surfaces of the tube may also be considered the same. The force acting on the internal surface is equal to the weight of the water raised into the capillary by the surface tension, while the change in the weight of the capillary is equal to twice the weight of this water.

Hence,

$$r = \frac{P}{4\pi\alpha}$$

277. *Solution.* Mercury effectively wets pure lead. Tightly fitted sheets of lead form fine capillary ducts and slits through which mercury is raised by the action of surface tension just like water in glass capillary tubes.

278. $F = 2\alpha l = 480$ dyn ≈ 0.5 gf; $A = FS = 960$ erg.

Solution. When the surface of the film is expanded the work done by the external mechanical forces will be converted into the potential energy of the liquid film associated with its surface tension. This energy is known as the surface energy. When the surface of the film is reduced the surface energy is decreased and is converted into the work of surface tension and then into other kinds of energy: the potential energy of the forces holding the movable side of the frame and the thermal energy.

279. The frame will be acted upon during the first moments by a force $F = (\alpha_1 - \alpha_2) l$ (Fig. 272) where α_1 and α_2 are the surface tensions of the water and the soap film. The frame will begin to move in the direction of the force F.

280. *Solution.* The water will not pour out if: (a) the sieve is made of a water repellent material; (b) if the height of the water layer in the sieve does not exceed

$$h_0 = \frac{2\alpha}{dgr} \approx 3 \text{ cm}$$

If the height of the sieve is less than h_0 the water can be drained; when the height is larger than h_0, then, if the sieve is inclined, a layer of water deeper than h_0 forms near its lower edge and the water begins to seep through the meshes of the sieve.

Fig. 272

281. It cannot. While calculating the loss in weight, a correction should be introduced for the action of surface tension.

Solution. A force $F = 2\pi r\alpha$ is exerted by the walls of the capillary on the liquid. According to Newton's third law, a force of the same magnitude but in the opposite direction will be exerted by the liquid on the capillary. The loss of weight in the case of the wetting agent will be less than the loss calculated by Archimedes law and larger in the case of a non-wetting agent.

282. *Solution.* The height to which the liquid rises in the capillary is $h_0 = \frac{2\alpha}{dgr}$. The work done by surface tension in this case is $A = Fh_0 = \frac{4\pi\alpha^2}{dg}$. The potential energy of the liquid raised in the capillary is

$$U = mg\,\frac{h_0}{2} = dg\pi r^2 h_0\,\frac{h_0}{2} = \frac{2\pi\alpha^2}{dg}$$

or

$$U = \frac{A}{2}$$

Only half of the work done by surface tension is converted into the potential energy of the liquid. The other half is expended on the work against the forces of friction and is converted into heat. If there were no viscosity and friction against the walls, the liquid level would perform harmonic oscillations in the capillary with the height h_0 as the position of equilibrium.

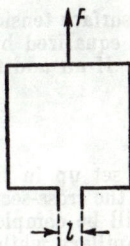

283. Fat is soaked into the paper faster because the capillary ducts in unsized paper are much smaller than in the fabric.

284. $\alpha = \dfrac{\Delta Pr}{2} \approx 70$ dyn/cm.

Solution. The additional pressure produced in the bubbles of air inside the liquid by surface tension can be found from the following simple reasoning.

When the end of the capillary touches the surface of the liquid the latter will rise in the capillary to a height $h = \dfrac{2\alpha}{dgr}$ under the action of a surface tension $F = 2\pi r\alpha$ directed upwards. In this case the force F is equalized by the weight of the liquid column.

If an additional pressure

$$\Delta P = \frac{F}{S} = \frac{2\pi r\alpha}{\pi r^2} = \frac{2\alpha}{r}$$

is set up in the capillary above the surface of the liquid ($S = \pi r^2$ is the cross-sectional area of the capillary) the action of surface tension will be completely balanced by the excess pressure of the air in the capillary while the weight of the liquid column in the capillary will remain unequalized. Therefore, the level of the liquid in the capillary should go down to the initial height and a bubble of air—a hemisphere of radius R equal to the radius of the capillary r—will form at the end of the tube. The required pressure in the bubble will be

$$\Delta P = \frac{2\alpha}{R} \qquad (1)$$

where R is the radius of the bubble.

It can be shown that this expression always determines the excess pressure built up by the surface tension in closed bubbles inside a liquid.

Formula (1) shows that the pressure in the bubble diminishes as the radius of the bubble increases. The formation of a bubble at the end of the capillary proves that the minimum radius of the bubble is equal to the radius of the capillary.

Therefore, when α is calculated from the data in the problem the radius of the capillary should be inserted, instead of R, in the calculation formula

$$\alpha = \frac{\Delta PR}{2}$$

285. $\Delta P = \dfrac{2\alpha}{g} \dfrac{r_1 - r_2}{r_1 r_2} \approx 3.6$ mm Hg.

The pump should be connected to the narrow capillary.

Solution. Let us denote the heights of the mercury levels before the air is pumped out by h_1 and h_2.

The mercury in the tube will be in equilibrium if the pressures produced by the columns of mercury on the two sides are equal in the cross section AB (Fig. 273). The total pressure in the cross section AB is composed on each side of the pressure gh (mm Hg) created by the weight of the mercury column and the pressure produced by surface tension and equal to

$$\frac{F}{S} = \frac{2\pi r \alpha}{\pi r^2} = \frac{2\alpha}{r}$$

For this reason the condition of equilibrium may be written as:

$$gh_1 + \frac{2\alpha}{r_1} = gh_2 + \frac{2\alpha}{r_2}$$

or

$$h_1 - h_2 = \frac{2\alpha}{g}\left(\frac{1}{r_2} - \frac{1}{r_1}\right) = \frac{2\alpha}{g}\left(\frac{r_1 - r_2}{r_1 r_2}\right)$$

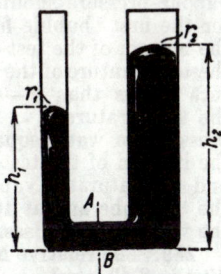

Fig. 273

The pressure difference of the air should compensate for this difference in the heights of the mercury columns, i.e ., it should be equal (in mm Hg) to

$$\Delta P = h_1 - h_2 = \frac{2\alpha}{g}\frac{r_1 - r_2}{r_1 r_2}$$

286. $h = \dfrac{4\alpha}{gr} \approx 3$ cm.

Solution. The column of water in the tube placed vertically will be held by two menisci, an upper and a lower one (Fig. 274), each acting on the water with a force $F = 2\pi r \alpha$. Therefore, the height of the column of water left in the tube can be determined from the equation

$$\pi r^2 gh = 2F = 4\pi r \alpha$$

287. $l = \dfrac{P_0 rh}{2\alpha - dg\,rh} + h \approx 552$ cm.

Solution. After rising to a height h in the tube the water will compress the air contained in it and produce an excess pressure ΔP which can be calculated by Boyle's law and will be equal to

Fig. 274

$$\Delta P = P - P_0 = \frac{P_0 h}{l - h}$$

The pressure $P_1 = \dfrac{2\alpha}{r}$ produced by surface tension should in our case balance the sum of the pressures created by the weight of the water column and by the air compressed in the capillary, i.e., the following equality should hold

$$\frac{2\alpha}{r} = \frac{P_0 h}{l - h} + dgh \quad (d \text{ is the density of water})$$

from which the formula for l can be calculated.

17. Humidity of Air

288. If the atmospheric pressure is H cm of water, the saturated vapour pressure should be not less than $H-h$ cm of water column for the first bubble filled with saturated water vapours to form near the bottom of the test-tube. Therefore, as soon as heating begins, when the temperature of the water is still low and the saturated vapour pressure is less than $H-h$, the water will fill the entire test-tube. When the temperature $T < 100°C$ which corresponds to a saturated vapour pressure for water equal to $H-h$, the water level will draw away from the bottom of the test-tube. Upon further heating, as the temperature and the saturated vapour pressure grow, the water level will sink in the test-tube and at 100°C will take the same position as the level of the water in the glass.

289. The relative humidity is 48.6 per cent and the absolute humidity is 8.42 g/m^3.

290. When the temperature is increased.

291. There will be no dew.

Note. It follows from the fact that both the masses of the air being mixed and their heat capacities are equal, after mixing the temperature of the mixture will be 15°C. The proportionality of the saturated vapour pressure to the temperature shows that the saturated vapour pressure at 15°C will be equal to 13 mm Hg. The absolute humidities at 10, 15 and 20°C will be 9, 13 and 17 g/m^3, respectively. The surplus amount of water vapour in the air at 15°C will be equal to $9 + 17 - 2 \times 13 = 0$.

292. 2.87 per cent.

293. 8.64 g.

Chapter III

ELECTRICITY

18. Coulomb's Law

294. $F = 9.2 \times 10^8 \dfrac{e_1 e_2}{r^2}$.

295. $F = 2.3 \times 10^{-3}$ dyn.

296. $v = \sqrt{\dfrac{Ze^2}{mr}}$. For hydrogen $v = 1.59 \times 10^8$ cm/s.

Note. The electrostatic interaction of the electron with the nucleus should generate the necessary centripetal acceleration, i.e., according to Newton's second law:

$$\frac{Ze^2}{r^2} = \frac{mv^2}{r}$$

297. At a distance of $l/3$ from the smaller charge. The equilibrium will be stable during longitudinal displacements, if the charge q is positive and unstable if q is negative.

Note. In order to determine the nature of equilibrium consider the forces arising for a small displacement of the charge q from the position of equilibrium.

298. The negative charge $q = \dfrac{4}{9}\, e$ should be placed at a distance $\dfrac{a}{3}$ from the charge e. In this case the sum of the forces acting on each charge in the system will be equal to zero.

299. The test charge should be placed at a distance $a = l\,(1 + \sqrt{2})$ behind the positive charge. The equilibrium will be stable.

Solution. The position of equilibrium can be determined from the equation

$$\frac{eq}{a^2} = \frac{2eq}{(l+a)^2}$$

The nature of equilibrium can be found if we consider the forces produced for small displacements of the charge q from the position of equilibrium.

When the charge q is displaced from the position of equilibrium the relative change in the distance from the charge $+e$ will always be larger than the relative change in the distance from the charge $-2e$.

In other words, if the charge q is moved a distance x from the position of equilibrium towards the system of charges, then

$$\frac{1}{(a-x)^2} > \frac{1}{[(l+a)-x]^2}$$

Therefore, when the charge q approaches the charge e, the forces of repulsion created by the charge e increase by a greater magnitude than the forces of attraction produced by the charge $-2e$, and the resultant appears which returns the unit charge q to the position of equilibrium. When the charge q is moved away from the charge e, the forces of repulsion will for the same reasons diminish faster than the forces of attraction. The resultant will be directed towards the system of the charges, i.e., it will again return the charge to the position of equilibrium.

The equilibrium will be stable.

The curve showing the dependence of the force acting on the charge q on the .distance from the charge $+e$ can be plotted qualitatively if we reason as follows.

If the charge q is moved closer to the charge e from the position of equilibrium, the difference in the relative change in the effect of the charges e and $-2e$ will become greater and greater and, accordingly, the force of repulsion acting on the charge q, as it approaches the system, will increase continuously and very rapidly (Fig. 275). As the charge q is being moved out of the system from the position of equilibrium the difference in the relative change in the effect of the charges e and $-2e$ will become less and the forces built up by these charges will rapidly diminish at the same time.

Therefore, when the charge q is moved out of the system from the position of equilibrium the force of attraction at first increases (the difference in the relative change of the distances is more pronounced than the decrease in the forces) and then, from a certain distance b onwards, diminishes and rapidly approaches zero. (The difference in the relative change in the distances becomes insignificantly small and the principal part is played by the decrease in each of the forces produced by the charges e and $-2e$.)

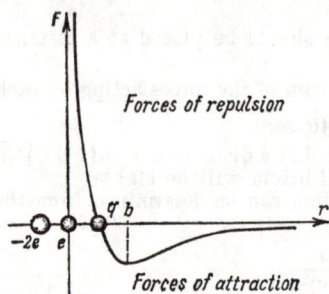

Fig. 275

300. $q = 2.6 \times 10^{-3}$ cgs electrostatic units.

Note. The magnitude of the charges can be determined from the equation

$$\frac{q^2}{r^2} = \gamma \frac{m^2}{r^2}$$

from which we get $q = m\sqrt{\gamma}$ where $\gamma = 6.66 \times 10^{-8}$ cm³/g·s² is the gravitational consant.

301. Before the balls are connected they interact with a force $F = 1$ dyn and after they are connected with a force equal to $F_2 \approx$ ≈ 1.6 dyn. After connection the charges on the balls will be the same and equal to 12.5 cgs electrostatic units.

Note. When the balls are connected by a wire the charges will be distributed equally between the balls.

302. $e_1 = 8$ cgs electrostatic units and $e_2 = -2$ cgs electrostatic units.

Solution. The force of interaction of the balls before they are connected is

$$F_1 = \frac{e_1 e_2}{l^2}$$

and after connection the charge of each ball will become $\frac{e_1 + e_2}{2}$ and the force of interaction to

$$F_2 = \frac{(e_1 + e_2)^2}{4l^2}$$

Hence,

$$e_1 e_2 = F_1 l^2$$
$$e_1 + e_2 = 2l\sqrt{F_2}$$

Solving these equations we get

$$e_1 = l\left(\sqrt{F_2} + \sqrt{F_2 - F_1}\right) = 8 \text{ cgs electrostatic units}$$
$$e_2 = l\left(\sqrt{F_2} - \sqrt{F_2 - F_1}\right) = -2 \text{ cgs electrostatic units}$$

When inserting the numerical data, remember that the forces of attraction and repulsion have opposite signs.

303. $e = l \sqrt{mg \tan \alpha} \approx 180$ cgs electrostatic units.

Solution. The force of interaction between the charges $F_1 = \dfrac{e^2}{l^2}$ should equalize the resultant of the forces of gravity and the tension in the thread (Fig. 276) equal to $F_2 = mg \tan \alpha$.

The value of e can be found from the equality $F_1 = F_2$.

304. The balls will first go down, touch each other and then move apart a distance $b = \dfrac{a}{\sqrt[3]{4}}$.

Solution. Let us denote the charge and the mass of each ball before contact by e and m, and the length of the threads by L.

Since $L \gg a$ and $L \gg b$, we may write the condition of equilibrium of the balls before contact (see the solution to Problem 303):

$$\frac{e^2}{a^2} = mg \tan \alpha = mg \frac{a}{2L}$$

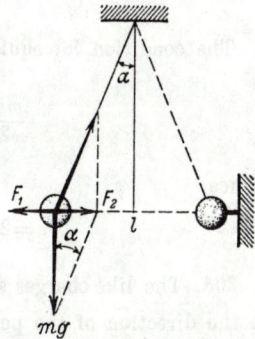

Fig. 276

On contact the charge e still remaining on one of the balls will be equally distributed between both balls and the condition for the new equilibrium of the balls will be

$$\frac{e^2}{4b^2} = mg \tan \beta = mg \frac{b}{2L} = \frac{e^2 b}{a^3}$$

Hence,

$$b = \frac{a}{\sqrt[3]{4}}$$

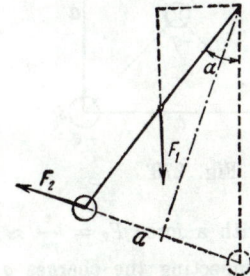

Fig. 277

305. $e = 2l \sin \dfrac{\alpha}{2} \sqrt{mg \sin \dfrac{\alpha}{2}}$.

Solution. The deflected thread will be acted upon by the weight $F_1 = mg$ acting through the centre of gravity of the thread and the force of interaction of the charges $F_2 = \dfrac{e^2}{a^2}$ (Fig. 277) acting on the end of the thread. The thread will be in equilibrium when the sum of the moments of these forces is equal to zero.

It follows from simple geometrical considerations that:
the moment of force F_1 is equal to $\dfrac{mgl}{2} \sin \alpha$;

the moment of force F_2 is equal to $\dfrac{e^2 l}{a^2} \cos \dfrac{\alpha}{2}$;

or, since $a = 2l \sin \dfrac{\alpha}{2}$, the moment of the force F_2 will be

$$\frac{e^2}{4l} \frac{\cot \dfrac{\alpha}{2}}{\sin \dfrac{\alpha}{2}}$$

The condition for equilibrium will take the form

$$\frac{mgl}{2} \sin \alpha = \frac{e^2}{4l} \frac{\cot \dfrac{\alpha}{2}}{\sin \dfrac{\alpha}{2}}$$

Hence,

$$e = 2l \sin \frac{\alpha}{2} \sqrt{mg \sin \frac{\alpha}{2}}$$

306. The like charges will act with a force $F_1 = \dfrac{e}{r^2} \sqrt{3} = 0.02$ dyn in the direction of the perpendicular to the line connecting the first

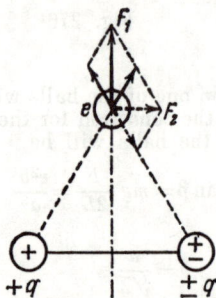

Fig. 278

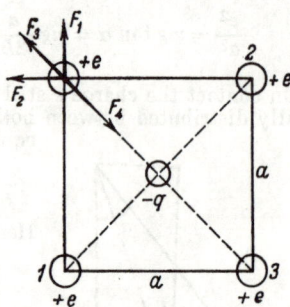

Fig. 279

two charges. The unlike charges will act with a force $F_2 = \dfrac{e}{r^2} \approx$ ≈ 0.01 dyn directed parallel to the line connecting the charges q (Fig. 278).

307. The negative charge $q = \dfrac{e}{4}(1 + 2\sqrt{2})$; the equilibrium of the system will be unstable.

Solution. Each charge at the four corners of the square is acted upon by four forces (Fig. 279): two forces $F_1 = F_2 = \dfrac{e^2}{a^2}$ set up by the charges at corners *1* and *2*; the force $F_3 = \dfrac{e^2}{2a^2}$ set up by the charge at

corner *3*; and the force $F_4 = \dfrac{2qe}{a^2}$ produced by the charge *q*.

For equilibrium to be established the geometrical sum of these forces should be equal to zero, i.e.,

$$\frac{2qe}{a^2} = \frac{e^2}{2a^2} + \frac{\sqrt{2e^2}}{a}$$

Hence,

$$q = \frac{e}{4}\left(1 + 2\sqrt{2}\right)$$

In order to determine the nature of the equilibrium of the system it is enough to impart a small displacement to one of the charges and estimate the change in the magnitude of the forces produced by the other charges.

For the sake of simplicity, let us consider a small displacement *s* of one of the charges $+e$ along the dia-
gonal in the direction from the centre of the square (Fig. 280).

Since the distance from this charge to the charge *q* is the smallest, the displacement *s* will cause a much larger relative change in the distance to the charge *q* than the relative change of the distances to the other charges. Therefore, the displacement *s* will decrease the force F_4 more than

Fig. 280

the forces F_1, F_2 and F_3. Moreover, the displacement *s* will decrease the angle between the forces F_1 and F_2 produced by the charges *1* and *2*. This reduction in the angle will slightly increase the resultant of the forces F_1 and F_2.

Thus, with the charge in the new position the force F_4 will delibe-
rately be smaller than the geometrical sum of the forces $F_1 + F_2 + F_3$.

In this new position the charge will be acted upon by the resultant directed away from the position of equilibrium.

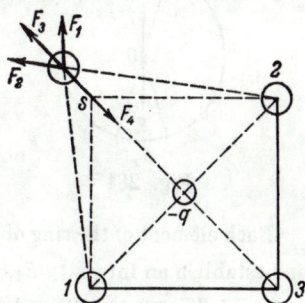

19. Electric Field. Field Intensity

308. $E = 1 \times 10^{-4}$ cgs electrostatic units $= 0.03$ V/cm.

309. $E = 0$; $V = \dfrac{2e}{a} = 24$ V.

Note. In order to solve the problem, use the principle of independ-
ent action of electric fields. The intensity of the field at the point *A* is equal to the geometrical sum of the intensities of the fields set up by each charge. The potential at the point *A* will be equal to the sum

of the potentials that would be established at this point by each charge separately.

310. $E_0 = 0$; $E_A = \dfrac{\sqrt{2}}{4}\dfrac{q}{R^2}$.

Solution. The charge will be uniformly distributed along the entire ring. Each unit of the ring length will accommodate a charge

$$\sigma = \frac{q}{2\pi R}$$

The intensity of the field set up by the charged ring at each point in space will be the geometrical sum of the intensities produced by the separate elements of the ring.

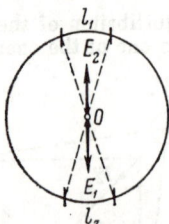

Fig. 281

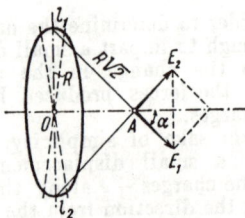

Fig. 282

Each element of the ring of length l_1 will carry a charge σl_1 (Fig. 281) and establish an intensity $E_1 = \dfrac{\sigma l_1}{R^2}$ at the point O. The symmetrically arranged element l_2 will produce an intensity E_2 of the same magnitude but in the opposite direction. Therefore, when the intensities are summed up over all elements of the ring they are mutually compensated and the total intensity of the field in the centre of the ring will be zero.

The element l_1 at the point A (Fig. 282) will set up an intensity $E_1 = \dfrac{\sigma l_1}{2R^2}$ directed at an angle $\alpha = 45°$ to the axis of the ring.

At this point the element l_2 establishes an intensity $E_2 = \dfrac{\sigma l_2}{2R^2}$.

When the intensities of these elements of the ring are added the sum will include only the projections of the vectors E_1 and E_2 on the axis of the ring. In exactly the same way the projections of the intensity vectors created by all the other elements of the ring will be included in pairs.

For this reason the intensity vector at the point A will be equal to

$$E_A = \frac{\sigma 2\pi R}{2R^2} \cos \alpha = \frac{q\sqrt{2}}{4R^2}$$

311. The leaves of the electroscope will be deflected through different distances. The maximum deflection will be observed when the charge is transferred from the point A, the minimum one during transfer from the point B and the one equal to zero after the contact at the point C.

Note. When the charges are transferred to the electroscope by the method described in the problem the divergence of the leaves of the electroscope is proportional to the density of charge distribution at the points of contact of the ball. The charges will be distributed on the surface so that their density is higher at the points on the surface having a greater curvature and lower at the points with a smaller curvature. The curvature and, therefore, the density of the charge is larger at the point A than at the point B.

312. See Fig. 283. The ball will have induced negative charges on the side of the positive plate and positive charges on the side of the negative plate.

The lines of force will be perpendicular to the surface of the ball.

The distortions in the shape and arrangement of the lines of force

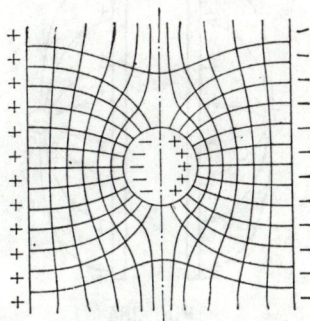

Fig. 283

are caused by the fact that the field of the capacitor is superposed by the electric field of the charges induced on the surface of the ball.

314. (a) A field will exist inside and outside the sphere.

(b) A negative charge will appear on the internal surface of the sphere and a positive charge on the external surface.

(c) The electric field inside the sphere will change.

(d) Only the electric field outside the sphere will change.

315. The charge will be distributed on the external surface of the sphere. The intensity of the field inside the sphere will be zero. An electric field similar to the field of the point charge e situated at the centre of the sphere will be set up outside the sphere.

316. The plates will begin to move apart due to the interaction of the point charges with the charges induced on each plate (Fig. 284).

317. See Fig. 285. The density of the induced charges will diminish from A to B on the surface of the plates facing the point charges. Induced charges of opposite sign will be distributed uniformly on the internal surfaces of the plates.

318. (a) 0; $\dfrac{\mathscr{E}}{3}$; $\dfrac{2\mathscr{E}}{3}$; $\mathscr{E}$.

(b) The potentials will be 0, $\dfrac{\mathscr{E}}{2}$, $\dfrac{\mathscr{E}}{2}$, $\mathscr{E}$. In the spaces *1*, *2*, and *3*, *4* the intensity of the field will increase, and in the space *2*, *3* it will become zero. The charges on plates *1* and *4* will increase.

(c) Plate *2* will have a positive charge and plate *3* a negative one.

319. $a = \dfrac{eE}{m} = 0.5$ cm/s².

Note. The force acting on the charge in the electric field will be $F = eE$. Newton's second law equation for the motion of a charge will take the form $eE = ma$.

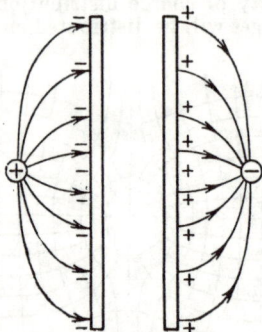

Fig. 284

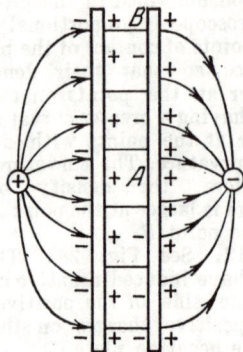

Fig. 285

320. Parabola; $h = 2.8$ mm.

Solution. The intensity of the field inside the capacitor will be

$$E = \frac{V}{d}$$

The electron will be acted upon in a vertical direction by the force $F = eE = e\frac{V}{d}$ (Fig. 286) which produces a vertical acceleration of

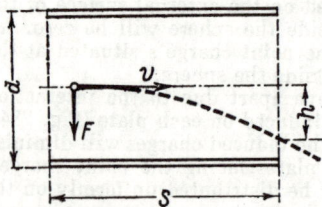

Fig. 286

the electron equal to

$$a = \frac{F}{m} = \frac{e}{m}\frac{V}{d}$$

The equations of motion of the electron are:

in the horizontal direction

$$l = vt$$

in the vertical direction

$$h = \frac{at^2}{2} = \frac{e}{m}\frac{V}{d}\frac{t^2}{2}$$

The electron will move as a body thrown horizontally above the surface of the Earth.

The vertical displacement of the electron at the moment it escapes from the capacitor will be

$$h = \frac{e}{m}\frac{V}{d}\frac{l^2}{2v^2} = 2.8 \text{ mm}$$

321. $E = \dfrac{mg}{e} \approx 10$ cgs electrostatic units $\approx 3{,}000$ V/cm.

322. (a) $T = 2\pi \sqrt{\dfrac{l}{g + \dfrac{e}{m} E}}$; (b) $T = 2\pi \sqrt{\dfrac{l}{g - \dfrac{e}{m} E}}$.

Solution. If a charge $+e$ is placed on the ball and the upper plate is charged positively the ball will be acted upon in a vertical direction not only by the force of gravity mg but by the force eE, where E is the intensity of the electric field of the capacitor. This additional force will change the acceleration of free fall of the ball in the capacitor. The magnitude of this acceleration can be determined from Newton's second law equation

$$mg' = mg + eE$$

and will be equal to

$$g' = g + \frac{e}{m} E$$

Introducing this value of g' into the formula for the period of oscillations of the pendulum we find that the period of oscillations decreases in the first case and increases in the second.

323. $F = \dfrac{T_1^2 - T_2^2}{T_2^2} \, mg = 3mg = 3gf;$ $\quad l = \dfrac{T_1^2 g}{4\pi^2} = 9.8$ cm;

$$T_3 = 2\pi \sqrt{\frac{l}{2g}}$$

Solution. The period of oscillations of the ball in the absence of the field is

$$T_1 = 2\pi \sqrt{\frac{l}{g}} \tag{1}$$

The period of oscillations after the ball and the capacitor have been charged (see the solution to the previous problem) will be

$$T_2 = 2\pi \sqrt{\frac{l}{g + \dfrac{F}{m}}} \tag{2}$$

Since $T_2 < T_1$, the upper plate of the capacitor and the ball had charges of the same sign.

Squaring (1) and (2) and solving them for F we obtain

$$F = \frac{T_1^2 - T_2^2}{T_2^2} \, mg = 3mg$$

Since the force of electric interaction of the ball with the plates of the capacitor is larger than the force of gravity, the position of equilibrium of the ball will change when the sign of the charge is changed.

The point A corresponding to the position of equilibrium of the ball will arrange itself above the point of suspension O (Fig. 287). The free fall acceleration of the ball under the simultaneous action of the force of gravity and the force produced by the electric field will be directed upwards and equal to

$$g' = \frac{F}{m} - g = 2g$$

Therefore, the period of oscillations of the ball about the point A will be

$$T_3 = 2\pi \sqrt{\frac{l}{\frac{F}{m} - g}} = 2\pi \sqrt{\frac{l}{2g}}$$

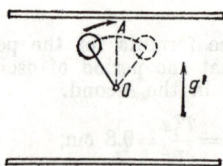

Fig. 287

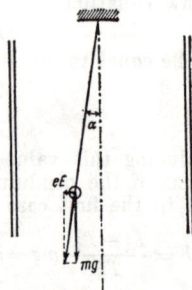

Fig. 288

324. The position of equilibrium of the ball will change and the period of oscillations will diminish.

Solution. If the mass of the ball is m, its charge $+e$ and the intensity of the field in the capacitor E, and the ball is in equilibrium, the thread will make such an angle α with the vertical line (Fig. 288) that

$$\tan \alpha = \frac{eE}{mg}$$

The free fall acceleration of the ball can be determined from Newton's second law equation

$$mg' = \sqrt{(mg)^2 + (eE)^2}$$

and will be equal to

$$g' = \frac{\sqrt{(mg)^2 + (eE)^2}}{m} = \sqrt{g^2 + \left(\frac{Ee}{m}\right)^2}$$

Hence, the period of oscillations of the pendulum will be

$$T = 2\pi \sqrt{\frac{l}{g'}} = 2\pi \sqrt{\frac{l}{\sqrt{g^2 + \left(\frac{Ee}{m}\right)^2}}}$$

325. $q \approx 5.9 \times 10^5$ coulombs.

Note. To solve the problem, use the expression for the intensity of the field of a point charge $E = \dfrac{q}{r^2}$, from which we have $q = Er^2$.

20. Work done by Forces in an Electrostatic Field. Potential

326. $v = 32,600$ km/s.

Solution. When the electron moves the work done by the forces of the electric field will be

$$A = Fd = eEd$$

According to the law of conservation of energy, the following must be true:

$$A = \frac{mv^2}{2} \quad \text{or} \quad eEd = \frac{mv^2}{2}$$

Hence,

$$v = \sqrt{\frac{2eEd}{m}} = 3.26 \times 10^9 \text{ cm/s}$$

327. $d = \dfrac{V}{E} = 5$ cm.

328. $\sigma = 8 \times 10^{-3}$ cgs electrostatic units.

Solution. The charged metal sphere creates in external space the same electric field as would be set up by a point charge q placed in its centre. The potential at any point in such a field is

$$V = \frac{q}{R}$$

Hence, the charge on the sphere $q = VR$ and the charge density on the surface of the sphere is

$$\sigma = \frac{q}{4\pi R^2} = \frac{V}{4\pi R} = \frac{1}{12.56 \times 10} \text{ cgs electrostatic units}$$

329. $V = 300$ V and 150 V.

Solution. The principle of independent action of electric fields makes it possible to calculate the potential at any point in the field established by a system of point charges as the sum of the potentials set up by each charge separately

$$V = V_1 + V_2 = \frac{e_1}{r_1} + \frac{e_2}{r_2} = 300 \text{ V}$$

When a dielectric is introduced the potentials at all the points in the field will be reduced ε times.

330. $A = q(V_B - V_A) = 270$ ergs.

331. $q_1 = +10.25$ cgs electrostatic units; $q_2 = -10.25$ cgs electrostatic units.

Solution. In order to solve the problem, use the principle of the independent action of electric fields.

The potential of the first ball V_1 is the sum of two potentials: the potential established by the charge on one ball and equal to $\frac{q_1}{r}$ and the potential set up by the charge on the second ball and equal to $\frac{q_2}{a}$ (knowing that $r \ll a$).

Thus,

$$V_1 = \frac{q_1}{r} + \frac{q_2}{a}$$

Similarly,

$$V_2 = \frac{q_2}{r} + \frac{q_1}{a}$$

Solving these equations for q_1 and q_2 we find that

$$q_1 = ar\frac{rV_2 - aV_1}{r^2 - a^2}, \qquad q_2 = ar\frac{rV_1 - aV_2}{r^2 - a^2}$$

Utilizing $r^2 \ll a^2$, we can simplify these expressions and obtain for the magnitude of the charges:

$$q_1 = -\frac{r}{a}(rV_2 - aV_1), \quad q_2 = -\frac{r}{a}(rV_1 - aV_2)$$

332. Outside the spheres $E = \frac{q+Q}{r^2}$ and $V = \frac{q+Q}{r}$; inside the large sphere $E = \frac{q}{r^2}$ and $V = \frac{q}{r} + \frac{Q}{b}$; inside the small sphere $E = 0$ and $V = \frac{q}{a} + \frac{Q}{b}$.

Solution. To solve the problem, use the fact that the charge distributed on the surface of the sphere produces outside the sphere a field similar to that of a point charge situated at the centre of the sphere.

Outside both spheres the charge Q produces an intensity $E_Q = \frac{Q}{r^2}$ and a potential $V_Q = \frac{Q}{r}$; the charge q establishes an intensity $E_q = \frac{q}{r^2}$ and a potential $V_q = \frac{q}{r}$, and therefore, on the basis of the principle of independent action of electric fields the intensity and the potential of the field outside the spheres will be

$$E = \frac{Q}{r^2} + \frac{q}{r^2} = \frac{Q+q}{r^2} \quad \text{and} \quad V = \frac{Q+q}{r}$$

Inside the large sphere the intensity of the field established by the charge Q is zero, and the potential in the field set up by this charge will be the same at all points and equal to $V_Q = \dfrac{Q}{b}$; the charge q sets up at these points an intensity $E_q = \dfrac{q}{r^2}$ and a potential $V_q = \dfrac{q}{r}$ and therefore the total intensity in the space between the spheres is $E = E_Q + E_q = \dfrac{q}{r^2}$ and the potential $V = V_Q + V_q = \dfrac{q}{r} + \dfrac{Q}{b}$.

Correspondingly, the intensity of the fields of both charges inside the small sphere will be zero and the potentials constant, i.e., $E_Q = E_q = 0$ and $E = 0$,

$$V_Q = \frac{Q}{b}, \quad V_q = \frac{q}{a} \quad \text{and} \quad V = \frac{Q}{b} + \frac{q}{a}$$

333. $Q = 83$ cgs electrostatic units.

Solution. Since, as is given in the problem, the charge is distributed with the same density σ on the surface of both spheres the charge on the external sphere will be $q_1 = 4\pi R^2 \sigma$ and on the internal one $q_2 = 4\pi r^2 \sigma$, and the required charge will be $Q = q_1 + q_2$.

The work needed to transfer one positive unit of electricity to the common centre of the spheres is numerically equal to the potential V at this centre. As in the solution of Problem 332 we shall have

$$V = \frac{q_1}{R} + \frac{q_2}{r}$$

After inserting the values of q_1 and q_2 we shall obtain the expression for the charge density

$$\sigma = \frac{V}{4\pi (R+r)}$$

for q_1 and q_2, respectively,

$$q_1 = \frac{R^2 V}{R+r} \quad \text{and} \quad q_2 = \frac{r^2 V}{R+r}$$

and, finally, for Q:

$$Q = \frac{r^2 + R^2}{r+R} V$$

334. $V_1 = Ed = 1{,}500$ V; $V_2 = E (d - 1) = 1{,}200$ V.

Note. The introduction of the metal bar removes the electric field in the entire volume occupied by the bar. When a unit charge is transferred from one capacitor plate to the other the electric field will only do work over the path $(d - 1)$ and, correspondingly, the potential difference between the plates will drop to $V_2 = E (d - 1)$ after the bar is introduced.

335. The leaves will all the time be deflected by the same angle.

Note. When the electroscope is charged as described in the problem its readings will be proportional to the potential on the surface of the body. But since the potentials at all the points on the surface of the conductor are the same in an electrostatic field the divergence of the leaves of the electroscope will also be the same for all the points.

Fig. 289

336. See Fig. 289. The lines of force are everywhere perpendicular to the equipotential surfaces in the direction of decreasing potential. The intensity of the field is higher where the equipotential surfaces are closer to each other.

337. $A = 0$.

Solution. The work done duing motion along straight lines *2, 3* and *4, 1* is equal to zero since the force $F = qE$ is perpendicular to the direction of motion (Fig. 290).

The work done by the force F in the sections *1, 2* and *3, 4* is equal in magnitude but opposite in sign. Therefore, the work done over the entire closed circuit will be zero. This result is true for all electrostatic fields and closed circuits of any shape.

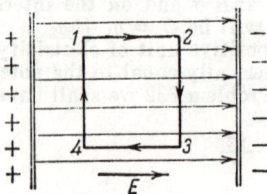

Fig. 290

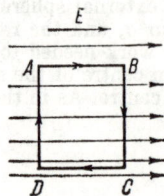

Fig. 291

338. *Solution.* To prove this, calculate the work done by the electric forces when the charge q moves in a closed rectangular circuit $ABCD$ (Fig. 291).

Since the lines of force are parallel the intensity of the field E along each line of force is constant.

As there are fewer lines of force in the section AB than in the section CD, the intensity of the field E_1 and, hence, the work A_1 done to move the charge in the section AB will of necessity be smaller in magnitude than the intensity E_2 and the work A_2 in the section CD.

The work done for motion in the sections BC and DA will be zero since the vector E is perpendicular to the direction of motion of the charge.

Therefore, the work done over the entire closed circuit $ABCD$ equal to $A_1 - A_2$ will not be zero.

Since the work done by the electric forces in an electrostatic field is always equal to zero in any closed circuit the result obtained is incompatible with the basic properties of electrostatic fields and the field described in the problem cannot exist.

339. *Solution.* To prove this, calculate the work done by electric forces in a circuit $ABCD$ (Fig. 292) enclosed by the sections of the radii

AD and BC and the arcs of the circles AB and CD coinciding with the respective lines of force.

Since the lines of force are parallel the intensity of the field E_1 is constant on the line AB and that of the field E_2 on the line CD.

The work in the section AB will be equal to $E_1 R\alpha$, in the section CD to $E_2 r\alpha$ and in the sections AD and BC to zero (the vector E is perpendicular to the direction of motion of the charge).

As the work done by electric forces in a closed circuit in an electrostatic field is always equal to zero (see Problems 337, 338) we have

$$E_1 R\alpha - E_2 r\alpha = 0$$

or

$$\frac{E_1}{E_2} = \frac{r}{R}$$

which was required to be proved.

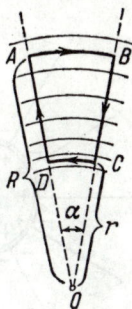

Fig. 292

21. Electric Field in a Dielectric

340. See Fig. 293. The sharp change in the number of the lines of force, as the boundary of the dielectric is passed, can be explained by the action of the polarizing charges set up on the boundaries of the dielectrics in electric fields.

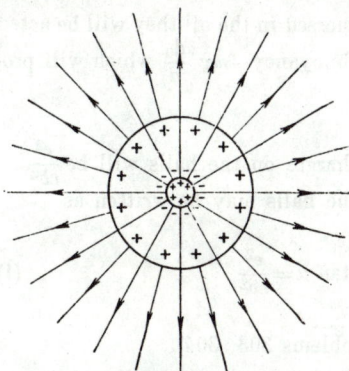

Fig. 293

341. $E_1 = \dfrac{q}{\varepsilon r_1^2} = 0.1$ cgs electrostatic unit; $E_2 = \dfrac{q}{r_2^2} = 0.075$ cgs electrostatic unit.

342. $q' = \dfrac{\varepsilon - 1}{\varepsilon} q$; $\sigma' = \dfrac{\varepsilon - 1}{\varepsilon} \sigma$.

Solution. If there were no dielectric around the ball, it would set up a field with an intensity

$$E_1 = \frac{q}{r^2}$$

When a dielectric is present a field of intensity

$$E_2 = \frac{q}{\varepsilon r^2}$$

will be generated.

The difference $E = E_1 - E_2 = \dfrac{q}{r^2}\dfrac{\varepsilon-1}{\varepsilon}$ is obviously equal to the intensity produced by the polarizing charges q' appearing near the charged body (Fig. 294). Since these charges are also distributed uniformly over the surface of the ball it may be assumed that

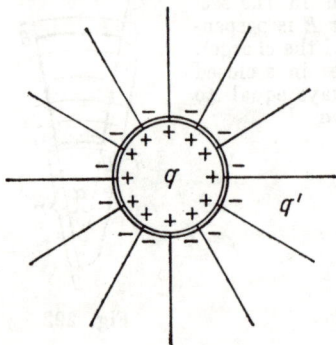

$$E = \frac{q'}{r^2}$$

Comparing the expressions obtained for E we find that

$$q' = \frac{\varepsilon-1}{\varepsilon}\,q$$

The surface density of the polarizing charges σ' will obviously be equal to

$$\sigma' = \frac{q'}{4\pi R^2} = \frac{\varepsilon-1}{\varepsilon}\,\frac{q}{4\pi R^2} = \frac{\varepsilon-1}{\varepsilon}\,\sigma$$

Fig. 294

where ε is the density of distribution of the charge q on the ball.

343. $b = a\sqrt[3]{\dfrac{d}{\varepsilon(d-d_0)}}$; $b < a$.

Solution. When the balls are immersed in the oil they will be acted upon by their weight mg and the buoyancy—$mg\dfrac{d_0}{d}$ which will produce the resultant $mg\dfrac{d-d_0}{d}$.

The electric interaction of the charges on the balls will be $\dfrac{e^2}{\varepsilon b^2}$. The condition for equilibrium of the balls may be written as

$$mg\,\frac{d-d_0}{d}\,\tan\alpha = \frac{e^2}{\varepsilon b^2} \tag{1}$$

(the solution is the same as in Problems 303, 304).
   Since

$$\tan\alpha = \frac{b}{2L}$$

and

$$L = \frac{mga^3}{2e^2}$$

(from the solution of Problem 304) and introducing these values into equation (1) and cancelling mg and e, we get

$$b = a \sqrt[3]{\frac{d}{\varepsilon(d-d_0)}}$$

22. Capacitance and Capacitors

344. $Q_1 = \dfrac{S\mathscr{E}}{4\pi d} = 3.2$ cgs electrostatic units;

$Q_2 = \dfrac{\varepsilon S\mathscr{E}}{4\pi d} = 7$ cgs electrostatic units.

Note. In the first case the magnitude of the charge on the plates will remain constant when the oil is poured in; the capacitance of the capacitor will increase ε times and, accordingly, the potential difference between the plates and the field intensity in the capacitor will also become ε times smaller.

In the second case, when the oil is poured in, the charge on the plates will increase ε times due to the increase in the capacitance, but the potential difference and the intensity of the field will not change.

345. *Solution.* If one of the bodies carries a charge q and the other body sets up a field intensity E at the point where the first body is situated, the force acting on the first body will be equal to $F = qE$.

Since the potentials of the conductors are maintained constant then, when the dielectric is poured in, the intensity of the field E set up by each body should also remain constant at all points. On the other hand, when the bodies are placed in a dielectric their capacitance will increase ε times. Therefore, if the potentials care to be kept constant, the charges on the bodies should also be increased ε times.

If q is the charge on the first body in the air, it should become εq after the bodies are placed in the dielectric and the interaction between the bodies will be $F_2 = \varepsilon qE = \varepsilon F_1$ where $F_1 = qE$ is the force acting on the body in the air.

346. In the first case the force will diminish in proportion to $1/\varepsilon$ and in the second it will increase in proportion to ε.

Solution. If the magnitude of the charges q remains unchanged, the intensity of the field E will diminish ε times when the dielectric is changed, i.e., $E_2 = \dfrac{E_1}{\varepsilon}$. Accordingly, the force equal to $F = qE$ acting on each ball will be decreased ε times.

Second case. See the solution to Problem 345.

347. The charges will move from the first ball to the second; $q_1 - Q_1 \approx 7$ cgs electrostatic units; $V = 2.6$ cgs electrostatic units; $Q_1 = 13$ cgs electrostatic units and $Q_2 = 27$ cgs electrostatic units (Q_1 and Q_2 are the charges of the balls after they are connected).

Solution. To solve the problem, determine the potentials of each ball. Since the balls are a long way apart it may be assumed that

$$V_1 = \frac{q_1}{r} \quad \text{and} \quad V_2 = \frac{q_2}{R}$$

since $V_1 > V_2$ the charges will move onto the second ball. The motion of the charges will cease when the potentials of the balls become the same. The following equalities will then hold

$$V = \frac{Q_1}{r} = \frac{Q_2}{R}, \qquad Q_1 + Q_2 = q_1 + q_2$$

Hence, the charge on the first ball Q_1 will be

$$Q_1 = \frac{r}{r+R}(q_1 + q_2)$$

and the quantity of electricity transferred from the first ball to the second will be

$$q_1 - Q_1 = \frac{Rq_1}{r+R} - \frac{rq_2}{r+R}$$

348. $V = \dfrac{C_1 V_1 + C_2 V_2}{C_1 + C_2} = 260$ V.

Note. In order to solve the problem, determine the total charges of the capacitors and the combined capacitance of the capacitors C_1 and C_2 connected in parallel.

349. The quantity of electricity transferred from the first capacitor to the second is

$$q = \frac{C_1 C_2 (V_1 + V_2)}{C_1 + C_2} = 6 \times 10^{-4} \text{ coulombs}$$

Solution. Before the capacitors are connected their charges are $Q_1 = C_1 V_1$ and $Q_2 = C_2 V_2$ respectively. The charge remaining in the battery after connection is $C_1 V_1 - C_2 V_2$. The capacitance of the two capacitors is $C_1 + C_2$. The potential difference between the plates of the capacitors after connection is $V = \dfrac{C_1 V_1 - C_2 V_2}{C_1 + C_2}$. The charge remaining across the plates of the first capacitor after connection will be $Q' = C_1 V = C_1 \dfrac{C_1 V_1 - C_2 V_2}{C_1 + C_2}$. The quantity of electricity transferred from the first capacitor to the second is

$$q = Q_1 - Q' = \frac{C_1 C_2 (V_1 + V_2)}{C_1 + C_2}$$

350. $V = \dfrac{q}{r} \sqrt[3]{N^2} = 2.7$ V where q is the charge on the small drop and N is the number of drops.

Note. In solving the problem use the formula for the capacitance of the ball and calculate the radius of the large drop.

351. It cannot because the capacitors would be punctured. The voltages in the capacitors will be $V_1 = 6{,}000$ V; $V_2 = 3{,}000$ V and $V_3 = 2{,}000$ V, respectively.

Solution. It follows from the fact that the charges across the plates of the capacitors are equal that

$$V_1 C_1 = V_2 C_2, \quad V_2 C_2 = V_3 C_3$$

and

$$V_1 + V_2 + V_3 = V$$

Solving these equations will give the required answer.

352. $C = \dfrac{\varepsilon S}{4\pi\,(d-1)} \approx 4.2$ cm. When the bar is shifted the capacitance will not change.

Note. In order to solve the problem consider the capacitor with the bar inserted in it as a system of two plane capacitors connected in series.

353. The capacitance will be different. It will be larger in the second case.

Solution. In the first case there will only be charges on the inside surface of the larger sphere. In the second case the charges will be on both sides (Fig. 295) and the capacitance of the entire capacitor must be calculated as the capacitance of a system of two capacitors connected in parallel and with plates AB and BC.

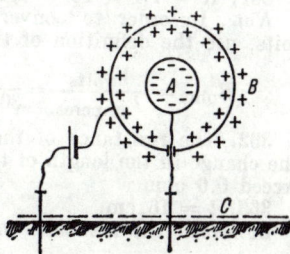

Fig. 295

354. $F = QE = 2\pi\,\dfrac{Q^2}{S}$; $\quad A = Fd = \dfrac{2\pi Q^2}{S}\,d = \dfrac{Q^2}{2C} = \dfrac{CV^2}{2}$.

355. $\sigma = \dfrac{1}{2\pi}\sqrt{\dfrac{F}{2dC}} \approx 5$ cgs electrostatic units.

356. $V = \sqrt{\dfrac{8\pi d^2 P}{S}} = 4$ cgs electrostatic units $= 1{,}200$ V.

Solution. The force acting on the upper plate is $P = \dfrac{CV^2}{2d}$ (see the solution to Problem 354) and the capacitance of the capacitor is

$$C = \dfrac{S}{4\pi d}$$

Hence,

$$P = \dfrac{SV^2}{8\pi d^2} \quad \text{and} \quad V = \sqrt{\dfrac{8\pi d^2 P}{S}}$$

357. In the second case.

Solution. In the first case when the plates are drawn apart the potential difference remains constant but the capacitance and, therefore, the charge across the plates diminish. This will gradually decrease the interaction between the plates.

In the second case the charge across the plates remains constant. Therefore, the interaction between the plates will keep the same value it had initially while the plates are being drawn apart.

Therefore, when the plates are moved identical distances more work will be done in the second case.

358. $\varepsilon = 3$.

23. The Laws of Direct Current

359. $R = 0.017$ ohm.

360. One Yakobi's unit is 5.75 ohms.

361. $R = 1.1 \times 10^{-11}$ cgs electrostatic units.

Note. In order to convert the resistance into cgs electrostatic units, use the definition of the resistance from Ohm's law:

$$R_{\text{ohm}} = \frac{V_{\text{volts}}}{I_{\text{amperes}}} = \frac{1}{300 \times 3 \times 10^9} \text{ cgs electrostatic units}$$

362. The resistance of the wire is 313 ohms higher in summer. The change in the length of the wire gives a correction that does not exceed 0.6 ohm.

363. $l = 16$ cm.

Solution. The resistance of the lamp filament is

$$R = \frac{V^2}{N} = \rho \frac{l}{S}$$

The resistivity of the incandescent filament is

$$\rho = \rho_0 \frac{T}{T_0}$$

The length of the filament is

$$l = \frac{RS}{\rho} = \frac{RST_0}{\rho_0 T} = \frac{V^2 S T_0}{N \rho_0 T}$$

364. $I = 2a$ is ten times larger than in normal burning.

365. $C = \frac{\varepsilon}{4\pi\lambda} \Lambda$.

Solution. The capacitance of the capacitor $C = \frac{\varepsilon S}{4\pi d}$.

The resistance of the capacitor after filling it with electrolyte $R = \frac{1}{\lambda} \frac{d}{S}$ and its conductivity $\Lambda = \frac{1}{R} = \frac{\lambda S}{d}$.

Hence, $C = \frac{\varepsilon}{4\pi\lambda} \Lambda$.

The expression obtained is of a general nature, is true of capacitors of any shape and is widely utilized in electrical engineering calculations.

366. Lenz's unit of current is 0.065 A.

Solution. It follows from the laws of electrolysis that the quantity of substance liberated on one electrode $M = \frac{1}{F} \frac{A}{n} It$ where F is Faraday's number; I is current in amperes; t is time in seconds and $\frac{A}{n}$ is the gram-equivalent of the substance.

On the basis of Avogadro's law, the volume of oxygen evolved when the current is passed will take 1/3 of the volume of detonating gas at a pressure of 760 mm Hg and will be equal to $V = 13.72$ cm³. Hence, the mass of the liberated oxygen $M = dV = 0.0196$ g. The current corresponding to Lenz's unit will be $I = \frac{MFn}{tA}$.

367. $R_1 = 10$ ohms; $R_2 = 20$ ohms; $R_3 = 60$ ohms.

Solution. When the rheostat is cut out the current is $I_0 = \frac{V}{R_0} = 4$ A. The resistance R_1 can be found from the equation

$$R_1 + R_0 = \frac{V}{I_0 - 1} \quad \text{or} \quad R_1 = \frac{V}{I_0 - 1} - R_0$$

Therefore,

$$R_2 = \frac{V}{I_0 - 2} - (R_1 + R_0)$$

and

$$R_3 = \frac{V}{I_0 - 3} - (R_2 + R_1 + R_0)$$

368. The galvanometer should be cut into the circuit in series. The scale of the instrument will be: ∞; 1.2×10^7 ohms; 6×10^6 ohms; 4.0×10^6 ohms; ...; $\frac{120}{n} \times 10^5$ ohms where n is the number of the division.

The minimum resistance that can be measured is 3×10^5 ohms.

Note. The values of the resistance R_n corresponding to separate divisions on the galvanometer scale can be determined from the formula

$$R_n = \frac{V}{nI_0}$$

where V is the mains voltage; n is the number of the scale division and I_0 is the current corresponding to one division on the galvanometer scale.

369. $I_0 = 5.05$ A.

Solution. If the voltage in the circuit is V, the current in it before the ammeter is cut in will be $I_0 = \frac{V}{R}$, and after the ammeter is cut in $I_1 = \frac{V}{R + R_0}$. Hence,

$$I_0 = \frac{R + R_0}{R} I_1$$

370. $R = \dfrac{R_0}{n-1} = 50$ ohms $(n = 20)$.

Note. The response of the galvanometer can be reduced n times if a current of $\dfrac{n-1}{n} I$ is passed through the shunt when the current in the circuit is I.

371. $R = 0.032$ ohm. The response of the instrument will be diminished 250 times.

372. 0.5 V per division.

Note. For a current $I = 1$ mA to flow through the instrument its terminals should have a voltage of

$$V = IR = 10^{-3} \times 500 = 0.5 \text{ V}$$

373. Before the voltmeter was connected the voltage was $V = 105$ V. The error is 5 V.

374. $R = \dfrac{VR_0}{IR_0 - V} = 61.2$ ohms. The resistance R' calculated on the assumption that $R_0 \to \infty$ will be 1.2 ohms less than the actual value.

375. For the 1 ohm resistance the measurement error using circuit *a* will be 0.1 ohm or 10 per cent, and using circuit *b* it will be 0.001 ohm or 0.1 per cent; for the 500 ohms resistance—0.1 ohm or 0.02 per cent and 167 ohms or 33.4 per cent, respectively.

Solution. If V and I are the readings of the voltmeter and the ammeter, the resistance $R' = \dfrac{V}{I}$ calculated from these readings will be equal to the total resistance of the section in the circuit bb' when measurements are made using (a) and to the resistance of the section cc' when measuring by (b), i.e., it will be related to the resistance R by

$$R_1' = R + R_a$$

in the first case and by

$$R_2' = \dfrac{RR_v}{R + R_v}$$

in the second.

Comparing the values calculated from these ratios with the actual value of the resistance R one can find the errors permitted when measurements are made using (a) and (b).

These errors are caused by the fact that in the first case (a) the voltage drop across the internal resistance of the ammeter is not subtracted from the voltmeter readings in calculations, and in the second case (b) the current taken by the voltmeter is not subtracted from the readings of the ammeter. Therefore, the resistance R' calculated only from the readings of the instruments is in the first case larger and in the second case smaller than the actual resistance R.

When the resistance R being measured drops in (a), the reduction of voltage shown by the ammeter will form an increasing share of the readings of the voltmeter and the circuit will produce increasingly larger relative errors. When the resistance is reduced in (b) the current taken by the voltmeter diminishes. The error in the readings of the ammeter and therefore the relative error in the calculation will also diminish.

The circuit (b) is more effective for low resistances and (a) for higher ones.

376. $V = 51.2$ V.

Solution. The resistance of the section AB is

$$R = \frac{R_0 R_1}{R_0 + 2R_1}$$

The current flowing through the potentiometer is

$$I = \frac{2V}{2R + R_0}$$

The voltage taken from the potentiometer is

$$V = IR = \frac{2VR_1}{R_0 + 4R_1} = 51.2 \text{ V}$$

377. By 10.4 V.

Solution. The resistances of the lamp and the appliance are

$$R_1 = \frac{V^2}{N_1} = 240 \text{ ohms} \quad \text{and} \quad R_2 = \frac{V^2}{N_2} = 60 \text{ ohms}$$

The resistance of the circuit before and after the appliance is switched on is

$$R' = R_0 + R_1 = 246 \text{ ohms} \quad \text{and} \quad R'' = R_0 + \frac{R_1 R_2}{R_1 + R_2} = 54 \text{ ohms}$$

The current in the circuit before and after the appliance is switched on is

$$I_1 = \frac{V}{R'} \approx 0.49 \text{ A},$$

$$I_2 = \frac{V}{R''} = 2.22 \text{ A}$$

The voltage drop in the wires is

$$V_0' = I_1 R_0 = 2.9 \text{ V} \quad \text{and}$$

$$V_0'' = I_2 R_0 = 13.3 \text{ V}$$

Fig. 296

378. $S = \frac{n I_0 2\rho l}{V_1}$.

Note. The resistance of the input wires is $R = \frac{\rho 2l}{S}$.

379. The current will flow since the potentials of the conductors AB and CD are different. The directions of all the currents which flow are shown in Fig. 296. The potentials at the points A, B, C and D will change. The potential difference between the points A and C,

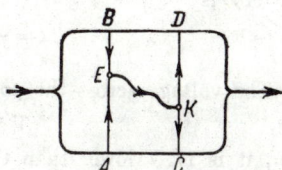

and also between B and D, will diminish. The potential at the point E will be lower than the potential at the points A and B, and the potential at the point K will be greater than the potentials at the points C and D.

380. If the bridge is in balance the readings on the galvanometer will be the same whether the switch is open or closed.

Solution. The bridge is not in balance. The potentials at the points A and B are different. When the switch is closed the conductor AB will carry a current and the entire distribution of the currents will be altered in the circuit. This will be tantamount to a change in the total resistance of the circuit and in the current flowing through the element. When the switch is open or closed the readings of the galvanometer in an unbalanced system will change.

The bridge is in balance. The potentials at the points A and B are the same. The distribution of currents in the circuit and the current flowing through the element will be the same whatever the position of the switch.

381. Lenz's unit for e.m.f. is equal to 0.38 V.

382. 6 A.

Solution. The internal resistance of the battery for a closed circuit can be found from Ohm's law

$$r = \frac{\mathscr{E}}{I_1} - R = 1 \text{ ohm}$$

The short-circuit current will be

$$I = \frac{\mathscr{E}}{r} = 6 \text{ A}$$

383. It will not.

Solution. The resistance of the lamp $R = \frac{V^2}{N} = 202$ ohms.

The current produced in the circuit composed of the lamp and the battery is

$$I = \frac{\mathscr{E}}{R+r} = 0.46 \text{ A}$$

The voltage across the poles of the battery is

$$V = IR = 93 \text{ V}$$

i.e., it is 17 V lower than the voltage corresponding to the normal intensity of the lamp. The lamp will not burn at full intensity.

The same result can be obtained by comparing the current flowing in the circuit of the batteries and the current needed for the lamp to burn at normal intensity and equal to $I = \frac{N}{V}$.

384. $r = \frac{I_2 R_2 - I_1 R_1}{I_1 - I_2} = 0.5$ ohm.

Solution. In the first case the current is related to the e.m.f. and the internal resistance of the storage battery by the equation

$$\mathscr{E} = I_1 \, (R_1 + r)$$

In the second case

$$\mathscr{E} = I_2 (R_2 + r)$$

The e.m.f. and the internal resistance of the storage battery are determined by solving these equations.

385. $\mathscr{E}_1 \approx 4.7$ V.

Solution. If R is the total resistance of the circuit, $\mathscr{E}_1$ is the e.m.f. of the storage battery and $\mathscr{E}_2$ is the e.m.f. of the element, the current in the circuit in the first case can be determined from the equation

$$I_1 R = \mathscr{E}_1 + \mathscr{E}_2$$

and in the second case from

$$I_2 R = \mathscr{E}_1 - \mathscr{E}_2$$

Hence,

$$\mathscr{E}_1 = \frac{I_1 + I_2}{I_1 - I_2} \mathscr{E}_2$$

386. $\mathscr{E}_1 = \dfrac{I_1 - I_2}{I_1 + I_2} \mathscr{E}_2 = 0.86$ V.

Note. See the solution to Problem 385. Bear in mind that when the storage battery and the cell are in opposition the current and the e.m.f. of the storage battery will have unlike signs and the Ohm's law equation for this case will take the form:

$$I_2 R = \mathscr{E}_2 - \mathscr{E}_1$$

387. $V = \dfrac{\mathscr{E}R}{R+r} \approx 1.43$ V.

388. $\mathscr{E}_2 = 1.8$ V.

Solution. The e.m.f. of the cell and the storage battery establish currents opposing each other in the section of the potentiometer AB. Obviously, the current in the galvanometer circuit will cease to flow when the potential difference V set up at the ends of the section AB by the cell becomes equal in magnitude to the e.m.f. of the storage battery, i.e.,

$$V = \mathscr{E}_2$$

When the circuit is in balance no current is taken by the galvanometer circuit. Therefore, it may be assumed that the increase in the potentials at different points in the potentiometer is proportional to the increase in the resistance of the section AB, i.e.,

$$\frac{V}{V_0} = \frac{r}{R}$$

Hence,

$$V = \frac{r}{R} V_0 \quad \text{and} \quad \mathscr{E}_2 = \frac{r}{R} V_0$$

389. 39.5 ohms.

Solution. When the slide is shifted from the position of equilibrium the current in the galvanometer circuit will be determined by the difference between the e.m.f. of the storage battery and the potential difference at the points AB set up by the cell. When the slide is shifted through one division the potential difference increases or decreases (see the solution to Problem 388) by

$$\Delta V = \frac{1}{n} V_0$$

where n is the number of divisions on the potentiometer scale.

If X is the resistance of the galvanometer, the current flowing in its circuit can be found from the equation

$$I (r + X) = \Delta V$$

Hence, $X = \dfrac{\Delta V}{I} - r = \dfrac{V_0}{nI} - r.$

When the slide is shifted through one division the maximum permissible value of X should produce a current of $I = 10^{-4}$ A, sufficient to deflect the pointer of the galvanometer by one division, i.e.,

$$X = \frac{2}{500 \times 10^{-4}} - 0.5 = 39.5 \text{ ohms}$$

390. $R = 6$ ohms; $r = \dfrac{\mathscr{E}}{I} - R = 4$ ohms.

Note. The unknown resistances can be found from the equations of Ohm's law for a closed circuit

$$I (R + r) = \mathscr{E}$$

and for a section of a circuit from

$$V = IR$$

391. $V = 0.$

Solution. Since the storage batteries are connected in series, the e.m.f. of the battery acting in the circuit will be 2 $\mathscr{E}$. The total resistance of the circuit is equal to $2r$. The current set up after the storage batteries are connected can be determined from the equation

$$2\mathscr{E} = I2r \quad \text{or} \quad I = \frac{\mathscr{E}}{r}$$

The potential difference across the terminals of any storage battery is

$$V = Ir - \mathscr{E} = 0$$

392. When the internal resistance of each storage battery is equal to R.

Solution. If $\mathscr{E}$ is e.m.f. and r the internal resistance of one storage battery, then for series connection an e.m.f. of NE will act in the circuit, the resistance of the circuit will be $R + Nr$ and the current

$$I_1 = \frac{N\mathscr{E}}{R + Nr}$$

in the case of parallel connection

$$I_2 = \frac{\mathscr{E}}{R + \dfrac{r}{N}} = \frac{N\mathscr{E}}{NR + r}$$

Comparing these equations we find that $I_1 = I_2$ at $R = r$.

393. Four lamps.
Solution. The resistance and current in each lamp will be

$$R_1 = \frac{V^2}{N} \quad \text{and} \quad I_1 = \frac{N}{V}$$

When m lamps are connected in parallel the resistance of the external circuit will be $R = \dfrac{R_1}{m} = \dfrac{V^2}{Nm}$. So that the lamps burn normally the current in the circuit should be

$$I = mI_1 = \frac{mN}{V}$$

Introducing these values of R and I into Ohm's law equation for an entire circuit, we get

$$\mathscr{E} = I(R + r) = \frac{mN}{V}\left(\frac{V^2}{mN} + r\right)$$

Hence,

$$m = \frac{(\mathscr{E} - V)V}{Nr} = 4$$

Another way of reasoning is also possible (see the solution to Problem 394).

394. $n = 110$.
Solution. If n storage batteries are connected in series, the e.m.f. of the battery will be $\mathscr{E} = n\mathscr{E}_1$ and the internal resistance $r = nr_1$. With a current I the voltage drop in the internal resistance of the battery will be equal to $V' = Ir$.

By Ohm's law the entire circuit should have

$$\mathscr{E} - V = V'$$

or

$$n\mathscr{E}_1 - V = Inr_1$$

Hence,

$$n = \frac{V}{\mathscr{E}_1 - Ir_1} = 110$$

395. $r = 1$ ohm; $\mathscr{E} = 3$ V.
Solution. It follows from Ohm's law that

$$\mathscr{E} - V_1 = I_1 r \quad \text{and} \quad V_1 = I_1 r_1$$

for the first case and

$$\mathscr{E} - V_2 = I_2 r \text{ and } V_2 = I_2 r_2$$

for the second case.

Solving these equations we find that

$$r = \frac{(V_2 - V_1)\, r_1 r_2}{V_1 r_2 - r_1 V_2}, \qquad \mathscr{E} = \frac{V_1 V_2\,(r_2 - r_1)}{V_1 r_2 - r_1 V_2}$$

396. $V = 3.2$ V; $I_1 = 1.6$ A; $I_2 = 0.4$ A.

Solution. The resistance of the external circuit is

$$R = \frac{r_1 r_2}{r_1 + r_2} = 1.6 \text{ ohms}$$

The current

$$I = \frac{\mathscr{E}}{R + r} = 2 \text{ A}$$

The voltage drop in the external circuit

$$V = IR = 3.2 \text{ V}$$

397. In each group there should be $m = 3$ storage batteries connected in series; $I = 10$ A.

Solution. If m storage batteries are connected in series in groups the resistance and the e.m.f. of each group will be $m r_0$ and $m \mathscr{E}_0$. If the total number of the storage batteries is N, one battery will contain $\dfrac{N}{m}$ groups, and the resistance and the e.m.f. of the battery will be $\dfrac{m^2 r_0}{N}$ and $m \mathscr{E}_0$ respectively.

The current in the circuit can be determined from the Ohm's law equation

$$I = \frac{m \mathscr{E}_0}{\dfrac{m^2 r_0}{N} + R} = \frac{N \mathscr{E}_0}{m r_0 + \dfrac{NR}{m}}$$

The current I will reach its maximum at that value of m for which the denominator of the fraction is smallest.

Since the product of the terms in the denominator does not depend on m and is constant $\left(m r_0 \dfrac{NR}{m} = N R r_0 \right)$ the values of the denominator will be smallest when its terms are equal to each other, i.e., when

$$m r_0 = \frac{NR}{m} \quad \text{or} \quad \frac{m^2 r_0}{N} = R$$

or, in other words, when the internal resistance of the battery becomes equal to the resistance of the external circuit.

Therefore,

$$m=\sqrt{\frac{NR}{r_0}}=3$$

will correspond to the minimum denominator and, hence, to the maximum current in the circuit.

398. $n=\sqrt{\frac{NR}{r_0}}$; $m=\sqrt{\frac{Nr_0}{R}}$.

Note. See the solution to Problem 397.

The resistance of the group is $\frac{r_0}{m}$, the number of groups is $n=\frac{N}{m}$ and the resistance and the e.m.f. of the battery is

$$r=\frac{nr_0}{m}=\frac{Nr_0}{m^2} ; \quad \mathscr{E}=n\mathscr{E}_0=\frac{N\mathscr{E}_0}{m}$$

With any value of m the current in the circuit is

$$I=\frac{N\mathscr{E}_0}{\dfrac{Nr_0}{m}+mR}$$

399. Number of storage batteries is 160. The battery should be composed of 40 groups connected in series. In each group four storage batteries are connected in parallel.

Solution. The current produced by the compound battery is equal (see the solution to Problem 398) to

$$I=\frac{N\mathscr{E}_0}{\dfrac{Nr_0}{m}+mR} \tag{1}$$

A battery of N elements will produce the maximum current when it is composed in such a way that its internal resistance is equal to the resistance of the external circuit (see the solution to Problem 397), i.e., when in the denominator of equation (1)

$$\frac{Nr_0}{m}=mR \tag{2}$$

Solving equations (1) and (2) simultaneously for N and m we find that

$$N=\frac{4r_0RI^2}{\mathscr{E}_0^2}=160$$

$$m=\sqrt{\frac{Nr_0}{R}}=4$$

N and m calculated in this manner determine the minimum number of the storage batteries that should be taken and also how they should be connected.

400. $\mathscr{E} = 12$ V.

Solution. If a source of current with an e.m.f. force $\mathscr{E}$ is cut into a section of a circuit, the current in this section will be determined by the joint action of this e.m.f: and the potential difference applied to the ends of the section.

The storage battery is connected for charging as shown in Fig. 297. The current flows in the opposite direction to the e.m.f. $\mathscr{E}$. The Ohm's law equation for the section of a circuit with a storage battery may be written as $V - \mathscr{E} = IR$.

Hence, $\mathscr{E} = V - IR$.

401. $R = 1$ ohm.

Solution. The Ohm's law equation for a section of a circuit with a storage battery and an auxiliary resistance R will be

$$V - \mathscr{E} = I(r + R)$$

Hence,

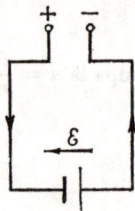

Fig. 297

$$R = \frac{V - \mathscr{E} - Ir}{I}$$

402. $R_0 = 5.5$ ohms. If $R > R_0$ the battery will be charged. If $R < R_0$ the battery will be discharged.

Solution. So that current does not flow through the battery the potential difference between the poles of the dynamo should be equal to the e.m.f. of the battery, i.e., $V = \mathscr{E}_2$ or, in other words, the voltage drop inside the dynamo should be

$$Ir = \mathscr{E}_1 - \mathscr{E}_2 \qquad (1)$$

Utilizing the equation $V = \mathscr{E}_2$ and knowing that the entire current produced by the dynamo passes through the resistance R_0 we may write

$$IR_0 = \mathscr{E}_2 \qquad (2)$$

It follows from equations (1) and (2) that

$$R_0 = \frac{\mathscr{E}_2 r}{\mathscr{E}_1 - \mathscr{E}_2} = 5.5 \text{ ohms}$$

403. 5 A.

Solution. The voltage supplied by the charging plant can be found from equations

$$V - \mathscr{E}_1 = I_1 r$$

$$V = \mathscr{E}_1 + I_1 r = 110 \text{ V}$$

The current at the end of charging is

$$I_2 = \frac{V - \mathscr{E}_2}{r} = 5 \text{ A}$$

24. Thermal Effect of Current. Power

404. $t = 1.42$ s.

405. $t = 4$ min 40.6 s.

406. $X = 2$ ohms.

Note. Use Ohm's law to determine the currents in the circuit before and after the shunt is switched on and calculate by the Joule-Lenz law the amount of heat liberated in the heater in both cases.

407. 40; 45; 37 W; 33; 50; 71 per cent.

Solution. The current in the circuit is $I = \dfrac{\mathscr{E}}{R+r}$.

The useful power $N = I^2 R = \dfrac{\mathscr{E}^2 R}{(R+r)^2}$.

The total power developed by the battery $N_0 = \mathscr{E}I = \dfrac{\mathscr{E}^2}{R+r}$.

The efficiency $\eta = \dfrac{N}{N_0} = \dfrac{R}{R+r}$.

The growth in the external resistance simultaneously reduces both the total power developed by the battery and the losses due to the liberation of heat by the internal resistance of the battery. In this case the losses diminish at a faster rate than the total power.

When the resistances are high the change in the useful power is affected primarily by the reduction in the total power of the battery. In the case of low resistances, the greater part is played by the reduction in the losses. For this reason, when a low resistance cut into the external circuit is increased, the useful power grows despite the drop in the total power.

The battery gives the maximum useful power when the external and internal resistances are equal.

408. $x = pn$.

Solution. Assume that the internal resistance of one cell is equal to r, its electromotive force is $\mathscr{E}_0$ and the resistance of a unit length of the wire is R_1.

Then, after the wire of length l is connected, the circuit will carry a current

$$I_1 = \frac{n\mathscr{E}_0}{nr + lR_1}$$

Every second an amount of heat

$$Q_1 = I_1^2 l R_1 = \frac{n^2 \mathscr{E}_0^2}{(nr + lR_1)^2} R_1 l$$

will be liberated in the wire and an amount of heat

$$q_1 = \frac{Q}{l} = \frac{n^2 \mathscr{E}_0^2}{(nr + lR_1)^2} R_1$$

on each unit length of the wire.

When a wire of length pl and x cells are switched in, the amount of heat liberated on each unit of wire length will be

$$q_2 = \frac{x^2 \mathscr{E}_0^2}{(xr + plR_1)^2} R_1$$

When both wires are heated to the same degree, a unit length of each should evolve the same amount of heat, i.e.,

$$\frac{n^2 \mathscr{E}_0^2}{(nr + lR_1)^2} = \frac{x^2 \mathscr{E}_0^2}{(xr + plR_1)^2}$$

Hence, $x = pn$.

409. 65 W; 15.4 per cent.

Solution. The current flowing through the storage battery is

$$I = \frac{V - \mathscr{E}}{r} = 5 \text{ A}$$

The power consumed by the plant is

$$N_1 = VI = 65 \text{ W}$$

The power expended to heat the storage battery is

$$N_2 = I^2 R = 10 \text{ W}$$

410. $N_1 = 1,100$ W; 82 per cent.

Note. The power consumed by the motor is $N_1 = VI$; the power expended to heat the windings of the motor is $N_2 = I^2 R$ and the power converted into mechanical energy is $N_3 = N_1 - N_2 = I(V - IR)$.

411. 45 min; 10 min.

Solution. If r_1 and r_2 are the resistances of the first and second coils and V is the mains voltage, the amount of heat liberated will be

$$Q = \frac{V^2 t_1}{r_1} = \frac{V^2 t_2}{r_2}$$

Hence,

$$\frac{r_1}{r_2} = \frac{t_1}{t_2} = \frac{1}{2}$$

In the case of a series connection the resistance of the electric kettle heater will be $r_3 = r_1 + r_2$ and the time of heating can be determined from the equation

$$Q = \frac{V^2 t_3}{r_1 + r_2} = \frac{V^2 t_1}{r_1}$$

i.e.,

$$\frac{t_3}{r_1 + r_2} = \frac{t_1}{r_1}$$

or

$$t_3 = \frac{r_1 + r_2}{r_1} t_1 = 3t_1 = 45 \text{ min}$$

In the case of parallel connection of the coils

$$Q = \frac{V^2 t_4 (r_1 + r_2)}{r_1 r_2} = \frac{V^2 t_1}{r_1}$$

Hence, $t_4 = \dfrac{r^2}{r_1 + r_2} t_1 = 10$ min.

412. The resistance of the cooled part of the wire becomes markedly less than the resistance of the part that is not cooled and the current accordingly grows in the circuit.

Since the same current is passed through both parts, most of the heat will begin to evolve from the uncooled portion of the wire.

413. $t = \dfrac{C_1 d_1 S_1^2 (T_1 - T_0)}{I^2 \rho} = 0.09$ s

$$T_3 - T_0 = \frac{I^2 \rho_2 t}{C_2 d_2 S_2^2} = \frac{C_1 d_1 S_1^2 \rho_2}{C_2 d_2 S_2^2 \rho_1} (T - T_0) = 0.1°$$

Note. The amount of heat liberated from each centimeter of the fuse is

$$Q = I^2 \frac{\rho_1}{S_1} t$$

The amount of heat necessary to heat this wire to its melting point is

$$Q = C_1 d_1 S_1 (T_1 - T_0)$$

The heating of copper wire can be calculated from the same equations.

414. $C = 0.59$ cal/g·deg.

Solution. If R is the resistance of each of the wires and I is the current, the amount of heat liberated in the calorimeters will be the same and equal to

$$Q = I^2 R t$$

The thermal balance equation for the calorimeter and water shows that $Q = m \Delta T_1$ where m is the mass of the water. In the calorimeter which contains the liquid, $Q = C m \Delta T_2$.

Hence, $C = \dfrac{\Delta T_1}{\Delta T_2} = 0.59$ cal/g·deg.

415. More heat will be evolved in the steel wire for a series connection and for a parallel one more in the copper wire.

416. It will be reduced by a factor of 2.25.

417. $R_0 = \sqrt{R_1 R_2}$.

25. Permanent Magnets

418. $m_1 = \sqrt{\dfrac{F r^2}{2}} \approx 620$ cgs electromagnetic units; $m_2 = 1,240$ cgs electromagnetic units.

419. $H = m \dfrac{l^2 + 2al}{a^2 (a+l)^2} \approx 0.36$ cgs electromagnetic unit.

Solution. The intensity of the field at the point A will be equal to the difference in the intensities set up by each pole separately, i.e.,

$$H = H_1 - H_2 = \frac{m}{(a+l)^2} - \frac{m}{a^2}$$

The vector H will be directed along the axis of the magnet towards the south pole.

420. $m \approx 65$ cgs electromagnetic units.

Solution. The interaction between the near like poles will be $F_1 = \dfrac{m^2}{a^2}$. Since $a \ll l$, the interaction of the like remote poles will to a good approximation be $F_2 = \dfrac{m^2}{4l^2}$ and that of the unlike poles $F_3 = \dfrac{m^2}{l^2}$

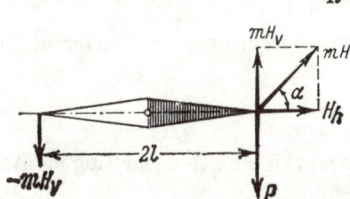

Fig. 298

$$\frac{F_2}{F_1} = \frac{a^2}{4l^2} \approx 0.001$$

and

$$\frac{F_3}{F_1} = \frac{a^2}{l^2} \approx 0.004$$

The forces F_2 and F_3 are infinitely small as compared with the force F_1 and therefore the magnetic masses can be determined with a sufficient degree of accuracy from the force F_1 assuming $F_1 = P$, i.e.,

$$m = \sqrt{Pa^2} = a \sqrt{P} \approx 65 \text{ cgs electromagnetic units}$$

421. $H_v = 0.5$ cgs electromagnetic unit; $H_h = 1$ cgs electromagnetic unit; $H = 1.12$ cgs electromagnetic units.

Solution. The magnetic needle will be acted upon by two forces tending to turn it (Fig. 298), their moments are: the moment of the force due to the terrestrial magnetic field acting on the poles of the needle

$$F_1 2l = m H_v 2l$$

and the moment produced by the load suspended from the needle and equal to Pl.

The condition for equilibrium of the needle will be

$$m H_v 2l = Pl$$

Hence, $H_v = \dfrac{P}{2m} = 0.5$ cgs electromagnetic unit.

The horizontal component and the total intensity of the terrestrial magnetic field can be found from the equation

$$H_h = H_v \cot \alpha \quad \text{and} \quad H = \sqrt{H_v^2 + H_h^2}$$

422. *Solution.* At distances equal to the length of the magnetic needle the terrestrial magnetic field of the Earth is practically uniform, i.e., its intensity remains constant both in magnitude and direction. For this reason, the terrestrial magnetic field acting on the magnetic needle can only give rise to rotating moments and fails to set up any resultant, other than zero.

The field of a permanent magnet is heterogeneous at distances equal to the length of the needle and changes appreciably. The intensity of the field at one end of the needle is stronger than at the other. Therefore, the field of the magnet acting on the needle sets up a resultant force which is not equal to zero and causes both rotational and translational motion of the needle.

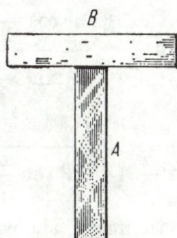

Fig. 299

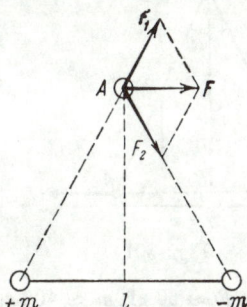

Fig. 300

423. The bars should be placed as shown in Fig. 299. If the bar A is made of soft iron it will not attract the bar B.

424. $F = \dfrac{8m}{5\sqrt{5}\,l^2} \approx 0.36$ dyn.

Solution. The poles of the magnet will act with forces F_1 and F_2 directed as shown in Fig. 300 and equal to

$$F_1 = F_2 = \frac{m}{2r_1^2}$$

The position and magnitude of the resultant can easily be found from simple geometrical considerations.

425. If the needle is arranged in the plane perpendicular to the magnetic meridian it will take a vertical position.

The direction of the magnetic meridian can be found if the instrument is revolved around a vertical axis to determine the position in which the needle will be vertical. In this case the magnetic meridian will coincide in direction with the axis of rotation of the needle.

426. At first the needles will be drawn apart since the magnet sets up like magnetic poles at the lower ends of the needles which repel each other. When the magnet is brought sufficiently close the interaction between the magnet and each of the needles will exceed that between the needles which will then sink being attracted to the magnet.

After the magnet is removed the needles will again be drawn apart due to the residual magnetisation.

427. $m \approx 6.5$ cgs electromagnetic units.

Solution. Let us consider one of the needles. It will be acted upon by the weight P acting through the centre of gravity B and the inter-action of the magnetic poles $F = \dfrac{m^2}{a^2}$ (Fig. 301) acting through the point A. For the needle to be in equilibrium the sum of the moments of the forces acting on the needle should be equal to zero, i.e.

$$P \frac{l}{2} \sin \frac{\alpha}{2} = Fl \cos \frac{\alpha}{2}$$

or $\dfrac{P}{2} \sin \dfrac{\alpha}{2} = \dfrac{m^2 \cos \dfrac{\alpha}{2}}{4l^2 \sin^2 \dfrac{\alpha}{2}}$

hence

$$m = l \sin \frac{\alpha}{2} \sqrt{2P \tan \frac{\alpha}{2}}$$

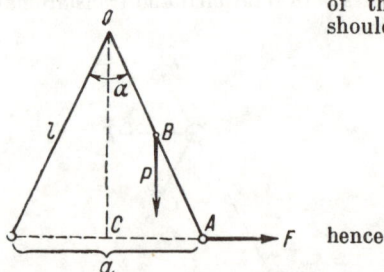

Fig. 301

428. $F \approx 60$ gf; $m \approx 406$ cgs electromagnetic units. The equilibrium is stable.

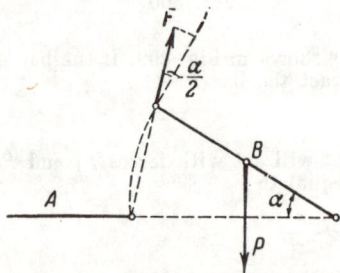

Fig. 302

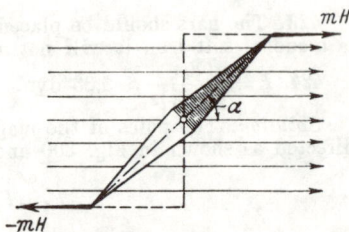

Fig. 303

Solution. The magnet B will be acted upon by the moment of weight $P \dfrac{l}{2} \cos \alpha$ and the moment of magnetic interaction

$$Fl \cos \frac{\alpha}{2} = \frac{m^2 l \cos \dfrac{\alpha}{2}}{4l^2 \sin^2 \dfrac{\alpha}{2}}$$

(Fig. 302). It follows from the condition of equilibrium that

$$\frac{P}{2}\cos\alpha = \frac{m^2\cos\dfrac{\alpha}{2}}{4l^2\sin^2\dfrac{\alpha}{2}}$$

and therefore the magnetic masses of the poles of the magnets will be

$$m = l\sin\frac{\alpha}{2}\sqrt{\frac{2P\cos\alpha}{\cos\dfrac{\alpha}{2}}}$$

429. $M = PH\sin\alpha$.
Solution. Each of the poles of the needle will be acted upon from the side of the magnetic field by a force $F = mH$ which with the needle

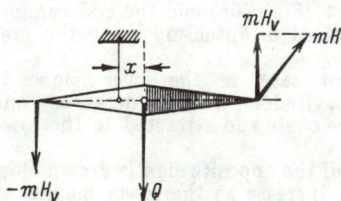

Fig. 304

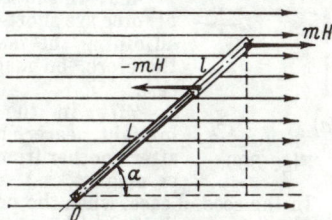

Fig. 305

ın the position shown in Fig. 303 has a rotational moment

$$F\frac{l}{2}\sin\alpha = \frac{1}{2}mHl\sin\alpha$$

The rotational moment of the couple of forces acting on the needle will   be

$$M = mlH\sin\alpha = PH\sin\alpha$$

430. $x \approx 0.05$ mm.
Solution. If x is the distance from the point of support to the centre of gravity of the needle (Fig. 304), the condition of equilibrium of the needle may be written as

$$Qx = PH_v$$

hence

$$x = \frac{PH_v}{Q}$$

431. $M = PH\sin\alpha$.
Solution. The moments of the forces acting upon each pole of the needle will be equal (Fig. 305) to

$$mH(l + L)\sin\alpha$$

and
$$-mHL \sin \alpha$$

Hence, the total moment of the force acting on the bar is
$$M = mHl \sin \alpha = PH \sin \alpha$$

432. $P_1 = m \dfrac{l}{2} = \dfrac{P}{2}$.

434. The arrangement shown in Fig. 306b corresponds to the position of unstable equilibrium and that in Fig. 306a to stable equilibrium.

435. Upon contact with plate B, part of the magnetic lines of force are short-circuited through this plate (Fig. 307). The number of the lines of force penetrating plate A sharply decreases. As a result the interaction between the magnet and plate A also decreases and the latter drops.

436. In the second case most of the magnetic lines of force are short-circuited inside the part of the rod adjoining the magnet (Fig. 308) and the rod cannot, therefore, be magnetized as intensely as in the first case.

437. In the first case, as the lower magnet is brought nearer, the cylinders will be detached one after another from the chain and attracted to the lower magnet.

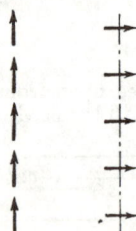
(a)   (b)
Fig. 306

In the second case, when the pole of the opposite sign is drawn closer, the "strength" of the chain will increase as the lower magnet is

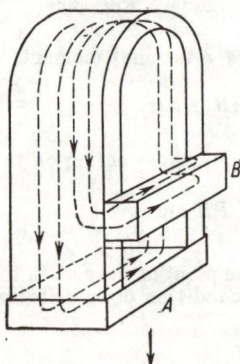
Fig. 307

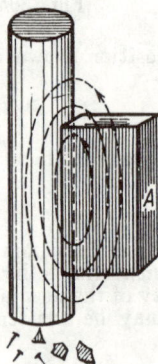
Fig. 308

brought near. As soon as the second magnet comes in contact with the lower cylinder, the magnet will be attracted to the chain and will remain hanging on it.

438. The magnets are detached owing to a sharp decrease in the number of the lines of force passing inside each magnet. At the moment of detachment an e.m.f. is induced in the coil due to the reduction in the number of the lines of force.

439. (a) The bar will be magnetized due to the action of the vertical component of the terrestrial magnetic field and the magnetic needle will be attracted as it is brought near the ends of the bar.

(b) The bar will be magnetized by the action of the horizontal component of the terrestrial magnetic field. The magnetic needle will always turn towards the nearest end of the bar.

(c) The bar will not be magnetized by the magnetic field of the Earth and the needle will not change its position when the bar is brought close.

It is assumed in all the three cases that when the needle is brought close to the bar the distance between them is still large enough for the additional magnetization of the bar due to the external magnetic field of the needle to be neglected.

If the bar is turned, the behaviour of the needle will not change in any of the three cases.

440. Iron loses its magnetic properties at quite a high temperature and behaves as any other non-magnetic substance (copper, glass, etc.). When the nail is heated in the flame of a burner to this temperature the interaction of the magnet and the nail abruptly decreases, the nail returns to the initial position. leaves the flame and gets cool. The magnetic properties of the nail thus cooled are regained, the forces of interaction between the nail and the magnet increase and the nail is again drawn to the magnet.

441. See the solution to Problem 440.

The impeller rotates because the force of attraction acting on the rods which are still outside of the flame of the burner is much larger than the forces acting on the hot rods or just emerging from the flame.

26. Magnetic Field of a Current

442. See Fig. 309.

Note. Since the intensity of the magnetic field of rectilinear current diminishes in proportion to r the lines of force will be closer together near the conductor and spaced further apart at some distance away from it.

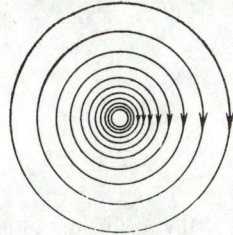

Fig. 309

443. $H = 0.08$ cgs electromagnetic unit; $F = 0.4$ dyn.

444. $H = \dfrac{0.2\,I}{R}$.

Solution. In order to derive the formula, calculate the work done by the magnetic field forces over the circuit enclosed by the sections of the radii drawn from the line of the current and the arcs of the concentric circles—the lines of force of the field. This calculation (see the solution to Problem 339) gives us

$$\frac{H_1}{H_2} = \frac{R_2}{R_1}$$

Since, when $R_0 = 1$, $H_0 = 0.2I$, it follows that

$$H = \frac{0.2I}{R}$$

445. The current should flow from west to east. The current-carrying conductor should pass at a distance $R = 5$ cm below the point A.

Solution. For the resultant magnetic field at the point A to have the vector H directed vertically the magnetic field of the current should completely compensate for the horizontal component of the terrestrial magnetic field, i.e.,

$$H_h = \frac{0.2I}{R}$$

Hence,

$$R = \frac{0.2I}{H_h}$$

446. The point will be located at a distance $R = \dfrac{0.2\,I}{\sqrt{H_h^2 + H_v^2}} = 1.9$ cm

in the northern hemisphere above and to the north of the conductor, and in the southern hemisphere above and to the south of the conductor.

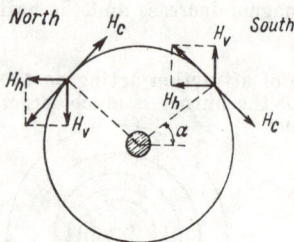

Fig. 310

The direction from the conductor to the point B will in both cases make an angle α with the horizontal such that $\tan \alpha = \dfrac{H_h}{H_v} = 0.4$.

Note. In the case considered in the problem the magnetic field of current should completely compensate for the magnetic field of the Earth. The vector for the intensity of the terrestrial magnetic field is equal to $H = \sqrt{H_h^2 + H_v^2}$ and makes an angle α with the horizontal such that $\tan \alpha = \dfrac{H_h}{H_v}$.

Obviously, the intensity vector of the magnetic field of current H_c should have the same magnitude and pass at the same angle to the horizontal, but in the opposite direction (Fig. 310).

447. $H = 0$.

Solution. The current flowing along the pipe may be regarded as the sum of many identical linear currents uniformly distributed over the surface of the pipe. Correspondingly, the intensity of the magnetic field at any point in space may be considered as the sum of the intensities of the fields established by such linear currents.

Fig. 311 shows the cross section of a pipe along which current flows. Let us compare the intensities of the magnetic fields set up at the point A by the linear currents passing through very small arcs S_1 and S_2. The currents I_1 and I_2 passing through S_1 and S_2 will be directly proportional to S_1 and S_2, in other words $\dfrac{I_1}{I_2}=\dfrac{S_1}{S_2}$. But S_1 and S_2 are proportional to the distances from the point A and therefore $\dfrac{I_1}{I_2}=\dfrac{R_1}{R_2}$. The intensity of the magnetic field created by each of these elements at the point A can be calculated from the formula for the magnetic field of rectilinear current, i.e.,

$$H_1=\frac{0.2I_1}{R_1} \quad \text{and} \quad H_2=\frac{0.2I_2}{R_2}$$

Hence,

$$\frac{H_1}{H_2}=\frac{I_1}{R_1}\frac{R_2}{I_2}=1$$

i.e., $H_1 = H_2$ or $H_1 - H_2 = 0$.

Since by this method it is possible to select for each element of the cross section of the pipe another corresponding element that completely compensates for the magnetic field of the first element at the point A, the resultant magnetic field of the current flowing along the pipe will be zero at any point inside the pipe.

Fig. 311

448. The intensity will be equal to that of the magnetic field set up by the current flowing along the axis of the cable in the inner conductor, i.e., $H = \dfrac{0.2I}{R}$ (see Problem 447).

449. $A=FS=mH \times 2\pi R=\dfrac{0.2Im}{R}2\pi R=0.4\pi Im=12.6$ ergs.

The work done by the magnetic field forces when the pole m is passed along a closed circuit depends only on the intensities of the currents penetrating the area confined within this circuit, and does not depend on the shape and size of the circuit.

450. It cannot. The surplus work obtained when the pole is moved along a closed path around the current-carrying conductor is produced by the energy of the current source. As the pole moves in the magnetic field the source of its e.m.f.'s acting in the circuit of the current spends only some of its energy in producing Joule heat, the rest being converted into mechanical work done by the magnetic field. The machine will stop as soon as the store of energy of the current source is exhausted.

451. $F = 0$.

Solution. All the elements of current in the branching are completely symmetrical with respect to the point O. Each element A (Fig. 312) corresponds to another element B parallel to A with the same direction of current and which is the same distance away from O, but situated on the other side of it. The intensities of the magnetic field produced by the elements A and B at the point O will be equal in magnitude

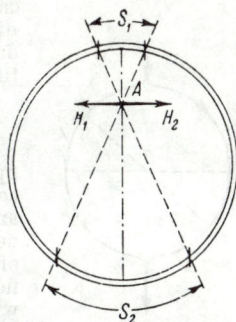

18–1325

but opposite in direction and, as they are added up, cancel each other out.

452. The cork will first turn so that the plane of the wire is perpendicular to the magnet and then it will approach the magnet.

453. $F = 0.3$ dyn.

454. The electric charges moving together with the disk set up in the surrounding space a magnetic field similar to that of a circular current. The lines of force of this field above the disk will be perpendicular to the plane of the drawing, behind it. The magnetic needle will turn clockwise (if viewed from below).

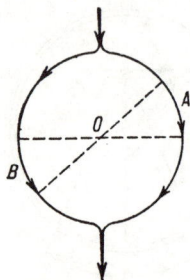

Fig. 312

455. $\tan \alpha = \dfrac{0.2\pi I}{H_h R} = 0.314$; $\alpha = 17°24'$.

Solution. The magnetic needle is acted upon by two magnetic fields: the horizontal component of the terrestrial magnetic field H_h and the magnetic field of the current H_c. The needle always arranges itself so that the sum of the rotating moments generated by these fields is equal to zero. The sum of the moments will be equal to zero if the resultant of all the forces is directed along the needle (Fig. 313), i.e., if

$$\tan \alpha = \frac{H_h}{H_c}$$

Since we are given that the needle is small and is arranged in the

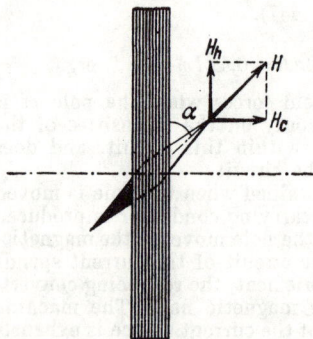

Fig. 313

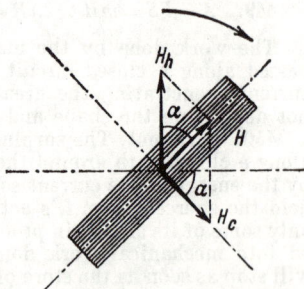

Fig. 314

centre of the circle, it may be assumed that the intensity of the field of the current acting on the needle is

$$H_c = \frac{0.2\pi I}{R}$$

(see Problem 453). Hence,

$$\tan \alpha = \frac{0.2\pi I}{H_h R}$$

456. $\sin \alpha = \frac{H_c}{H_h} = \frac{1}{2}$, $\alpha = 30°$.

Solution. When the circle turns through an angle α so also does the intensity vector of the magnetic field of current H_c (Fig. 314). For the needle to lie in the plane of the circle after rotation, this plane should accommodate vector H—the intensity of the resultant field formed by the summation of the magnetic fields of the Earth and the current. Since H_c is always perpendicular to the plane of the circle with current it follows from simple geometrical considerations that

$$H = \frac{H_c}{\tan \alpha} \quad \text{and} \quad H = H_h \cos \alpha$$

Hence,

$$\frac{H_c}{\tan \alpha} = H_h \cos \alpha \quad \text{or} \quad \sin \alpha = \frac{H_c}{H_h}$$

457. $H = 50.4$ oersteds.

27. Forces Acting in a Magnetic Field on Current-Carrying Conductors

458. The conductor will first turn counterclockwise in a horizontal plane (if viewed from the top) and will then go down.

Note. The lines of force of the magnetic field at the point A (Fig. 315) pass from the bottom to the top at an angle to the line of the current. At the point O the lines of force pass parallel to the line of current and at the point B from the top to the bottom at an angle to the line of current.

The nature of motion of the conductor can be determined by applying the left-hand rule consecutively to the sections of the conductor adjoining the points A, O and B.

459. The conductor will wind itself around the magnet as shown in Fig. 316.

Note. In order to determine how the conductor moves, find the direction of the lines of force in the sections adjoining the points A and B and apply the left-hand rule to establish the direction of motion of these sections.

460. The conductors will tend to turn so that they become parallel to each other and then will be mutually attracted.

Note. In order to solve the problem, consider the action of the magnetic field of current I_1 on the sections of the conductor with current I_2 adjoining the points A, O and B (Fig. 317).

461. $F = 0$.

Solution. The lines of force of the magnetic field of current I_2 are concentric circles. The current I_1 passes along one of these lines of force. For this reason the magnetic field will not act on the current I_1. All the elements of the conductor with current I_2 also coincide everywhere in direction with the axial line of force of the magnetic field

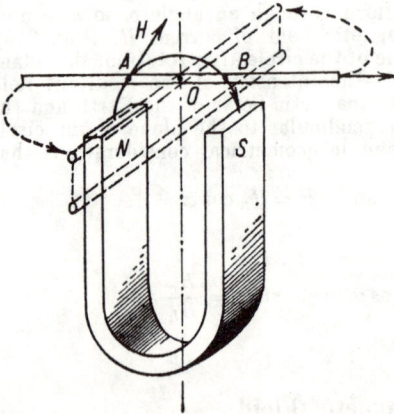

Fig. 315

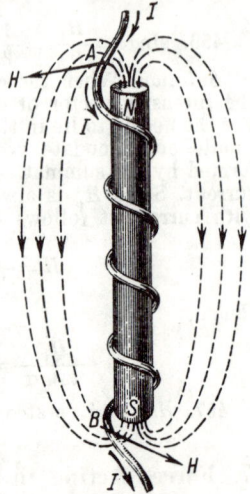

Fig. 316

set up by the current I_1. Likewise, the current I_2 will not be acted upon by any forces from the side of the magnetic field.

462. The end of the spring will perform periodic oscillating motions.

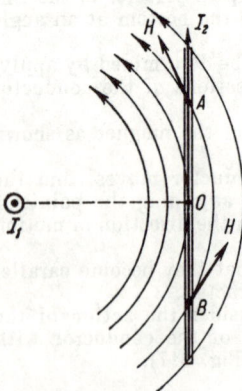

Fig. 317

Solution. When the circuit is closed each coil of the spring will, in the same way as circulating current, set up its own magnetic field and attract the adjacent coils. The spring will be compressed and its lower end will leave the mercury. The current circuit will be interrupted, the magnetic field will vanish and the spring will then straighten itself out. As soon as the end of the spring touches the mercury the entire process will be repeated again.

463. Along a circumference.

Solution. A beam of moving charged particles is similar to a certain current I_1 having the direction of the velocity v of the particles. If the lines of force of the magnetic field are directed towards the observer (Fig. 318) the particles moving with a velocity v will be acted upon from the side of the field by the force F directed perpendicularly to the velocity v and distorting the path of the particles (apply the left-hand rule to find the direction of the force).

Since we are given that the magnetic field is uniform, the force F will be constant in magnitude and impart centripetal accelerations a which are also constant in magnitude to the particles. It follows from the fact that the velocity of the particles and the centripetal acceleration is constant, the radius of curvature of the path of the particles

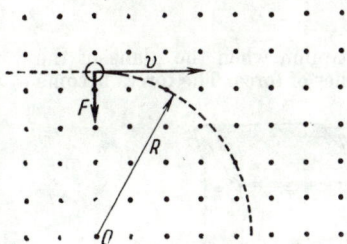

Fig. 318

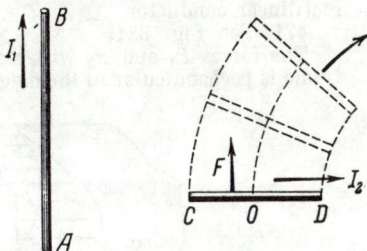

Fig. 319

should everywhere be constant to $\left(a = \dfrac{v^2}{R}\right)$, i.e., the path should be circular.

464. The conductor CD will first move upwards along the conductor AB, turning at the same time as shown in Fig. 319, and then will move away from it.

Solution. The direction of motion of each element in the conductor CD can be found from the left-hand rule. Since it is given that the conductor is uniform its centre of gravity will lie at the point O.

The intensity of the magnetic field at the point C will be greater than at the point D (see Problems 442, 444). Larger forces will act on the elements adjoining the point C from the side of the magnetic field than on the identical elements in contact with the point D. The point of application of the resultant of all the forces acting on the conductor

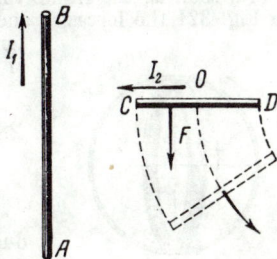

Fig. 320

CD will lie to the left of its centre of gravity. Therefore, as the conductor CD moves up it will at the same time begin to revolve clockwise around the point O.

465. See Fig. 320 and the solution to Problem 464.

466. They will turn and set themselves parallel so that the directions of the currents flowing in them are the same.

467. The ring will be attracted to the magnet, fit itself round it and move along, stopping at the neutral line. In this case the direction of the lines of force of the magnetic field of the current will coincide with the lines of force of the magnet field.

468. The ring will jump off the magnet, turn over and fit round the magnet with its other side foremost.

469. The disk will begin to rotate clockwise.

470. If the initial position of the frame is arbitrary it will tend to turn and set itself in the plane passing through the rectilinear conductor so that the direction of current in the side of the frame closest to the conductor coincides with the direction of current in the rectilinear conductor.

471. See Fig. 321.

The forces F_1 and F_2 will reach maximum when the plane of the frame is perpendicular to the magnetic lines of force. The forces become

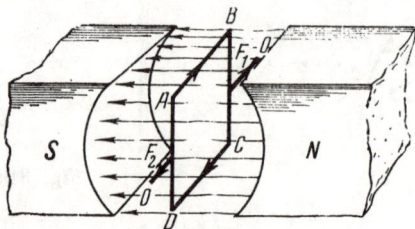

Fig. 321

zero when the plane of the frame lies in the same direction as the lines of force.

As soon as the frame turns through 180° from the position shown in Fig. 321 the forces F_1 and F_2 will reverse their directions and will tend to compress the frame along its axis of rotation.

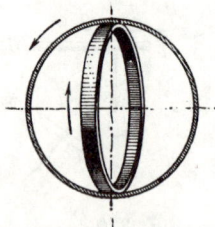

Fig. 322

28. Electromagnetic Induction

472. See Fig. 322.

473. The current will flow from C to A.

When the direction of motion of the conductor is changed the induction current is reversed.

474. If the conductor is arranged above the magnet and the latter is turned westwards, the conductor will carry a current from north to south. If the magnet is turned eastwards, the current will flow from south to north. If the conductor is under the magnet, the current will flow from south to north in the first case and from north to south in the second.

475. In the first case the current will flow from the axis of the disk towards the lower edge and in the second it will flow in the opposite direction.

476. When the conductors are moved towards each other the direction of the current induced in the second one will be opposite to the direction of the current I. If the conductors are drawn apart, the directions of the currents will coincide.

477. The current will flow counterclockwise.

478. As it passes through the position A the current will flow counterclockwise. When passing through the position B there will be no induced current. In the case of the position C the current will flow clockwise.

479. As the pendulum oscillates, the periodic changes in the area enclosed by the circuit will induce currents in the latter. The induced currents will be directed so that their magnetic field compensates for the change in the flux of the magnetic lines of force penetrating the area of the circuit.

When the pendulum swings so as to increase the area enclosed by the circuit the current will flow counterclockwise, and if the motion is such as to decrease the area enclosed by the circuit, the current will be clockwise. The interaction of the magnetic field of induced currents with the field of a permanent magnet will further damp the oscillations of the pendulum.

480. An e.m.f. will be induced because the introduction of the wire into the space between the poles of the magnet will change the number of the magnetic lines of force passing through the area enclosed by the circuit.

481. The potentials at the ends of the wings will be different.

If the aircraft flies in any other direction the potential difference will not change its value because it depends only on the vertical component of the terrestrial magnetic field and on the horizontal velocity of the aircraft.

482. The e.m.f. will be minimum when the frame arranges itself in the plane passing through the rectilinear conductor.

The maximum e.m.f. will be induced when the frame is perpendicular to this plane.

483. There will be no current.

Chapter IV

OPTICS

29. The Nature of Light

484. $\lambda - \lambda_1 = 250$ millimicrons.

Solution. The wavelength of red light in vacuum will be $\lambda = \dfrac{c}{v}$

and the velocity of these rays in glass will be $v = \dfrac{c}{n}$.

The wavelength of red light in glass is $\lambda_1 = \dfrac{v}{\nu}$.

The change in the wavelength is $\lambda_1 - \lambda = \dfrac{c}{\nu} \cdot \dfrac{1-n}{n}$.

485. $v_1 = \dfrac{c}{n_1} = 2 \times 10^{10}$ cm/s; $v_2 = \dfrac{c}{n_2} = 1.95 \times 10^{10}$ cm/s.

486. $v > 2 \times 10^{10}$ cm/s.

487. Coloured bands in thin films are caused by the interference of light waves reflected from the upper and lower boundaries of the film. A wave reflected from the lower boundary should traverse a longer path than a wave reflected from the upper boundary. For this reason the wave reflected from the lower boundary lags in phase behind the wave reflected from the upper boundary. The amount of this lag expressed in terms of the length of a light wave depends on the thickness of the film at the point of reflection and on the length of the light waves in the film.

Upon reflection, the waves corresponding to various colours will acquire a path difference equal to an odd number of half-waves at the points of various thickness. At each given point in the film the interference of the reflected rays will damp some colours of the spectrum and intensify others. Therefore, the points in a film of varying thickness will seem to be coloured differently.

488. Each of the horizontal interference bands corresponds to some definite thickness of the film. The water in the internal layer of the film gradually flows into its lower part and makes it thicker while the upper part grows thinner. The points corresponding to some definite thickness of the film are gradually displaced and the respective interference bands move downwards with them. After some time the film in the upper part becomes one quarter the thickness of the length of the shortest light wave incident on the film. During the interference of rays reflected from the film the waves of all lengths will be damped at the points in the film, and the spot will appear dark in the reflected light.

489. Since after the space is filled with liquid the conditions of reflection of the waves from the lower surface of the lens and from the upper surface of the glass become identical (both waves are reflected from an optically denser medium), a bright spot will appear in the centre of the rings in the reflected light instead of the dark spot that was there before the space between the glass and the lens was filled with liquid. The rings will be displaced and their width altered in the space between the glass and the lens due to the decrease in the velocity of light. The rings will become narrower and denser.

490. The light will be reflected from the front and rear surfaces of the film. The conditions of reflection will be the same in both cases. For this reason the reflected rays leaving the film will have a path difference equal to half the length of the wave and will completely damp each other in the case of interference.

491. $E = 3.31 \times 10^{-13}$ erg.

492. $E = h\nu = 3.03 \times 10^{-12}$ erg.

493. $F = 6 \times 10^4$ tons.

Solution. The surface of the Earth receives the entire quantity of light coming from the Sun inside a solid angle formed by the circle equal to the area of the cross section of the globe. The total energy absorbed by the Earth is $E = \pi R^2 \times 1.9$ cal where $R = 6,400$ km is the radius of the Earth.

The force of the sunrays on the Earth, if they are completely absorbed by the terrestrial surface, is $F = \dfrac{E}{c}$.

494. $F = \dfrac{E}{c} = 6.8 \times 10^{-6}$ dyn.

Note. See Problem 493.

495. *Note.* The quantity of light from the Sun incident on any area S is proportional to the solid angle which this area makes with the Sun. As the area is moved away this angle diminishes in proportion to the square of the distance of the area from the Sun. Accordingly, the quantity of light falling on the area and therefore the force exerted by the light should also diminish in proportion to the square of the distance as the area is moved away.

30. Fundamentals of Photometry

496. $h = 1$ m.

497. By 40,000 times; 160,000 lx.

498. *Solution.* $E = \dfrac{I}{r^2} \cos \alpha = \dfrac{Ih}{(h^2 + a^2)^{3/2}} = 25$ lx.

499. $l = 55$ m.

Note. The illumination provided by one lamp on the ground at a distance $a = \dfrac{l}{2}$ will be

$$\frac{E}{2} = \frac{Ih}{(h^2 + a^2)^{3/2}}$$

Hence,

$$a = \sqrt{\left(\frac{2Ih}{E}\right)^{2/3} - h^2} = 27.5 \text{ m}$$

500. The illumination will be $\sqrt{2}$ times greater at the point C than at the point B.

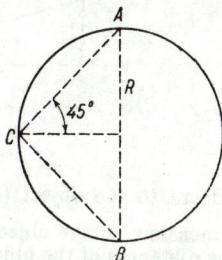

Fig. 323

Solution. The illumination at the point B is

$$E_0 = \frac{I}{4R^2}$$

and at the point C

$$E_1 = \frac{I \cos \alpha}{r^2}$$

From triangle ABC (Fig. 323)
$$r = AC = 2R \cos \beta$$
where β is the angle at the vertex A. Therefore
$$E_1 = \frac{E_0 \cos \alpha}{\cos^2 \beta}$$

When $\alpha = \beta = 45°$
$$E_1 = E_0 \sqrt{2}$$

501. $E = 5$ lx.

502. $E = \dfrac{3l}{l^2}$ and is the same for both sides.

503. The illumination of a plate in a camera depends on the quantity of light passed through the lens and on the ratio of the area of the object being photographed to the area of its image on the plate.

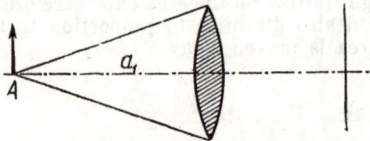

Fig. 324

The quantity of light Q passing through the lens is proportional to the solid angle which the lens makes with the point of the object, i.e., it is directly proportional to the area of the aperture of the lens S and is inversely proportional to the square of the distance a_1 from the

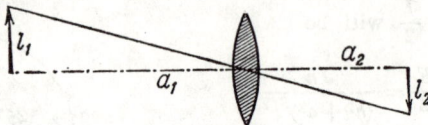

Fig. 325

camera to the object (Fig. 324) or $Q \sim \dfrac{S}{a_1^2}$. The ratio of the linear dimensions of the object to those of the image is equal to the ratio of the distances of the object and the image to the camera lens (Fig. 325).

Therefore, the area of the object σ_1 is related to the area of the image σ_2 as the square of the distances of the object and the image from the lens, i.e.,
$$\frac{\sigma_1}{\sigma_2} = \frac{a_1^2}{a_2^2}$$

Comparing the results obtained, we find the illumination of the image
$$E \sim \frac{Q\sigma_1}{\sigma_2} = \frac{S}{a_1^2} \frac{a_1^2}{a_2^2} = \frac{S}{a_2^2}$$

i.e., the illumination of the image in the camera is inversely proportional to the square of the distance from the lens to the image.

The image of a distant object is closer to the lens than that of an object located nearby. Hence, the illumination of the image of a distant object will always be greater than that of the image of a near object. In the first case (near object) a longer exposure is required than in the second case.

504. $\eta \approx 4$ per cent.

The quantity of light emitted by the lamp is approximately equal to two joules $= 2 \times 10^7$ ergs.

505. $Q = 2.4 \times 10^{15}$ kcal; 0.441×10^{-9} of all the energy of the light emission from the Sun; the total amount of energy received by the Earth is 0.22 of the energy received by Jupiter.

Solution. The amount of energy received by the Earth is

$$Q_1 = \pi r_1^2 q_1$$

where πr_1^2 is the cross-sectional area of the Earth.

The ratio of Q to the total energy of emission E is

$$\frac{Q_1}{E} = \frac{\omega_1}{4\pi} = \frac{r_1^2}{4R_1^2}$$

where ω_1 is the solid angle which the Earth makes with the Sun. The ratio of the energies received by the Earth and Jupiter is

$$\frac{Q_1}{Q_2} = \frac{\omega_1}{\omega_2} = \frac{r_1^2 R_2^2}{r_2^2 R_1^2}$$

31. The Law of Rectilinear Propagation and Reflection of Light

506. On one straight line so that the planes of the object and the screen are perpendicular to this straight line.

507. The radius of the half-shadow $R_1 = 15$ cm and the radius of the full shadow $R_2 = 7.5$ cm. The shadow will disappear when the ball is at a height of 2.5 m. The dimensions of the shadow will be constant if the radius of the ball is equal to that of the sphere.

Note. The radius of the half-shadow can be found from the similarity of the triangles CC_2D, BB_1D and AA_2D (see Fig. 326). The radius of the shadow is clear from the triangles OA_1A, OBB_1 and OCC_1. The straight line C_2C_1 is equal to the diameter of the sphere and BB_1 to the radius of the ball. The sections AC and AB are equal respectively to the heights of the sphere and the ball above the floor.

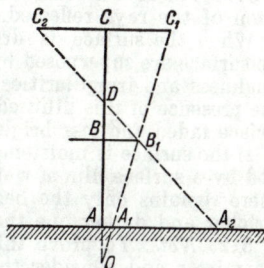

Fig. 326

508. The sources should be moved along the tangents to the rod passing through the point O.

When motion occurs in other directions the shadows diverge or are superimposed on each other.

509. With the given arrangement each point of the object will be represented by a bright circle whose diameter can be found from the ratio (Fig. 327)

$$\frac{d'}{d} = \frac{ED}{CD}$$

i.e.,

$$d' = \frac{ED}{CD}\, d = 2 \ \text{mm}$$

Therefore, the parts less than 2 mm in size cannot be distinguished because the bright circles representing the separate points of these parts will be superimposed on each other.

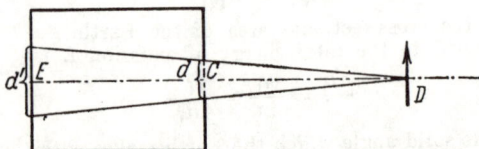

Fig. 327

510. The shape of the light spot will depend on the form of the source of light and on the position of the screen onto which the spot is projected. For example, if the source is circular in shape and the screen is placed at various angles with respect to the incident rays the spot will take the form of a circle or a more or less elongated ellipse.

For the conditions specified in the problem the shape of the spot will not depend on the shape of the mirror.

511. The colour of any surface is determined by the spectral composition of the rays reflected by it.

When the surface is dry the rays corresponding to the colour of the surface are superposed by randomly diffused white light due to the roughness and irregularities of the surface (cloth fibres, for example). The presence of this diffused white light makes the basic colour of the surface faded and less bright.

If the surface is moistened with water all the irregularities are covered by a surface film of water and the diffused white light disappears. There remains only the basic hue on the surface which we see as a a richer and darker one than before moistening.

512. *Note.* To prove this, construct the image of the point A in the mirror and consider the ratio between the lengths of the paths A_1CB and A_1DB (Fig. 328).

513. If the observer looks along the line passing through the images A' and B' of the pins in the mirror (Fig. 329), he will see these images superimposed on each other. In the position C the observer will see the image of the pin B to the right of the image of the pin A.

In the position D he will see the image of the pin B to the left of the image of the pin A.

514. See Fig. 330. The rays coming from the point O' will be propagated inside the band restricted by the straight lines AB and CD

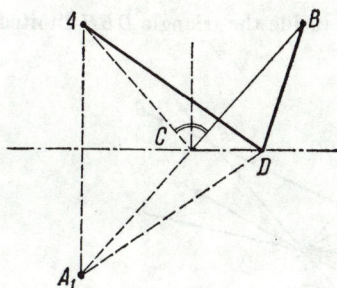

Fig. 328

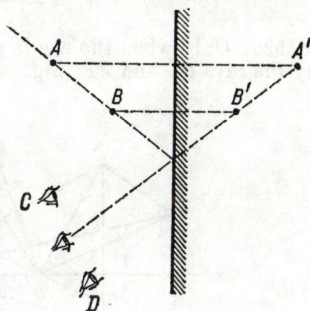

Fig. 329

after reflection from the mirror. The rays coming from O will be inside the bands AE and CF. The rays coming from all the points on the object will only arrive at each point in space between the straight lines

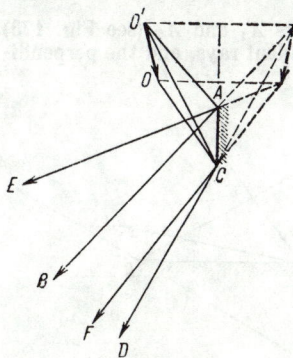

Fig. 330

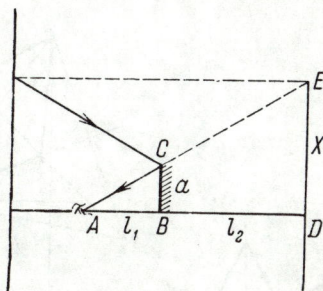

Fig. 331

AB and CF. The eye can only see the entire image of the object if it is at one of the points enclosed between the rays AB and CF.

515. By 10 cm.

517. At an angle of 45°.

518. $\alpha = 2°$; $x = l \tan \alpha \approx l\alpha = 5 \times 0.035 = 17.5$ cm.

519. 3 m.

Solution. The image of the wall will be behind the mirror at a distance $l_2 = 4$ m. If the eye is placed at the point A (Fig. 331) it will see only the rays coming from all the points in the section of the wall image DE after the reflection in the mirror BC. Thus, the section of the wall visible in the mirror will have dimensions

$$X = \frac{l_1 + l_2}{l_1} a = 3 \text{ m}$$

520. Only when the eye is placed inside the triangle DEH limited by the rays DG and EF (Fig. 332).

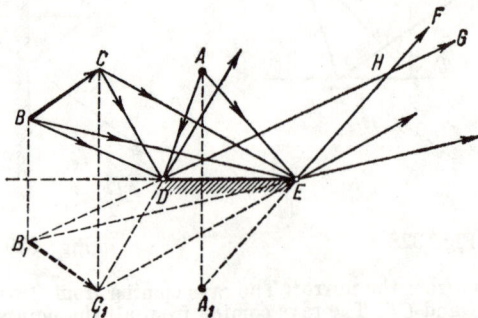

Fig. 332

521. The perpendiculars to the mirrors A_1 and A_2 (see Fig. 173) should make angles of 22°30′ with the incident rays, and the perpendi-

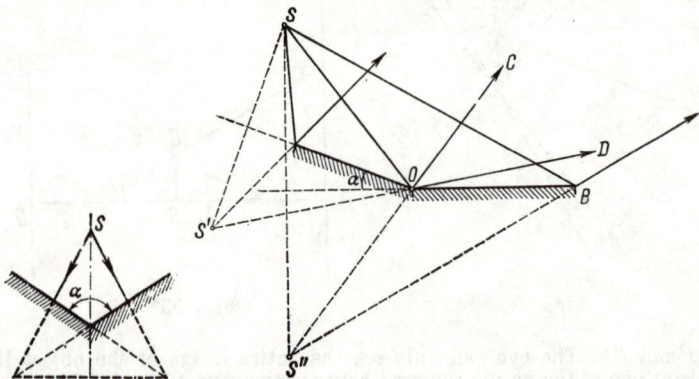

Fig. 333   Fig. 334

culars to the mirrors A_3 and A_5—angles of 77°30′. The height of all the mirrors should not be less than the diameter of the lenses d, the width of the mirrors A_1 and A_2 should be equal to $\dfrac{d}{\cos 22°30′} \approx 1.03d$ and the width of the mirrors A_3 and A_5 should be 2.61d.

522. See Fig. 333; $\alpha = 120°$.

523. The centre of the circle lies at the point O where the mirrors intersect.

524. Inside the band limited by the rays OC and OD (Fig. 334).

32. Spherical Mirrors

526. $f = \sqrt{pq} = 40$ cm.

527. *Solution.* It follows from the similarity of the triangles ABF and CDF (Fig. 335) that

$$\frac{l_2}{l_1} = \frac{f}{a_1 - f}$$

and from the concave mirror formula

$$a_2 = \frac{a_1 f}{a_1 - f}$$

Hence,

$$\frac{l_2}{l_1} = \frac{a_2}{a_1}$$

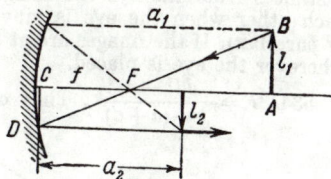

Fig. 335

528. $a_2 = \frac{1}{3}$ m; $R = 0.50$ cm; $f = 25$ cm (see Problem 527).

529. $f = 2.5$ cm.

Note. If a_1 and a_2 are the initial distances of the object and the image from the mirror, l_1 and l_2 are the respective lengths of the object and the image, and a_3 is the distance from the image after the object is moved, the focal length can be found from the following system of equations:

$$\frac{l_1}{l_2} = \frac{a_1}{a_2} = 4, \quad \frac{a_1 - b}{a_3} = 2, \quad \frac{1}{a_1} + \frac{1}{a_2} = \frac{1}{f} \text{ and } \frac{1}{a_1 - b} + \frac{1}{a_3} = \frac{1}{f}$$

530. $\frac{l_2}{l_1} = \frac{f}{p}$.

Note. The ratio $\frac{l_2}{l_1}$ can be found from the equations:

$$\frac{l_2}{l_1} = \frac{a_2}{a_1}, \quad a_1 = p + f, \quad a_2 = q + f, \quad pq = f^2$$

See Problem 526.

531. $f = \frac{l}{2} = 50$ cm; $d = 2l\varphi$.

532. At a distance of 50 cm from the mirror and 2 cm from each other.

Note. When the two halves of the mirror are drawn apart the source is displaced 0.5 cm from the optical axes of the halves. The distances of the images from the new optical axes of the halves can be calculated in the same way as in Problem 527.

533. $b = 15$ cm.

Solution. If a_1 and a_2 are the distances from the mirror to the source and its image respectively, then, from the given conditions, the ratios $a_1 = a + b$ and $a_2 + a = b$ should hold. Inserting the values of a_1 and a_2 obtained from these ratios in the convex mirror formula we get

$$b = \sqrt{2aF + a^2}$$

The coincidence of the image can be established by observing the changes in the relative position of the images when the eye is moved away from the optical axis of the mirror. If the images are at various distances from the eye the images will be displaced with respect to each other when the eye is moved as described above (phenomenon of parallax). If the images are at the same distance, they will coincide wherever the eye is placed.

534. $F = \dfrac{d(b-a)}{b-(a+d)}$. They cannot. See Fig. 336.

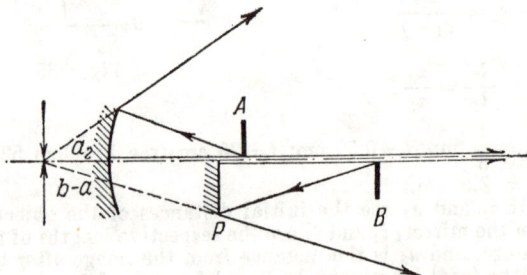

Fig. 336

Note. The distances a_1 and a_2 from the concave mirror to the first needle and its images should satisfy the ratios $a_1 = d$ and $a_2 = b - a$. When these values of a_1 and a_2 are inserted in the mirror formula, remember that a_2 should be negative.

In order to find whether the images can be observed at the same time, consider the path of the rays that actually take part in the formation of the images. All the rays reflected from the concave mirror and forming the image of the first needle pass above the optical axis. All the rays forming the image of the second needle in the flat mirror pass below the optical axis of the concave mirror. Since the rays reflected from the two mirrors do not overlap at any point it is impossible to observe both images at the same time. To compare the position of the images the observer should move his eye in the vertical plane near the optical axis and view the images in turn.

535. See Fig. 337; $h_1 = 5$ cm.

Solution. If K_1P_1 is the image of the object KP, the rays forming the image of the point K will only be propagated inside the cone enclosed by the rays K_1A and K_1B. The rays forming the image of the point P will pass inside the cone enclosed by the rays P_1P and P_1C.

In order to see the entire image the observer should place his eye inside the band between the straight lines K_1A and P_1C in which the rays coming from all the points on the object are superposed. The maximum dimensions of the object are determined from the similarity

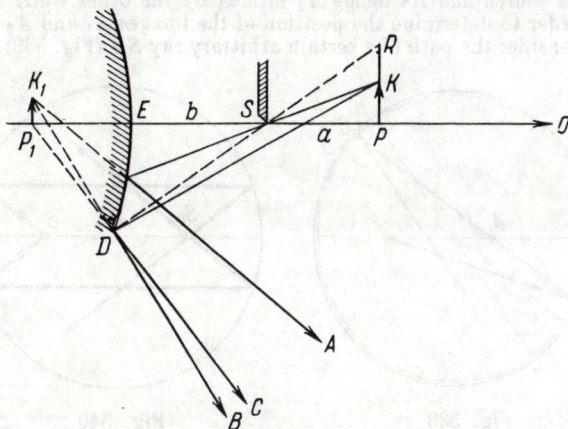

Fig. 337

of the triangles DES and SPR (in this case the curvature of the section DE is neglected as is common in elementary optics):

$$\frac{PR}{DE} = \frac{a}{b}, \quad PR = h_1 = \frac{ad}{2b} = 5 \text{ cm}$$

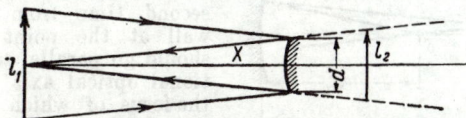

Fig. 338

536. $X = 45$ cm.

Note. If l_2 is the image of the face (Fig. 338) and a_2 is the distance from the image to the mirror, the eye will see all of the image for the minimum distance X from the mirror when the following condition is observed:

$$\frac{X}{d} = \frac{X + a_2}{l_2}$$

The values of a_2 and l_2 can be determined from the convex mirror formulas (see Problem 526) and used to find

$$X = F \frac{l_1 + 2d}{d}$$

537. At a distance of $5/6R$ from the nearest wall; at a distance of $R/2$ from the remote wall.

Note. To solve the problem, calculate in the first case the position of the image A_1 produced by the remote wall and then considering this as a source find its image A_2 formed by the other wall.

In order to determine the position of the images A_1 and A_2 graphically, consider the path of a certain arbitrary ray SB (Fig. 339) coming

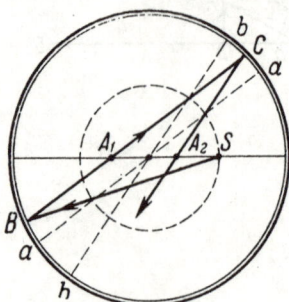

Fig. 339

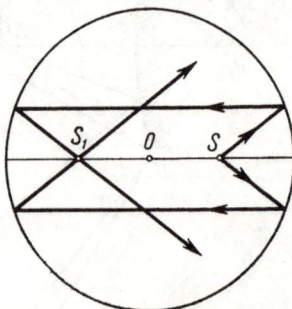

Fig. 340

from the source at a small angle to the optical axis. An additional optical axis aa drawn so as to be intersected by the ray SB at the focus is necessary to determine the direction of this ray after the first reflection at the point B. The reflected ray BC will be parallel to this axis. The image A_1 will be at the point of intersection of the ray BC with

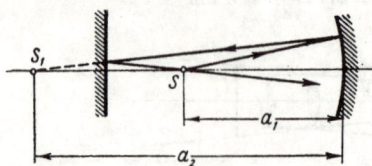

Fig. 341

the principal optical axis. After the ray is reflected for the second time from the nearest wall at the point C the ray should go parallel to the additional optical axis bb through the focus of which the ray BC passes. The image A_2 is at the point of intersection of the ray CA_2 and the principal optical axis.

The sequence of operations for graphical construction of the image in the second case is shown in Fig. 340.

538. $X = 90$ cm; it will not change.

Note. The flat mirror should be placed halfway between the source S and its image S_1, i.e., the following should hold (Fig. 341):

$$X = \frac{a_2 - a_1}{2} + a_1 = \frac{a_1 + a_2}{2} = \frac{a_1^2}{2(a_1 - F)}$$

539. $X = 0.28R$.

Solution. Let us denote the distance of the source from the concave mirror by X and the distance of the image produced by the convex mirror from this mirror by y (Fig. 342). The ratio

$$\frac{1}{2R-X} - \frac{1}{y} = \frac{2}{R}$$

will hold for the image produced by the convex mirror.

The image in the convex mirror is the source with respect to the

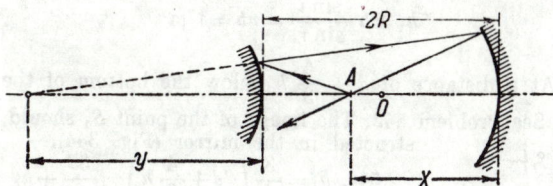

Fig. 342

concave mirror. If the point where the rays meet after two reflections coincides with the source, then

$$\frac{1}{2R+y} + \frac{1}{X} = \frac{2}{R}$$

The required distance is determined by solving these equations.

Since the path of the light rays is reversible when the initial direction of the rays is changed, the position of the point where the rays meet remains the same.

33. Refraction of Light at Plane Boundary

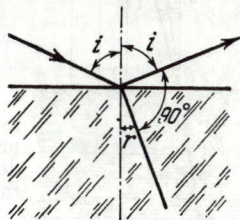

Fig. 343

540. $i = 56°24'$.

Solution. It follows from geometrical construction that $i + r = 90°$, $r = 90° - i$ (Fig. 343). From the law of refraction $\frac{\sin i}{\sin r} = n$. Since $\sin r = \cos i$ we get $\tan i = n = 1.5$.

541. 2.9 m.

Note. The length of the shadow of the pile will be

$$l_1 = h_1 \tan r = 3 \times 0.62 \approx 1.9 \text{ m}$$

542. $h = 1$ m.

Solution. The object will appear to be at a point S_1 where the extensions of the rays striking the eye of the swimmer meet (see Fig. 344). From triangles OBS and OBS_1

$$OB = OS \tan i = h \tan i$$
$$OB = OS_1 \tan r = h_1 \tan r$$

Hence,

$$h_1 = h \frac{\tan i}{\tan r}$$

Since the angles i and r are small we may assume that $\tan i \approx \sin i$ and $\tan r \approx \sin r$. Therefore

$$h_1 = h \frac{\sin i}{\sin r} = nh = 1 \text{ m}$$

543. At a distance of $d + \dfrac{4}{3} h$ below the bottom of the vessel.

Note. See Problem 542. The image of the point S_1 should be constructed in the mirror (Fig. 344).

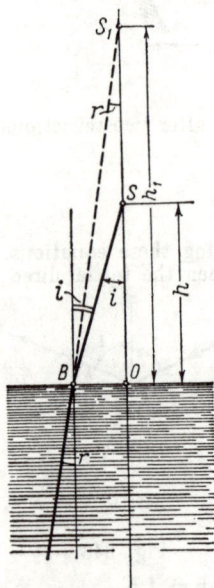

544. $h_1 = \dfrac{3}{4} \left(2d + \dfrac{4}{3} h \right) = \dfrac{3d}{2} + h.$

Solution. If S is the position of the image found in Problem 543 and $OS = H = 2d + \dfrac{4}{3} h$ the observer will see this image at the point S_1 which is at a distance h_1 from the surface of the water.

It follows from triangles OAS and OAS_1 (Fig. 345) (assuming that the angles i and r are small) that

$$h_1 = \frac{H}{n} = \frac{3}{4} H$$

545. $n = 1.41$.

Note. Since it is given that the refracted ray is perpendicular to the second face of the prism it follows from simple geometrical considerations that the angle of refraction of the ray $r = 30°$.

546. $h = 30$ cm.

The absence of the parallax shows that the images coincide.

Note. See the solutions to Problems 526 and 533.

547. If $n < 2$ the ray will be refracted and emerge from the second face.

Fig. 344

If $n > 2$ the ray will be subjected to full internal reflection at the second face and emerge from the prism through the third face perpendicularly to the latter.

548. $n = \dfrac{\sqrt{4d^2 - a^2}}{a} = 1.34.$

Solution. If a bright image of the point source appears on the upper boundary of the plate, the rays coming from the source into the plate at small angles i (Fig. 346) pass unhindered through the lower boundary. If the angle of incidence of the rays on the lower boundary is larger than the critical angle the rays are subjected to total internal reflection, illuminate the sensitive photolayer from below and form a halo.

The refractive index can be calculated directly from Fig. 346 and from the definition of the critical angle

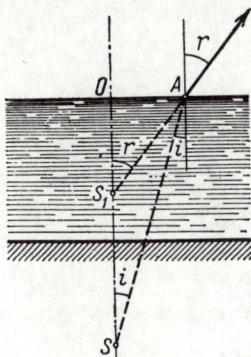

$$\sin i' = \frac{1}{n}$$

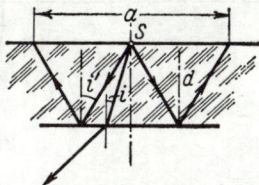

Fig. 345   Fig. 346

34. Lenses and Composite Optical Systems

551. $d = f\varphi = 2.35$ mm.

Note. See Fig. 347. The image of the Sun will be in the focal plane of the lens and will be seen from the optical centre of the lens at an

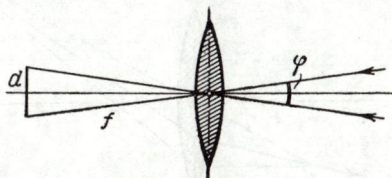

Fig. 347

angle φ just like the Sun. Since the angle φ is small it may be assumed that

$$\tan \varphi \approx \varphi$$

552. In the plane passing through the optical centre of the lens.

Note. To prove this it is enough to follow the motion of the image when the object is brought up to the lens (Fig. 348).

Remember that in any position of the object the direction of the ray AF remains constant. The ray passing through O slowly turns about this point, as the object is brought up to the lens, making an increasing angle with the optical axis.

553. See Fig. 349.

554. It will move 5 cm closer to the screen.

Note. In calculating the new position of the apex of the beam from the thin lens formula the apex of the beam A should be regarded as an object.

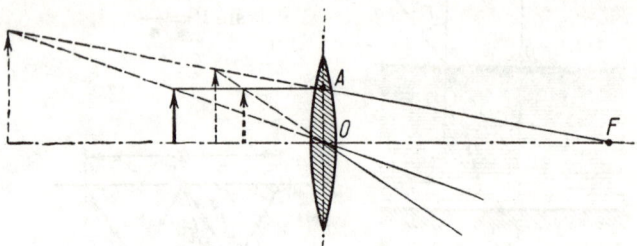

Fig. 348

Remember that although in the normal case (the point of the object is the apex of the diverging beam of rays) the apex of the beam lies on the side where the rays are incident on the lens, in this particular case the apex of the beam lies on the other side of the lens with respect

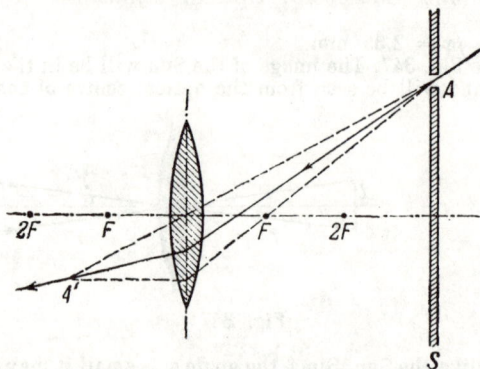

Fig. 349

to the incident rays. For this reason, in calculations the distance a_1 to the object should be introduced into the thin lens formula with the minus sign, i.e., $a_1 = -15$ cm.

In the case of graphical construction, determine the path of the auxiliary rays BA and CA impinging on the lens from the left in the direction of the point A. The point where these rays meet on the other side of the lens will show the new position of the apex of the beam A' (Fig. 350).

555. $f = 30$ cm.

Note. See the solution to Problem 554.

556. See Fig. 351.

557. The source should be more than twice the focal length away and the observer at one of the points in the area BAC (Fig. 352).

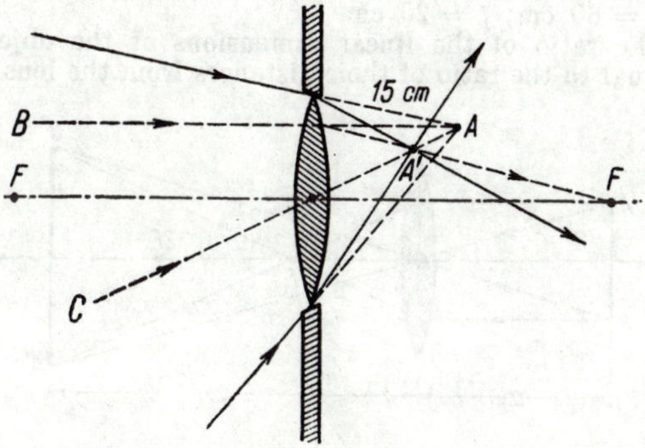

Fig. 350

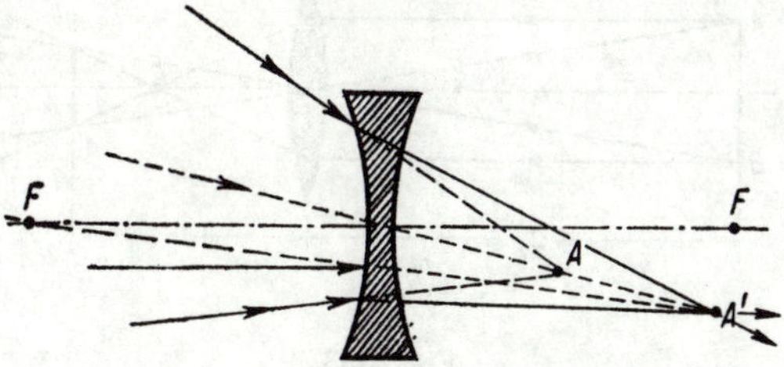

Fig. 351

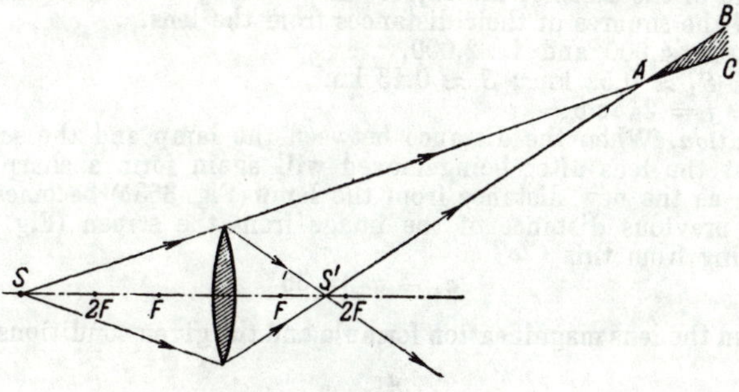

Fig. 352

Note. The rays coming from the source past the mounting of the lens towards the observer and the rays from the image are propagated inside the cones shown in Fig. 352.

The source and its image can only be seen simultaneously when there are regions in space where the beams overlap.

558. 4 cm.

559. $a_2 = 60$ cm; $f = 20$ cm.

Note. The ratio of the linear dimensions of the object and the image is equal to the ratio of their distances from the lens. Therefore,

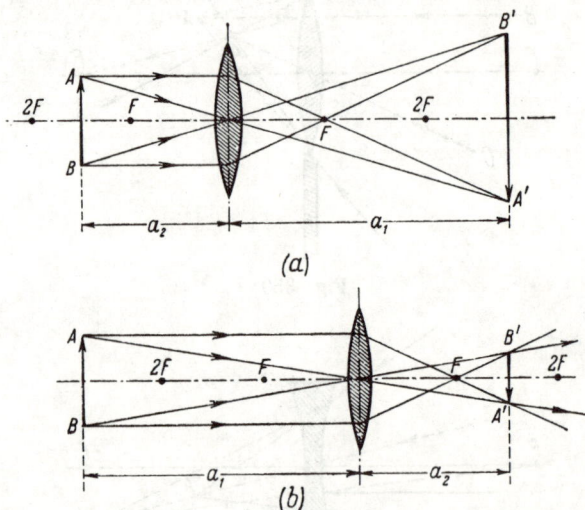

(a)

(b)

Fig. 353

the ratio of the areas of the object and the image will be equal to the ratio of the squares of their distances from the lens.

560. $1 : 4,000$ and $1 : 2,000$.

561. $S_1 \approx 0.52$ km²; $S \approx 0.13$ km².

562. $f = 24$ cm.

Solution. When the distance between the lamp and the screen is constant the lens after being moved will again form a sharp image as soon as the new distance from the lamp (Fig. 353b) becomes equal to the previous distance of the image from the screen (Fig. 353a). Following from this

$$a_1 - a_2 = 36$$

From the lens magnification formula and the given conditions we get

$$\frac{a_1}{a_2} = 2$$

Solving these equations simultaneously and utilizing the lens formula we obtain

$$f = \frac{2a_2}{3} = 24 \text{ cm}$$

563. $a = l \tan \varphi = 60$ cm.

Note. The size of the object is determined by the minimum viewing angle of the eye.

564. At the principal focus of the lens.

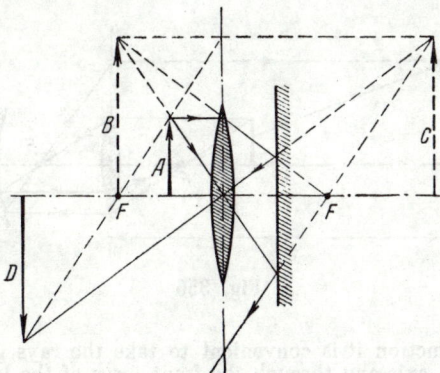

Fig. 354

565. The image will be at a distance $a_2 = 60$ cm on the same side of the lens as the object (see Fig. 354).

Solution. In order to determine the position of the image produced by the system as a whole, calculate the positions of the images formed by the separate parts of the system consecutively along the path of the rays.

The lens for the object A will produce a virtual image B lying to the left of the lens at a distance

$$a = \frac{a_1 F}{a_1 - F} = 30 \text{ cm}$$

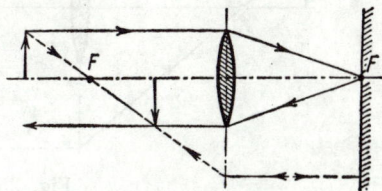

Fig. 355

The mirror having B as the object will form an image C lying at a distance $a + b = 45$ cm behind the mirror or, in other words, at a distance $a' = a + 2b = 60$ cm from the lens.

On the right the lens receives rays from C as the object and the lens will form for C a real image D a distance

$$a_2 = \frac{a'F}{a' - F} = 60 \text{ cm}$$

to the left.

566. The image will be real and will lie between the lens and its focus. See Fig. 355.

567. $a_2 = 100$ cm. See Fig. 356.

Note. See the solution to Problem 565. In calculations, bear in mind that the first image formed by the lens lies behind the mirror.

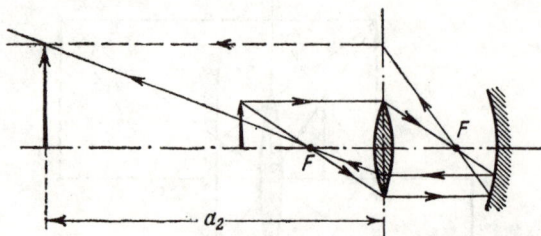

Fig. 356

For construction it is convenient to take the rays going parallel to the optical axis and through the front focus of the lens.

568. The source should be at infinity.

569. See Fig. 357; $a_2 = 2.5$ cm.

570. If the distance between the halves is infinitely small, the beam will, for all intents and purposes, remain parallel. If this distance

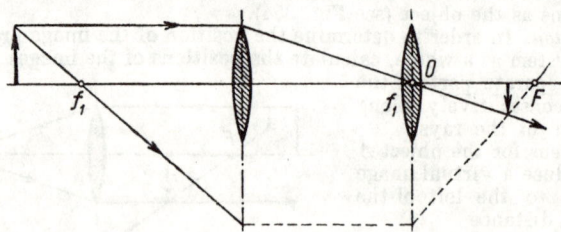

Fig. 357

is large but less than the focal length of each half, the beam of parallel rays will be transformed into a beam of converging rays.

When the distance between the lenses is larger than the focal length of each, the parallel beam, will be converted by the system into a diverging beam,

TO THE READER

Mir Publishers welcome your comments on the content, translation and design of this book.

We would also be pleased to receive any suggestions you care to make about our publications.

Our address is:

USSR, 129820, Moscow I-110, GSP
Pervy Rizhsky Pereulok, 2
MIR PUBLISHERS

Other Books on Physics for Your Library

PROBLEMS IN PHYSICS

A. Pinsky, Cand. Sc. (Phys.-Math.)

The material of this book is arranged in accordance with the two-volume course *Fundamentals of Physics* by B. Yavorsky and A. Pinsky (Mir Publishers, 1975). It contains more than 750 problems covering all the topics discussed in the textbook. In addition to the traditional material, the book contains problems on theory of relativity (including relativistic collision, accelerators; creation of particles, etc.), quantum mechanics (uncertainty principle, de Broglie waves, potential barrier, degenerate state of matter), statistics, wave and quantum optics, atomic and nuclear physics. The problems in astro-physics illustrate the applications of laws of physics to cosmic objects. Most of the problems, especially the difficult ones, carry detailed solutions or hints. The book is meant for students of physics and mathematics at teachers-training institutes and for physics teachers at secondary schools and polytechnics.

Contents. Motion and Force. Conservation Laws. Molecular-Kinetic Theory of Gases. Molecular Forces and States of Aggregation of Matter. Electrodynamics. Vibrations and Waves. Fundamentals of Quantum Physics. Nuclear and Elementary Particle Physics. Tables.

PHYSICS FOR THE TECHNICIAN

L. Zhdanov, D. Sc.

This book is meant to serve as a textbook for polytechnics. The material of the text has been arranged in accordance with the syllabus in physics for polytechnics and secondary schools. A considerable effort has been made to bring out the engineering applications of physics and to illustrate the basic facts behind various physical phenomena. The International System (SI system) of units has been used throughout the book. Different sections of the book have been augmented by exercises in the form of questions on the subject and numerical examples.

The book is intended for a wide circle of readers: students of polytechnics and senior secondary schools, and all those interested in self-study.

Contents. Physical Quantities and Their Measurement. Molecular Physics and Heat. Electricity. Oscillations and Waves. Optics. Fundamentals of the Theory of Relativity. Physics of the Atomic Nucleus. Fundamental Aspects of Astronomy.

JUNIOR PHYSICS

A. PERYSHKIN, Corr. Mem. USSR Acad. Ped. Sc., and N. RODINA, D. Sc. (Ped.)

The authors of this textbook were awarded the USSR State Prize for 1978. The book contains a preliminary course in physics, introducing to the basic ideas of the science, viz. the structure of matter, mechanical motion and forces, heat phenomena, electricity and magnetism. The chief methodological idea is to identify theoretical propositions by generalizing empirical facts. The textbook has a great deal of material illustrating the relationship between physics and life. It provides questions and assignments for the students and describes laboratory work.

SENIOR PHYSICS. Part II

B. BUKHOVTSEV, D. Sc.,   Yu. KLIMONTOVICH,   Cand. Sc.,   and G. MYAKISHEV, D. Sc.

This is the second volume of the textbook prescribed by the USSR Ministry of Education for high-school students. It is a continuation of Senior Physics, Part I, by A. Kikoin and I. Kikoin dealing with basic concepts of Mechanics. This book aims at acquainting the reader with the fundamentals of thermal phenomena and molecular physics. The description has been confined to the grass-root level and does not involve higher mathematics. The authors have been teaching physics at the Moscow State University for many years.

Contents. Molecular-Kinetic Theory. Gas Laws. Ideal Gas. The First Law of Thermodynamics. Phase Transformations in Liquids and Gases. Surface Tension of Liquids. Solids. Fundamentals of Electrodynamics. Electrostatics. Direct Current. Electric Current in Various Media. Magnetic Field of Currents. Electromagnetic Induction.

FUNDAMENTALS OF PHYSICS, Vols. I-II

B. Yavorsky, D. Sc. and A. Pinsky, Cand. Sc.

This textbook explains the concepts and most important advances of modern physics without resort to higher mathematics. Avoids the traditional division between classical and modern physics and endeavours to present all material so as to develop quantum mechanical concepts.

The textbook is intended for secondary schools and as a teaching aid for physics teachers in general and technical secondary schools. Will be found useful by correspondence students studying 'A' level and first year physics.

Volume I

Contents. Motion and Forges. Conservation Laws. Molecular-Kinetic Theory of Gases. Molecular Forges and States of Aggregation of Matter. Electrodynamics. Index.

Volume II

Contents. Vibrations and Waves. Basic Quantum Physics of Atoms, Molecules and Solids. The Basic Physics of the Nucleus and Elementary Particles. Index.

HANDBOOK OF PHYSICS

B. Yavorsky, D. Sc. and A. Detlaf, Cand. Sc.

A companion volume to Vygodsky's *Handbook of Higher Mathematics*, designed for use by engineers, technicians, research workers, students, and teachers of physics. Includes definitions of basic physical concepts, brief formulations of physical laws, concise descriptions of phenomena, tables of physical quantities in various systems of units, universal physical constants, etc.

This is a third English edition.

Contents. Physical Basis of Classical Mechanics. Fundamentals of Thermodynamics and Molecular Physics. Fundamentals of Fluid Mechanics. Electricity and Magnetism. Wave Phenomena. Atomic and Nuclear Physics.